# SΛSOL

# PROTE

TONY REBELO

SASOL

# PROTEAS

*A Field Guide to the Proteas of*
*Southern Africa*

Photographs by
COLIN PATERSON-JONES

Line illustrations by
NICCI PAGE

FERNWOOD PRESS

IN ASSOCIATION WITH
THE NATIONAL BOTANICAL INSTITUTE

FERNWOOD
PRESS
P O Box 15344
8018 Vlaeberg

Registration no. 90/04463/07

First published 1995
Second edition 2001

Botanical editor: Emsie du Plessis, Pretoria
Project co-ordinator: Leni Martin
Cover design by Abdul Amien
Production control by Abdul Latief (Bunny) Gallie
Typesetting and reproduction by Cape Imaging Bureau (Pty) Ltd, Cape Town
Printed by Tien Wah Press (Pte) Ltd, Singapore

ISBN 1 874950 40 7

**COVER PHOTOGRAPHS**
Top: *Leucadendron argenteum*
Bottom left: *Leucospermum cordifolium* cultivar
Bottom right: *Protea cynaroides*
Spine: *Protea eximia*

HALF-TITLE PAGE: *Orothamnus zeyheri*
FRONTISPIECE: *Leucadendron microcephalum*
PAGE 8: *Leucospermum lineare*

**WWF**

This field guide has been published with the support
of WWF South Africa

# CONTENTS

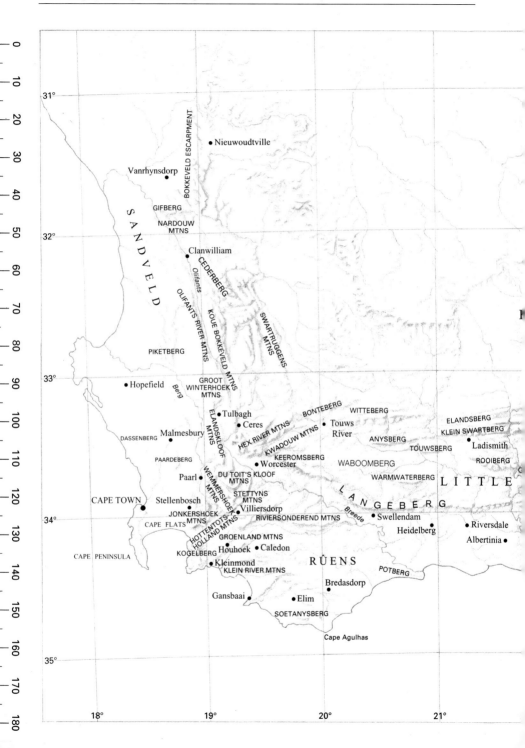

# MAP OF THE CAPE FLORAL KINGDOM

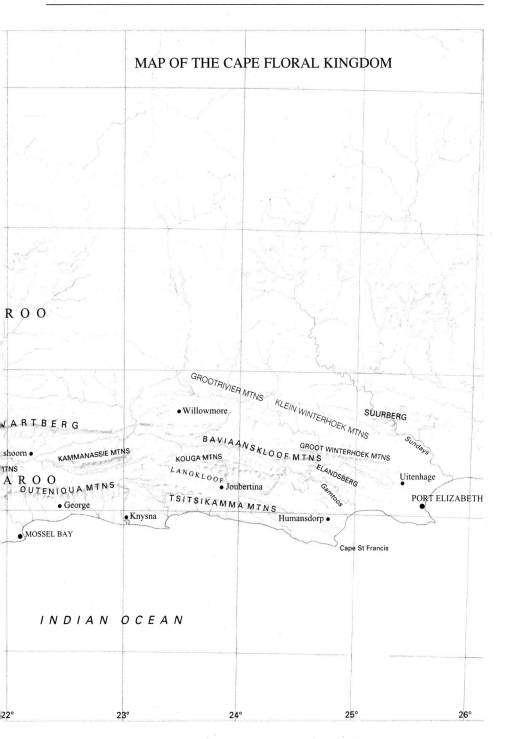

ROO

GROOTRIVIER MTNS

KLEIN WINTERHOEK MTNS

SUURBERG

● Willowmore

ARTBERG

BAVIAANSKLOOF MTNS

Sundays

shoorn ●

KAMMANASSIE MTNS

GROOT WINTERHOEK MTNS

TNS

KOUGA MTNS

AROO

LANGKLOOF

ELANDSBERG

Uitenhage ●

OUTENIQUA MTNS

● Joubertina

Gamtoos

PORT ELIZABETH

● George

TSITSIKAMMA MTNS

●

● Knysna

Humansdorp ●

● MOSSEL BAY

Cape St Francis

*INDIAN OCEAN*

22°          23°          24°          25°          26°

# FOREWORD

## Protea conservation is key to maintaining biodiversity

Southern Africa is blessed with a great diversity and wealth of ecosystems and minerals. While the subcontinent is renowned internationally for its vast numbers of mammals, birds, insects and other fauna, we should not lose sight of the region's treasure chest of flora. For example, more plant species thrive on the Cape Peninsula, a World Heritage Site, than in the whole of the United Kingdom. The Cape Floral Kingdom has the richest array of temperate flora with an estimated 8000 plant species and is one of the world's top ten floral kingdoms.

Of these extensive plant species, none are more uniquely South African than the 380 species of proteas (Proteaceae). These species include South Africa's national flower, the giant King Protea. Worldwide, there is increasing interest being expressed in proteas, as is borne out by the growing numbers of ecotourists who travel to South Africa to admire these beautiful flowers, along with the rest of the country's flora and fauna.

Sadly, the Cape Floral Kingdom has been classified as a mega extinction zone – one of the few areas in the world where thousands of species could become extinct over the next few years unless concerted initiatives are maintained to counter this ecological threat. About one-third of all proteas have been listed in the *Red Data Book* for plants – and this fraction could rise without carefully managed conservation programmes.

Sasol is pleased to sponsor this second edition of *Sasol Proteas: A Field Guide to Proteas in Southern Africa*. We hope that this indispensable field guide will carry on where the first edition left off – helping botanists and conservationists, as well as lay enthusiasts, to become more knowledgeable about, and appreciative of, South Africa's treasure chest of proteas. We believe that greater knowledge and appreciation, in turn, will lead to a far stronger programme to protect and conserve all proteas, thereby helping the region to maintain its irreplaceable biodiversity for many more generations.

PAUL DU P. KRUGER
CHAIRMAN
SASOL LIMITED

## PREFACE TO THE FIRST EDITION

Proteus was the mythological Greek god who could see into the future and always spoke the truth. However, in order to extract a prophecy, one had to grasp him tightly while he changed into numerous animate or inanimate forms. Exactly why Carl Linnaeus, the 'father' of taxonomy, bestowed this name on the protea family is open to debate, but there can be no doubt that the variability within the family is remarkable.

Unrivalled in their beauty and variety, proteas represent one of the best-known plant families in southern Africa. Yet many of its species have only ever been seen by a privileged few. Of the 360 or so species in southern Africa, more than 125 appear in the *Red Data Book* for plants, which lists species in imminent danger of obliteration at the hand of man.

I have written this book with one goal in mind: to enable interested amateurs to identify proteas *in situ* with ease. There is an urgent need for a field guide that concisely illustrates the differences between species. Other popular books about proteas have been published, but none of these explains either the interrelationships between the different species or the features characterizing any particular group of related species. This is a pity, as the very features neglected are those which unite species into close-knit 'guilds' in which common pollinators, pests or growth requirements may be shared. On the other hand, closely related species within a guild are usually quite distinct in other respects such as distribution range, habitat, habit, or flowering and growth times. This interplay of changeable and immutable features, which effectively reduces competition and shapes the paths of potential evolution, will determine the future of the proteas over the next few decades of global climate change and urbanization.

I firmly believe that interested amateurs can contribute significantly to conservation on our subcontinent, and in many different spheres. Their participation is invariably based on a keen appreciation of living organisms, an appreciation initiated and nurtured by the availability of interesting information and enhanced by personal discovery. Where plant conservation is concerned, there has never been a greater need for their contribution. Taxonomists are overworked, herbaria are understaffed and university subsidies are being drastically reduced. Most of our knowledge of protea ecology has been documented only during the last two decades, which suggests that many interesting discoveries have yet to be made. We are woefully ignorant of the details of protea distribution ranges, the significance of their population dynamics, and their optimal management.

The protea family therefore seems the ideal group with which to encourage amateur involvement in plants and their natural environment. It encompasses both common and rare species, its seeds are dispersed by unusual agents, and it manifests a great diversity of pollination and fire survival strategies. In these and many other respects the family is a veritable treasure-chest of potential discoveries. The Protea Atlas Project is one attempt to get the public involved with our plants. If you would like to participate in the project, which involves noting where you see proteas and submitting the data to us at the University of Cape Town, you can not only discover the protea family for yourself, but also contribute to the understanding and conservation of our flora.

Let us hope that, like the mythological prophet Proteus, the proteas will provide an indication of the options available to us for conserving our floral wealth. It can still be done, but it must be done now. Ours is the last generation able to make these decisions. All we have to do is hold on tightly to what we have, never let go, and ensure that the variety and splendour of the proteas will remain forever available to our descendants.

TONY REBELO
PROTEA ATLAS PROJECT, CAPE TOWN 1995

# PREFACE TO THE SECOND EDITION

The Protea Atlas Project came to an end in March 2001 after nearly ten glorious years of atlassing proteas. Almost 500 people sent in records of proteas from their hikes, walks, travels and work. An estimated 2000 more persons assisted them. This has increased the number of recorded localities for proteas from a few thousand to more than 200 000 records. During this process eight new species have been discovered. We have new localities for over two-thirds of the species, and for one-third of our proteas these are significant range extensions. For a synopsis of our achievements, why not visit the website *www.nbi.ac.za/protea*. The cornerstone of all this endeavour was the first edition of *Sasol Proteas*.

This second edition includes many of these findings. We have added most of the new species and modified some of the species descriptions based on the data now available. Although we used Protea Atlas data in the first edition, new significant range extensions have meant that our maps and distributions needed to be revised. The large volume of data resulted in our being able to combine herbarium and amateur data directly to generate our maps in this edition. These maps are thus not generalizations about where proteas are likely to occur, but provide information based on over 100 times more data than the previous edition.

But this is not the end of the project. We do not know everything. There is still no sign that range extensions are tailing off. We cannot even tell how much more data we will need to be able to say that we now know where all our proteas occur. More record data will be appreciated. Indeed, more data are essential for conservation planning. For instance, we discovered our eighth new species during the last two weeks of the Protea Atlas Project. Sadly, it came too late for inclusion in this edition, as it will only flower after this book is printed. The new species is related to *Leucadendron comosum* and has a habitat best described as 'lollipops standing on a green carpet'. Once flowering material has been obtained, the species can be formally described. However, most of the veld in the Riviersonderend area where it was found is just two months old; we will have to wait five more years to map its full distribution.

The data we have obtained are impressive. They will be used to reassess the *Red Data Book* status of our proteas later this year, and an atlas of our proteas will be published in 2002. The data are so 'hot' that we have obtained a US$200 000 grant from the United States National Science Foundation for preliminary analysis. This will be used to investigate the centres of endemism, the evolution of the flora, the possible effects of global warming, and the conservation priorities in the Cape Flora. In addition, our data are already being used by developers, planners and conservation authorities to evaluate proposals for development and conservation.

For those few sceptics, there can now be no doubt that amateur botanists, hikers and laymen can contribute significant data on our flora. It will take decades to realize fully the benefits that these data will confer on science, planning, conservation and communities. To all those who contributed – I salute you! This is your achievement and a heritage for future generations.

This book then is the product of, and a tribute to the many atlassers who participated in this project, to the conservation officials, landowners and keen enthusiasts who granted permission and showed atlassers their gems, and to those who checked and processed the data and helped in many other ways. I trust that it will be the seed for many other field guides, the inspiration for more atlassing projects, and the stimulus for more amateur involvement in our natural heritage.

TONY REBELO
PROTEA ATLAS PROJECT, APRIL 2001

# AUTHOR'S ACKNOWLEDGEMENTS

Many people, some unknowingly, have contributed substantially to this book reaching fruition. I cannot thank them all individually; indeed, there are many whose names I do not know.

It seems fitting to begin by thanking Peter Linder, who kindled my interest in taxonomy. Without his enthusiastic plying of his trade, this book would never have been conceived. Gert Brits, Gert Jacobs, Byron Lamont, Mr Smit, Marie Vogts and Sharon von Broembsen sparked a particular interest in the protea family at an extra-mural study course on the Proteaceae in 1980. To my colleagues William Bond, Jan Coetzee, Brian Collins, Richard Cowling, Ian Newton, Cristián Samper, Peter Slingsby, Del Wiens and Brian van Wilgen, who have shared freely of data, experiences and criticism: may the voyage of discovery never end. I am especially grateful to John Rourke, who spent weeks tutoring me in the nuances of proteas. But for his patient assistance, I could never have contemplated producing this book.

The distribution maps were compiled from published accounts and herbarium records. I thank Beth Gibbs Russell and the directors of the National Botanical Institute for additional distribution data. Ted Oliver and Professors Roy Siegfried and Eugene Moll all encouraged me during the development of the book. Professor W.P.U. Jackson and Richard Brooke helped determine the meanings of Greek and Latin scientific names and suggested possible reasons for their use. Professor Jackson was also responsible for illustrating to me the importance of amateurs in discovering new aspects of botany. His Botanical Society A-team is a continuing source of inspiration, and embodies his desire to learn and teach about plants. Peter Slingsby (who rediscovered myrmecochory in the Cape Flora, and who, to me, symbolizes what a keen amateur can achieve) and his wife Maggie put up with me during the period this book was conceived and initiated: many thanks.

My wife Pat and Alanna, Janet and Alexander have patiently endured having a husband and father devoted to far more than he should have been. Hopefully, we can now spend more time hiking, and getting to see the plants.

To those Protea Atlassers who have contributed to this book with a continuous stream of unknown specimens, 'silly' questions which have left me pondering and wondering for weeks before being able to produce a reasonable answer, and endless tips, advice and suggestions for improvements to the prototypes of this book, very many thanks. A special thanks goes to Jimmy Dunn, Nigel Forshaw, Simon Gardner, Gerard Hansford, Nick Helme, Reuben Heydenrych, Ivor and Cora Jardine, Marc and Amida Johns, Dave and Fay Jones, Victor and Jean Keightly, Tom Lloyd-Evans, Mervyn Lotter, David Louw, Lyn McCallum, Libby McGill, Adrian Mohl, David Osborne, the Outramps, Wendy Paisley, Penny Palmer, Gail Reeves, Stephen Richardson, Peter Ross, Martin Scott, Pindar Sidisunthorn, Ruth Smart, Ann Steele, Andrew and Eve Tiltman, and Kitty and Austen Williams, who provided valuable data and range extensions and who honed my skills by forcing me to identify species from unrecognizable scraps. Nigel Forshaw is especially thanked for his superb data captive packages and his Protea Web Page.

This guide was produced for all amateur botanists and naturalists. I hope that proteas can provide you with the same inspiration and awe that made me choose botany as my career. I appreciate that there is always room for improvement in a publication of this nature, and would welcome any criticism or ideas that may enhance future editions.

# INTRODUCTION

## Proteas in the world
The Proteaceae is one of the most prominent flowering plant families in the southern hemi-sphere. An ancient family, it existed before Gondwana began to break up some 140 million years ago, at the time when dinosaurs roamed the earth. The break-up of the continents occurred only after the family had divided into two subfamilies: the Proteoideae, which occurs mainly in southern Africa but also in Australia and New Zealand; and the Grevilleoideae, which occurs predominantly in Australia but also in South America and on the southwestern Pacific islands, and has a single species in Africa.

Currently about 1400 species (in more than 60 genera) are recognized in the Proteaceae. Virtually all the species occur in the southern hemisphere, mostly in Australia which harbours more than 800 species representing 45 genera. Of these, 550 species are found in southwestern Australia. About 400 species occur in Africa, of which more than 330 species (in 14 genera) are in the southwestern Cape. Central and South America host about 90 species, while 80 species occur on the islands east of New Guinea, 45 species in New Caledonia and a few species in Madagascar, Southeast Asia, New Guinea and New Zealand.

## Protea distribution in southern Africa
About 360 species of proteas are found in southern Africa, of which more than 330 species are confined to the Cape Floral Kingdom, between Nieuwoudtville in the northwest and Grahamstown in the east. Only four of the 14 genera are represented outside the Cape Floral Kingdom: *Faurea*, which has six species in southern Africa and another nine elsewhere in Africa and in Madagascar; *Protea*, which has 35 species in tropical Africa; and *Leucospermum* and *Leucadendron*, each of which has three species or subspecies outside the Cape Floral Kingdom. Six genera (*Brabejum*, *Diastella*, *Orothamnus*, *Serruria*, *Sorocephalus* and *Vexatorella*) do not occur much east of Mossel Bay.

Most protea species in the Cape Floral Kingdom are confined to nutrient-poor soils derived from Table Mountain Sandstone. A few species occur in limestone and calcareous sands, and very few grow in dry, shale-derived soils. More than two-thirds of the species are confined to the area west of 20°E (Cape Agulhas to Ceres). More spectacularly, more than 130 species occur in the Caledon region alone.

Some proteas are confined to specific mountain ranges in the western Cape, and an analysis of distributions reveals clearly defined boundaries. The pattern is less clear in the east, where the most common species tend to be those which occur throughout the Cape Floral Kingdom.

## What is a protea?
A 'protea' is any member of the protea family, or Proteaceae. In order to distinguish between a member of the protea family and a member of the *Protea* genus, the latter is referred to as a 'sugarbush' in this book.

### Habit
The habit of proteas is very variable, and in the Cape Floral Kingdom it includes trees, upright shrubs, plants with a spherical underground bole from which several erect branches emerge, plants with creeping stems and plants with underground stems (as in ferns). In temperate and tropical Africa, the last-mentioned growth form is absent. One constant feature of proteas' habit is that they are neither herbaceous nor annual, but are always woody.

### Leaves
The leaves of proteas are sclerophyllous (i.e. hard and leathery, snapping rather than folding over when bent) and either entire or dissected into needle-like lobes. And, in contrast to the very

small leaves of most plant species in the Cape Floral Kingdom (hence the term 'fynbos'), they are often large. The function of leaves is to capture carbon dioxide and sunlight in order to produce carbohydrates, without losing more water than is necessary. The sclerophyllous qualities of protea leaves help to prevent water loss, and their heavily lignified tissue stops them from collapsing when water is scarce. By restricting water loss, sclerophyllous leaves slow down the process of photosynthesis but, being drought-resistant, they can continue to photosynthesize long after ordinary leaves have wilted. They are also longer-lived than ordinary leaves, a factor which compensates for the high cost of producing them.

The leathery, woody nature of sclerophyllous leaves appears to be a structural feature of plants growing on nutrient-poor soils, especially where nitrogen and phosphorus are scarce. Because the nitrogen and phosphorus needed for protein synthesis are lacking, excess organic carbon is produced from photosynthesis. This excess carbon is channelled into the production of non-proteinaceous compounds, such as woody fibres and tannins. With their high ratio of carbon to nitrogen, sclerophyllous leaves are indigestible to most insect larvae (since insects require nitrogen for proteins). Similarly, very few mammals will eat protea leaves, as the high carbon to nitrogen ratio is compounded by low levels of trace elements which are essential in the herbivore's diet, and by high levels of chemicals (tannins) which impair the action of digestive enzymes in the gut, making digestion inefficient.

In the Cape Floral Kingdom there are four major types of protea leaves:
**1 *Isobilateral leaves*,** which are flat leaves without differences between the two surfaces. Ordinary (dorsiventral) plant leaves have a harder upper surface which faces the sun, and a lower shaded surface through which most of the carbon dioxide and water vapour exchange takes place. An isobilateral leaf exchanges carbon and water equally through the two surfaces, albeit at a lower rate than a dorsiventral leaf. It has the advantage that, when orientated vertically, it photosynthesizes through one surface in the morning and through the other in the afternoon. At midday, however, when the sun is overhead, its edge faces the sun and overheating and water loss are thus reduced.
**2 *Needle-like (terete) leaves*,** which are in essence thin, cylindrical and isobilateral. They have a reduced surface area compared to their volume, so that water loss is further minimized.
**3 *Grooved or channelled (canaliculate) leaves*,** which in proteas can be considered an intermediate stage between thin isobilateral leaves and needle-like leaves. However, where a grooved leaf clasps the stem or is tightly folded, the inner surface is shaded from sunlight and protected from wind, just as the lower surface of a dorsiventral leaf is. This allows for faster carbon dioxide exchange on the inner surface.
**4 *Divided leaves*,** such as those of *Serruria* and *Paranomus* species, which are branched and needle-like or grooved, respectively. Divided leaves are a solution to many problems: they increase the surface area of a leaf while minimizing volume (thus saving water by preventing overheating); they increase the surface area of a leaf without shading lower leaves; they prevent caterpillars (or other animals) from taking large mouthfuls of leaf; and they make it more difficult for diseases to spread through a leaf.

In proteas the tips of leaves differ considerably from one species to another. In some the leaves end in a small, sharp, red or black point, called a mucro. These may be very sharp (as in *Protea mucronifolia*), and probably serve to discourage browsers. However, in other cases mucros are fleshy in young leaves and probably serve the same function as glandular teeth.

Glandular teeth on the leaves occur in most genera but are particularly conspicuous in the pincushions (*Leucospermum*), which may have up to 20 teeth per leaf. They secrete a sugary solution and are therefore extrafloral nectaries. Their exact function is unknown: it is possible that they excrete excess water, thus cooling the leaves, or they may contain substances that prevent herbivory. However, leaves are visited extensively by wasps, ants and flies, and as wasps and ants parasitize and prey upon other leaf-eating insects, their presence may be more effective in reducing herbivore numbers. In species that produce little floral nectar, the teeth may help to attract insects to flowerheads. Many *Protea* and *Paranomus* species have thickened leaf margins which do not appear to secrete nectar. Their precise function is not known, but they may serve as a strengthening and cooling device for the large leaves.

Protea leaves may be hairless or covered with hairs or denticles. Hairs are either long or short, straight or (in *Leucospermum* only) curly. Most silver and grey leaves have dense layers of hairs which reflect bright sunlight, thus preventing overheating. Hairs also prevent wind from disturbing the air at the leaf surface, allowing efficient carbon dioxide uptake while reducing water loss. In addition, hairs may hinder insect herbivory by clogging up the insect's mouthparts or increasing its chewing time. In some bird-pollinated *Mimetes* species, hairs contribute to the visibility of the flowerheads. Some protea leaves have fine denticles that make them sandpapery to the touch (scabrous). These denticles are modified hairs that probably have both a supportive and an anti-herbivore function. In *Protea denticulata* the denticles are so rough that the bushes with their interlocking branches resemble barbed wire entanglements.

Some blue-grey (glaucous) leaves are covered not with hairs but with fine waxy scales or 'bloom'. These scales reflect light, and by reducing the amount of light reaching the leaf surface, they prevent the leaf from overheating. The wax also helps to keep the leaf surfaces impermeable to water, and may hinder herbivory.

Young leaves present a problem for proteas growing in nutrient-poor soils. They are soft, since they must expand before the strengthening woody components can be laid down, and they are full of the protein needed for rapid growth. Consequently, they are choice items on any herbivore's menu. Because they are soft, they cannot resist desiccation as the older leaves can. In order to overcome these problems, young leaves must grow quickly and they are usually covered with dense hairs or bloom. They are often a different colour to the mature leaves, frequently red or yellow. The reason for this is not known, but it may be related to reducing the heat load (red leaves reflect more heat) and thus water loss. Also, many insects cannot readily see red light, and although red leaves appear brightly coloured to humans, they may be relatively inconspicuous to insect herbivores.

FLOWERS AND FLOWERHEADS
Plant classification is based largely on the shape of the plant's flower, and the protea flower must rank as one of the easiest to identify. The secret is to ensure that you are looking at a flower and not at the flowerhead – which comprises many flowers together with some colourful bracts. It is a feature of southern African proteas that their flowers, like those of daisies, are grouped into large flowerheads that are easily mistaken for flowers. The manner in which the flowers are grouped into heads facilitates the ready recognition of the different genera.

The most common flowerhead type is the capitulum, in which the flowers are borne on a receptacle which may be flat or pointed. The receptacle is surrounded by involucral bracts, and these may be prominent (in *Protea*, *Orothamnus* and *Diastella* species) or inconspicuous (in *Leucospermum* and *Vexatorella* species). In *Leucadendron* the involucral bracts are also inconspicuous, but the floral bracts of female plants are large, developing into woody cones.

Perhaps the most primitive flowerhead type is the spike, a modified branch bearing stalkless flowers. Found in *Faurea*, this is probably the type from which all other African protea flowerheads developed. Stalked flowers are borne on a modified branch known as a raceme, which occurs in the genus *Aulax*. In male plants the racemes are obvious, but in the female plants they are not easily seen, being situated in a 'cup' of modified branches. *Grevillea* and *Brabejum* species also produce racemes, but in both cases the flowers are borne in pairs.

The remaining genera have compound flowerheads. In *Mimetes* the flowerhead is a single pollination unit (a conflorescence) comprising headlets with the leaves and branch. In *Paranomus*, *Serruria*, *Spatalla* and *Sorocephalus* (which could be collectively termed the Spiderhead allies) the flowerhead is typically a raceme, panicle, spike or umbel bearing lateral headlets. There are many variations on this theme, but in this book technical complexities have

## A stalkless protea flower

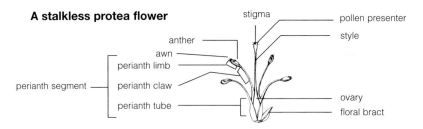

## A protea flowerhead

## A compound protea flowerhead

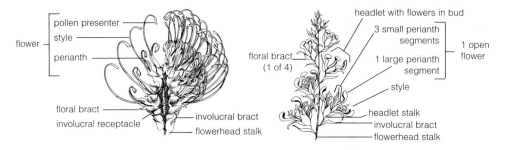

been avoided as far as possible by referring to the entire unit as the flowerhead and to the sub-units as headlets. In the Spiderhead allies the number of flowers per headlet (1 or 3 in *Spatalla*, 4 in *Paranomus*, 4 to 9 in *Sorocephalus* and many in *Serruria*) are crucial for the identification of these genera.

Unlike most flowering plants, protea flowers do not have separate sepals and petals. Instead, they have a single set of four segments (often called tepals) which make up the perianth. This is most unusual and is an important diagnostic feature. Each perianth segment is divided into three regions: the tube at the base (which may be absent), the limb at the tip which bears the anthers, and the claw connecting the tube and the limb. In the bud these segments abut one another, but never overlap. As the bud opens, the four perianth segments separate and curl back to expose the style (the stalk which extends from ovary to stigma). The manner in which the perianth segments separate, and how much of the lower portions remain fused to form a tube, are used to distinguish between the different genera.

The male organs (anthers) of proteas are also distinctive. Instead of having long stalks (fila-ments) as do the anthers of most other flowers, protea anthers are joined directly to the base of the perianth limb. Another unusual feature is that they shed their pollen onto the topmost por-tion of the style just before the flowers open.

The female organs of protea flowers, similar to those of other flowers, consist of an ovary, a style and a stigma. The ovary is superior (i.e. not enveloped by or fused with the perianth seg-ments) and in all southern African species it contains one ovule. After flowering it develops into a small dry fruit that contains one seed. Often the fruit itself is incorrectly identified as the seed. The style is a long thin stalk, modified at the tip to form a pollen presenter, another diagnostic feature of proteas. It effectively 'presents' the pollen in a position suitable for placing onto a visiting pollinator and, in order to ensure adequate transfer of pollen to pollinators, is often elaborately shaped. The stigma, a tiny groove situated at the top of the pollen presenter, is dry and seldom sticky.

In some species four minute floral nectaries are situated at the base of the ovary, between it and the base of the perianth segments. These secrete nectar to attract pollinators. They always alternate with the perianth segments, and may be all that remains of the petals. Below each flower is the floral bract, situated either adjacent to stalkless flowers or on the flower stalk. In genera which have separate male and female plants the female features are absent in male flowers and *vice versa*. However, all the proteaceous characteristics are still prominent.

ROOTS
On nutrient-poor soils many plant families form associations with soil-living fungi to assist with water and nutrient uptake. Proteas, however, do not appear to form these associations, producing instead little bunches (up to 200 mm long) of thousands of short-lived rootlets (proteoid roots) at intervals along their normal roots. Produced just below the soil surface, these rootlets may account for more than half of the total plant root mass and cover 15 times the area of a normal root of the same mass. Proteoid roots are almost twice as efficient at absorbing nutrients and water as normal roots. They are usually produced only after rain, since moisture promotes the decay which results in the release of the necessary nutrients from the leaf litter.

Proteas growing in nutrient-rich soils tend not to produce proteoid roots, as they could absorb lethal doses of nutrients. Similarly, seedlings do not produce proteoid roots for the first few months of their life, since they have an internal supply of nutrients. Only when this supply has been exhausted do they produce proteoid roots.

**Defences against fire, herbivory and disease**
Fire is one of the characteristic features of both the Cape Floral Kingdom and the African savannas and grasslands, and most proteas are adapted to survive fires in one of four ways:
1 Storage of seeds in fire-safe environments by serotiny (e.g. *Protea repens*) or myrmecochory (e.g. *Leucospermum cordifolium*) (see FRUIT DISPERSAL AND SAFE STORAGE, page 19). In Africa, these fire survival strategies are largely confined to the Cape Floral Kingdom where many species have no other fire survival mechanism. Species which take from three to 15 years to flower for the first time are vulnerable to fires that occur at intervals shorter than those needed to produce seeds.
2 Growing in a fire-safe environment (escape strategy), such as in rocky crags (e.g. *Protea rupicola*), by creeping along the ground where fires are cooler (e.g. *P. scabriuscula),* or by creeping underground like ferns (e.g. *P. acaulos).* Protection in these environments is relative, and fierce fires might well kill these plants.
3 Producing a thick bark which protects buds in the stem (stem resprouting strategy, e.g. *Protea nitida*). Growth of these buds is stimulated when branch tips are killed by fire. However, fierce fires may kill the buds beneath the bark, and some species with very thick bark seem to be easily killed by fire (e.g. *Leucadendron argenteum*).
4 Growing from large boles or rootstocks, which are thick underground stems (bole resprouting strategy, e.g. *Protea cynaroides*). The boles or rootstocks contain many dormant buds which are stimulated to produce more growth after a fire has killed the above-ground parts of the plant. Many of these species flower only for a few years following a fire and then become inconspicuous. Plants adopting this strategy are easily recognized by their multiple-stemmed habit, with many erect stems arising at ground level.

Proteas face the problems of herbivory and disease as do all other plants, but as yet very little research has been done on the mechanical and chemical defences they use. The high carbon to nitrogen ratio in the leaves may help to prevent herbivory, and may also be effective against disease. Extrafloral nectaries, hairs, thickened leaf margins and divided leaves may also play defensive roles. There are also few records of rusts, smuts or mildews, or bacterial infection affecting proteas, but this may be due to a lack of research.

Proteoid roots are prone to infection by *Phytophthora* fungus, but different species vary in the degree of susceptibility. An antifungal substance, p-hydroxybenzoylcalleryanin, which is secreted by *Protea cynaroides* roots, may confer resistance to *Phytophthora.*

## Reproduction

Most proteas flower in spring and summer, with fewest species flowering in autumn. This pattern may relate to the abundance of pollinators, to the optimal conditions for nectar secretion, or to the need for myrmecochorous species to synchronize seed release with the season of maximum ant activity.

Flowerheads remain open for a few days or up to several months. Flowers almost always open from the outside towards the middle of a flowerhead. However, when headlets are grouped into compound flowerheads, the inner headlets may open before the outer ones.

POLLINATON

A feature of protea pollination is that pollen is deposited by the anthers onto the pollen presenter of the same flower. Flowers usually remain closed until they are triggered by a visiting bird, mammal or insect into snapping open. As they do so, they release the style, from which pollen is transferred onto the visitor. If no visitors arrive, flowers may open during the heat of day. Pollen falls off the pollen presenter after a few hours of exposure to air.

Closed when the flowers first open, the stigmatic grooves of proteas open to their full extent only after 24 to 36 hours. The stigma is then ready to receive pollen brought by a visitor from another plant. Thus proteas are protandrous: the male organs mature before the female to prevent self-pollination. Most *Protea* species seem incapable of self-pollination (i.e. are self-incompatible), although certain *Serruria* and *Leucospermum* species do set seed when pollinated with pollen from the same plant. Dioecious proteas (i.e. *Leucadendron* and *Aulax* species, which have separate male and female plants) are obviously unable to pollinate themselves.

There are four main syndromes of pollination in our proteas:

**1 *By rodents.*** Several species of gerbils, mice, rats and shrews visit the flowerheads of Hook Pincushions and some *Protea* species, attracted by their strong musty odour and a reward of nectar which is secreted in large quantities and is rich in sucrose. The flowerheads of rodent-pollinated proteas are usually hidden inside the bush at ground level, and the colours of the insides of the involucral bracts (pale white) and of the tips of the flowers (shiny red) guide the rodent to the nectar in the dark. In order to prevent birds and insects from stealing this nectar, the proteas have inconspicuous brown or black involucral bracts. The distance between the pollen presenter and the nectar in the perianth tube matches the length of the rodent's snout (about 10 mm), allowing pollen to be deposited on its head. Since most of these proteas flower in spring, nectar is available during the rodents' breeding period.

**2 *By birds.*** Many *Mimetes*, *Protea* and *Leucospermum* species are pollinated by birds. Their flowerheads are often brightly coloured, and because bird vision and human vision are similar, they are aesthetically pleasing to us. The bright red, orange, yellow, green and pink colouring on involucral bracts and styles serve as visual attraction to the birds, but are relatively inconspicuous to many insects which cannot see red and orange. Since birds do not rely on smell, bird-pollinated proteas have little scent. Copious quantities of easily digested, glucose-rich nectar are secreted. The most important bird visitors are sugarbirds and sunbirds.

**3 *By insects.*** Many of the bird-pollinated proteas are also visited by large numbers of insects – up to 2 000 beetles may occur in a single flowerhead. Among the most important of these are the Scarab Beetles (Scarabaeidae) such as the Protea Beetle (*Trichostetha fascicularis*) and Monkey Beetles, and Rover Beetles (Staphylinidae). The relative importance of birds and insects in pollinating these species is not known. Although insects in sugarbush flowerheads often end up as bird-food, they pollinate the flowers adequately when birds are absent.

Another feature of bird- and insect-pollinated proteas is the occurrence of thousands of Protea Itch Mites (*Proctolaelaps vandenbergi*) in flowerheads. These mites 'hitchhike' to the flowerheads on birds and beetles and feed on nectar and pollen. They do not occur on young flowerheads, but a mature *Protea* flowerhead may contain more than 6 000 breeding mites. It is not known whether these mites play a role in pollination.

Certain proteas are visited exclusively by insects: smaller *Protea* (the Shale Proteas) and *Leucospermum* species are insect-pollinated, mainly by bees and wasps; *Leucadendron* species are visited by a number of beetles; and most of the genera with smaller flowerheads are visited by a variety of beetles, flies and wasps. These species can usually be distinguished by their sweet, spicy or sour smells, and by their relatively meagre production of nectar. The flowerheads tend to be pink, cream or yellow in colour, and are usually considerably smaller in size than those of bird-pollinated species. Some *Diastella* species do not produce nectar and are visited only for their pollen by bees and flies.

**4 By wind.** The ten wind-pollinated proteas in southern Africa are all *Leucadendron* species. They have two main characteristics: they do not secrete nectar (most do not even have nectaries) and they are odourless. The flowers of the female plants have large stigmas for filtering pollen out of the air. In the male plants, the pollen does not adhere to the pollen presenter, but when the flower opens it is scattered in large showers and drifts away in the wind.

SEED SET

A characteristic of protea reproduction is the extremely low production of seeds in hermaphrodite species: only 1-30 per cent of flowers result in seeds. It has been surmised that the 70-99 per cent of flowers which do not set seed may function as male flowers, ensuring that there is sufficient pollen for fertilization. The high seed set of dioecious species (70-100 per cent) suggests that the surmised male function may be part of the answer, and the similar ratios of male to female flowers in dioecious species and flowers (males) to seeds (females) in hermaphrodite species support this hypothesis. Moreover, it should be borne in mind that most protea flowerheads physically could not accommodate a higher seed set due to lack of space.

Another factor affecting the low seed production is probably the plant's need to produce nutrient-rich seeds in a nutrient-poor environment. The shortage of nutrients restricts the total seed production, with the result that each flowerhead bears only a few large seeds.

FRUIT DISPERSAL AND SAFE STORAGE

In proteas of the Cape Floral Kingdom fruits can be classified into three broad types depending on how they are stored and dispersed, with those of *Brabejum stellatifolium* in a fourth category of their own. Serotinous, myrmecochorous and cached fruits all represent adaptations to the need to store nutrient-rich seeds safely in a fire-prone and nutrient-poor environment.

**1 Serotinous fruits** are relatively soft-shelled nutlets which are flat or cylindrical in shape and often have hairs or wings. They are produced by *Aulax*, *Protea* and half the *Leucadendron* species. In most members of these genera in the Cape Floral Kingdom, fruits are retained with the flowerheads on the plant (serotiny) after a ripening period of about seven months. These seedheads are fire-safe and release their fruits when the water supply to them stops. This occurs when the plant dies or is killed by fire, or when insects consume the seedhead stalk. Thus fruits accumulate on the plant from year to year, and the entire crop (minus that destroyed by insects) is stored on the plant. In the savannas, where fires are annual, and in dry areas, where fires may not occur for centuries, fruits of *Protea*, *Faurea* and certain *Leucadendron* species are not stored, but drop to the ground after a two- to four-month ripening period.

The function of the hairs on serotinous fruits is fourfold: in the opening seedhead they expand, forcing the fruits free of the head; on an airborne fruit they are buoyancy devices in high winds; when the fruit lands they function as grapnels, anchoring it to the ground; and they orientate the fruit on the soil surface to ensure optimum water uptake for germination.

When the fruits of serotinous species are released onto the soil surface after a fire they are available as food to rodents and birds until their seeds germinate after the winter rains Serotinous species in fynbos are thus vulnerable to local extinction should fires occur in spring. Only one serotinous species, *Leucadendron platyspermum*, has overcome this predation problem – its fruits are retained in the cones until after the onset of the rains has initiated germination. The growing root then pushes the fruit out of the cone.

**2 *Myrmecochorous fruits*** are relatively hard-shelled nutlets which are rounded or ovoid in shape, hairless, and usually covered by a fleshy skin, the elaiosome. Often called the *Leucospermum* fruit type, they also occur in the *Serruria, Spatalla, Sorocephalus, Orothamnus, Diastella, Vexatorella* and *Paranomus* genera and a few of the *Leucadendron* species. The fleshy skin is too thin to attract birds as seed dispersers, but ants are partial to it. After a six- to eight-week ripening period, it secretes a chemical substance that attracts the ants, and they carry the fruits (sometimes removing them from the seedheads) to their nests where they consume the elaiosomes. The hard, smooth nutlets are then left in the nest and the seeds in them, which are very much in demand as a nutrient-rich food source, are thus safely buried. However, the invasive Argentinian Ant (*Iridomyrmex humilis*) may have upset the entire relationship because it consumes the elaiosome without burying the fruits, thereby leaving them exposed to predation.

Buried fruits 'know' when conditions are suitable for germination by reading subtle clues that indicate when a fire has occurred. For example, ants secrete formic acid, causing a low pH in their nest. When they are killed by fire or starved by the lack of food after it, the pH in the abandoned nest increases. Similarly, when the ants are active they maintain a high concentration of carbon dioxide in their nest, but when they abandon it oxygen levels increase. In addition, the absence of vegetation after a fire results in extreme diurnal fluctuations in soil temperature and these also promote the germination of myrmecochorous fruits.

**3 *Cached fruits*** are large, rounded nuts and are borne only by *Leucadendron* species in the subsections Arid Conebushes (*Membranacea*) and Sun Conebushes (*Nucifera*). They are produced in enormous quantities over a very short period, about two to four months after flowering. Although many of the fruits are eaten, most are buried by rodents, and from the underground caches they germinate after fire, prompted by the same cues as are the myrmecochorous fruits.

**4 *Brabejum stellatifolium*,** a riverine species, has water-dispersed fruits which ripen in March and are washed downriver during autumn and winter floods. The seeds germinate immediately on suitable substrates. Since riverine habitats are unstable, offering a short-lived substratum for germination, the fruits themselves are short-lived.

# IDENTIFYING PROTEAS IN THE FIELD

**How to use this book to identify proteas**

In the species descriptions each species is given its full scientific name, which includes the author(s) of the name. This is followed by a short description of the plant, with features that uniquely identify it printed in italics. A short account of its geographical distribution, habitat, status and normal flowering and fruiting seasons is also provided.

Take a good look at the plant you wish to identify. Note its leaf size and shape, and the structure and size of the flowerhead. Then:

1  Decide whether it is in fact a member of the protea family (see 'What is a protea?', page 13).
2  Determine to which genus it belongs by using the generic key (see pages 22-23). Ensure that you have correctly identified the genus by checking its diagnostic features, which are printed in boxes at the beginning of each chapter devoted to a genus.
3  If the genus has been divided into a number of groupings, determine to which grouping your plant belongs by using the keys following the genus description. Check that you have the correct grouping by comparing your plant with the grouping description.
4  Flip through the pages of that grouping until you find a description that fits your plant. Check that its leaf, flowerhead and locality tally with those of your specimen.
5  IMPORTANT: Check that all the diagnostic features (*printed in italics*) apply to your plant.

Alternatively, you may page through the plates and match your plant to a photograph. Having done so, however, you should always check your specimen against the diagnostic features relating to the species in the photograph you have decided upon. This is important if you wish to have confidence in your identification. Only by making a habit of doing this will you learn how the different proteas are related.

Looking at the written description first has the advantage that it highlights what is needed to identify different species within genera. For example, in the *Paranomus* genus a leaf and a headlet are sufficient to identify any species, whereas for *Leucadendron* species fruits are essential for identification. As a rule, a leaf and a flowerhead are always needed. Remember always to note the habit of the plant: whether, for example, it has a single erect stem, erect multiple stems from an underground rootstock, underground stems or creeping stems.

Most proteas can be identified even when they are not in flower. To do so you will need to rely on leaf shape and old flowerheads that you may find around the bush. Identify the genus, compare leaf shapes and sizes within the genera and then check the diagnostic notes.

USING THE KEYS

Botanical keys can be remarkably easy to use and save much time in identifying species. However, the terminology used in many keys, their curt descriptions and their complex pathways often bewilder amateurs. For this reason, I have replaced detailed keys with 'quick keys' in which the plant is illustrated and diagnostic features are given in brief. These keys are provided to guide you to the genera (pages 22-23) and to the groupings within the larger genera.

Remember that keys are no more than guides – they work most of the time but are not infallible. However, short of providing pages and pages of tedious text, no key will provide the correct answer every time. The keys in this field guide have been designed for simplicity and ease of use, and as such they should be correct in 90 per cent of cases.

Immediately after finishing with the key, check the diagnostic features in the short descriptions of the genus or grouping that the key has led you to, in order to find out whether you have ended at the correct place in the key.

## A QUICK KEY TO THE GENERA OF THE PROTEA FAMILY

### A FLOWERHEAD COMPRISING CLOSELY PACKED, STALKLESS FLOWERS ON A ROUNDED BASE

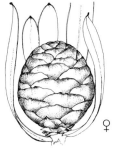

**Protea The Sugarbushes** (page 25)
Flowerheads either terminal or basal
Involucral bracts large and showy
Involucral receptacle flattened

**Leucadendron The Conebushes** (page 169)
Flowerheads terminal
Floral bracts large in female
Involucral bracts small and brown
Upper leaves (involucral leaves) larger and colourful
Seedhead a cone of floral bracts

**Vexatorella
The Vexators**
(page 159)
Leaves somewhat succulent
Flowerheads small and terminal
Style conspicuous and pin-like
Involucral bracts inconspicuous

**Orothamnus
The Marsh Rose**
(page 168)
An erect, unbranched shrub
Flowerheads pendulous, axillary
Involucral bracts large,
rounded and red

**Serruria
The Spiderheads**
(page 82)
Leaves divided
Flowerheads terminal or axillary
Involucral bracts inconspicuous
to large

**Diastella
The Silkypuffs**
(page 155)
Flowerheads very small and terminal
Style conspicuous and pin-like
Involucral bracts thin and papery

**Hakea
The Needlebushes** (page 218)
Flowerheads axillary
Flowers in pairs per floral bract
Fruit a cone-like follicle,
bearing 2 seeds

**Leucospermum
The Pincushions** (page 130)
Leaves with 1 to many glandular teeth
Flowerheads axillary
Style conspicuous and pin-like
Involucral bracts inconspicuous

### A FLOWERHEAD COMPRISING STALKLESS FLOWERS ON AN ELONGATED BASE (SPIKE)

**Faurea The Beechwoods** (page 80)
A tree
Flowerheads terminal

# A FLOWERHEAD COMPRISING STALKED FLOWERS ON AN ELONGATED BASE (RACEME)

*Brabejum*
**The Wild Almond**
(page 217)
Leaves in star-like whorls of 6 to 12
Flowers in pairs per floral bract
Fruit a furry brown 'almond'

*Grevillea*
**The Silky Oaks**
(page 220)
Leaves deeply lobed and
with grey, hairy lower surfaces
Flowers in pairs per floral bract
Fruit a leathery follicle,
bearing 2 seeds

*Aulax*
**The Featherbushes** (page 78)
Male flowerheads yellow
Flowers single per floral bract
Male flowers fall off, leaving
short stalks
Female flowers on short stalks,
borne on a central conical column
that is surrounded by modified
branches, forming a woody cup

# A COMPOUND FLOWERHEAD COMPRISING AGGLOMERATIONS OF HEADLETS

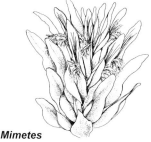

*Serruria*
**The Spiderheads** (page 82)
Leaves divided
Flowerheads comprise many
stalked headlets and may be terminal
or borne in the axils of terminal leaves
Flowers straight or curved in bud

*Mimetes*
**The Pagodas** (page 161)
Flowerheads large and cylindrical
on upper stem, comprising densely
packed headlets and leaves
Headlets stalkless, axillary, with
3 to 35 flowers
Involucral bracts conspicuous,
forming a tube, sometimes hidden
by modified leaves

*Paranomus*
**The Sceptres** (page 105)
Leaves usually divided,
except sometimes the upper
leaves
Headlet comprises 4 flowers
Flowers straight in bud

*Spatalla*
**The Spoons**
(page 121)
Leaves needle-like
Headlet comprises either 1 or 3 flowers
Flowers curved outward in bud

*Sorocephalus*
**The Clusterheads**
(page 114)
Leaves needle-like or awl shaped
Flowerheads globose
Headlets numerous,
comprising 4 to 9 flowers
Flowers straight in bud

**When you cannot identify a plant in the field**

If all else fails and you cannot identify a plant, turn to page 22 and slowly go through the key. Having done this, you should be absolutely certain of the genus. If you are not, then read again 'What is a protea?' (page 13) and carefully check that you do in fact have a member of the protea family.

If, for some reason, you still cannot identify your plant, you should take a small snippet home. For this you will need a permit if the plant is on state or forestry land, or permission from the owner if it is on privately owned land. Use a sharp knife or secateurs so as to cause minimal damage to the plant, and do not take more than one flowerhead with three or four leaves below it. In the case of *Leucadendron* and *Aulax*, take one snippet from each sex and collect a cone with seeds from a bush or from the ground beneath the bush. Record in your notebook the locality (which mountain peak, how far from the turn-off to the nearest major road, the road number, etc.) and note the height, stature and number of stems the plant has (your snippet will not help you with this information). Also, guess the number of plants at the locality and make a note of the habitat, including the soil type. This will help taxonomists should you need to seek professional help and will be invaluable data if you have discovered a new species or race. Take your information to your neighbourhood enthusiasts, such as the local branch of the Botanical Society or Wildlife Society, and ask their advice.

Most herbaria will identify your snippets, at a cost of about R5 for each one. To present a worth-while specimen you need to dry and compress your snippet while it is fresh. Put it between several sheets of newspaper and then in a plant press. If the latter is not available, use two flat pieces of wood to keep the plant material flat and a belt to squeeze the pieces together tightly. It is wise to make a copy of your notes, adding your name and address and the colour of the flowerhead, and tie it to your snippet before pressing. It is also a good idea to attach a collector's number to each spec-imen to distinguish it from others you may have collected or may still collect. Serious collectors usually number their specimens consecutively from 1, keeping records to avoid using the same num-ber for different specimens.

Never take more than the smallest snippet. If you cannot identify the plant, it may be rare or new. Always bear in mind that one-third of our proteas are threatened with extinction, and that it would be unpardonable to contribute to their demise. If you suspect that the species is rare, take photo-graphs and notes rather than a snippet. Be careful not to trample too much in the vicinity of the plants as proteas are particularly vulnerable to soil disturbances, especially trampling which seems to promote fungal diseases.

**Field equipment**

All you need to study proteas in the field is this guide, a notebook and pencil, and a 10x magnify-ing glass or lens. The last-mentioned is very important for determining whether leaves are hairy or not, and the shape of the smaller floral parts such as the floral nectaries and pollen presenters. It will also increase your appreciation of the complexity of apparently bland structures.

Should you intend picking snippets, you will need a permit or permission from the landowner and a sharp knife or secateurs. Make sure these are sterilized regularly (any commercial disinfectant will do) so that no infection is transferred from the wild to your garden or, more importantly, from your garden into the wild.

If you wish to become a serious collector, you will need special permits from your local Department of Nature Conservation. Most herbaria will advise you on the best techniques for col-lecting and the equipment you will need, provided that you can justify your hobby as beneficial to science or conservation.

## *PROTEA* L.  The Sugarbushes

The common name 'protea' has come into everyday use for the genus *Protea* in South Africa. However, the International Protea Association has ruled that the term can be applied to any member of the Proteaceae. This unfortunate state of affairs means that plants as diverse as banksias, hakeas and macadamias are now sold worldwide as 'proteas'. For this reason the older, but until recently ignored name 'sugarbush' is used in this book to refer to *Protea* species.

The genus Protea is easily recognized by the *involucral bracts which surround the flowerheads; the flowers with 3 completely fused perianth parts and 1 free; and hairy, woody fruits.* Additional features include a long, narrow pollen presenter which is almost always joined to the style by a knee-bend; linear to broad leaves with a thickened red or yellow edge and tips with a fine black point or glandular region; perianth parts which often have awns; and *a hard, woody involucral receptacle which shows clear spirals when the flowers are removed.*

# A QUICK KEY TO THE CAPE SUGARBUSHES

**FLOWERHEADS AT BRANCH TIPS; STEMS ERECT OR SPRAWLING**

**The 'True' Sugarbushes**
(Page 52, Plate 14)
Flowerhead obconic
Involucral bracts hairless

**The Bearded Sugarbushes**
(Page 54, Plate 15)
Inner involucral bracts with
a 'beard' of long, dense hairs

**The King Sugarbush**
(Page 45, Plate 10)
Leaves borne on a long stalk
Flowerhead large

**The White Sugarbushes**
(Page 63, Plate 20)
Flowerhead shorter than 80 mm
Perianth collapses into the flowerhead
after flowering

**The Spoon-bract Sugarbushes**
(Page 48, Plate 12)
Inner involucral bracts spatulate

**The Shaving-brush Sugarbushes**
(Page 36, Plate 4)
Flowerhead bowl-shaped, erect
Involucral bracts relatively inconspicuous

**The Penduline Sugarbushes**
(Page 75, Plate 27)
Leaves ovate, wider than 5 mm
Flowerhead pendulous

**The Shale Sugarbushes**
(Page 72, Plate 25)
Flowerhead shorter than 25 mm

**The Rose Sugarbushes** (Page 73, Plate 26)
Leaves needle-like if flowerheads pendulous
Flowerhead 20-50 mm long

## FLOWERHEADS AT BRANCH TIPS; STEMS CREEPING OR UNDERGROUND

**The Bishop Sugarbush**
(Page 66, Plate 22)
Flowerhead surrounded
by large, oval, brown leaves

**The Western Ground
Sugarbushes**
(Page 69, Plate 24)
Leaves silky smooth
Style strongly curved
Occurs west of Mossel Bay

**The Eastern Ground
Sugarbushes**
(Page 67, Plate 22)
Style slightly curved
Occurs in the Swartberg and
east of George

**The Snow Sugarbushes**
(Page 46, Plate 11)
Involucral bracts with long points,
and white, woolly hairs on outer
surface

**The Dwarf-tufted Sugarbushes**
(Page 60, Plate 18)
Leaves tufted, with sandpapery texture
Style straight or slightly curved
Occurs west of Mossel Bay

## FLOWERHEADS BASAL, ON OLD STEMS

**The Rodent Sugarbushes** (Page 29, Plate 1)
Involucral bracts brown or black

# A QUICK KEY TO THE TROPICAL AND SUBTROPICAL SUGARBUSHES

**Protea roupelliae**
(Page 48, Plate 12)
Inner involucral bracts spatulate

**The Mountain Sugarbushes**
(Page 38, Plate 6)
Leaves large (100-200 mm long)
Flowerhead large
(longer than 70 mm)
Involucral receptacle dome-shaped
Involucral bracts stay open
in seedhead

**The Grassland Sugarbushes**
(Page 32, Plate 2)
Involucral bracts and
stems hairless or
with few hairs
Involucral bracts
close in seedhead

**Protea lorifolia**
(Page 56, Plate 16)
Leaves broadly oblanceolate
Involucral bracts bearded

**The Moorland Sugarbushes** (Page 44, Plate 9)
Perianth tube slender
Perianth segments recoil to base
of style on opening
Occurs in high mountain areas

**The Savanna Sugarbushes**
(Page 42, Plate 8)
Stems hairy when young
Flowerhead medium-sized
(about 50 mm across)
Style slightly longer than
involucral bracts
Flowerheads often
clustered at branch tips

**Protea subvestita**
(Page 63, Plate 20)
Flowerhead small, oblong
Perianth segments collapse into
the flowerhead after opening

**The Red Sugarbush**
(Page 38, Plate 5)
A small, prostrate bush
Flowerhead conical to turban-shaped
Involucral bracts red and hairless

## *Protea* The Rodent Sugarbushes

The Rodent Sugarbushes (section *Hypocephalae)* are characterized by the *flowerheads borne in the axils of leaves*, unlike the terminal flowerheads of all other sugarbushes. The flowerheads are produced at *ground level, at the bases of branches and stems*, and are thus hidden by foliage and branches. The *involucral bracts are covered by dark brown or purple hairs* which make the flowers inconspicuous, and this often gives the appearance that flowering is over. Together with the *shallow, bowl-shaped flowerheads and the yeasty odour*, these are adaptations for pollination by rodents, and to the need to hide the flowerheads from nectar-thieving birds and bees. Although several species have woody bases, these do not allow the plants to survive fires, unlike the rootstocks of other sugarbush species.

*Protea amplexicaulis* (Salisb.) R. Br.　　　　　Clasping-leaf Sugarbush　**Plate 1**

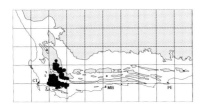

A low, sprawling shrub up to 0.4 m tall, 1.3 m across, with a single main stem. Stems prostrate and hairless. *Leaves at right angles to stem, base clasping stem, heart-shaped to elliptic*, 30-80 mm long, 15-50 mm wide, becoming smaller at branch tips, dull green to glaucous. *Flowerhead axillary on lower branches*, cup-shaped, 60-80 mm across, with a strong yeasty odour. *Involucral bracts purple-black with velvety to short hairs on outer surface and margin*, inner surface ivory; outer series ovate, tip pointed, 10-15 mm long, 10 mm wide, overlapping; inner series oblong-spatulate, 45-50 mm long, 8-15 mm wide, slightly curved inwards. Perianth 25-28 mm long, tube 15-18 mm long, tips red and sparsely covered with white hairs. Style strongly curved inwards, 25-30 mm long. Pollen presenter 5-7 mm long, linear, tip pointed, grooved, not distinct from style. DISTRIBUTION: Koue Bokkeveld to Langeberg, Hottentots-Holland and Riviersonderend Mountains and Caledon Swartberg. HABITAT: Sandstone soils, 180-1600 m. STATUS: Extensive stands of dense plants occur on dry, north-facing slopes, with scattered plants in moister south-facing sites. FLOWERS: June to September, mainly July and August. FRUITS: Retained.
□ VARIATIONS: Blue-grey leaves are produced at elevated, sunny locations and tend to blush pink or purple with frost. Dull green leaves are more common at lower elevations.

**Protea cordata** Thunb.                                    Heart-leaf Sugarbush    **Plate 1**

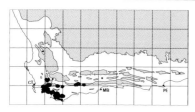

A *low, erect shrublet up to 0.5 m tall, 0.3 m across, with a woody base bearing several erect, unbranched stems. Stems hairless, red-flushed, up to 500 mm long, with brown, lanceolate, pointed scale leaves at base, zigzagging between leaves. Leaves heart-shaped,* 30-140 mm long, 20-160 mm wide, hairless, glaucous, becoming smaller towards tip of stem, crimson, grey-green when mature; stalkless. *Flowerhead axillary, clustered at base of stems,* long-stalked, cup-shaped, 40-50 mm across. *Involucral bracts brown, dry-papery, widely spread,* occasionally with minute brown hairs on the margin; outer series lanceolate, tip pointed, 8-10 mm long, 3-5 mm wide; inner series lanceolate, 25-40 mm long, 12-15 mm wide. Perianth 20-25 mm long, tube indistinct, tips hairless, bright red. Style strongly curved inwards, 28-30 mm long, ivory. Pollen presenter 3 mm long, linear, tip rounded. DISTRIBUTION: Du Toit's Kloof Mountains to Kogelberg and Bredasdorp Mountains to Agulhas; Riviersonderend Mountains to central Langeberg. HABITAT: Varied, but favours Cederberg shales, 0-1200 m. STATUS: Isolated clumps of a few dozen plants are typical, although extensive stands may occur locally. FLOWERS: June and July. FRUITS: Retained.

**Protea humiflora** Andrews                                 Patent-leaf Sugarbush    **Plate 1**

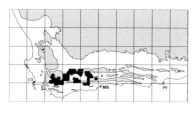

An erect to sprawling shrub up to 1 m tall, 1-2 m across. Trunk up to 80 mm in diameter. Stems hairless. *Leaves linear to sickle-shaped, 55-110 mm long, 2-6 mm wide, midrib distinct, tip pointed, hairless, glaucous, flushed dark reddish brown; stalkless. Flowerhead axillary, cup-shaped, 60-80 mm across. Involucral bracts ivory with pink tips inside, outer surface densely covered with dark purple-black, downy-velvety hairs;* outer series ovate, tip rounded, 6-10 mm long, 8-10 mm wide, tightly overlapping; inner series oblong to spatulate, 30-40 mm long, 6-10 mm wide. Perianth 20-25 mm long, tube 10-12 mm long, tips red, with delicate white hairs. Style strongly curved inwards, 30-40 mm long, cream. Pollen presenter 6 mm long, linear to thread-like, not distinct from style. DISTRIBUTION: Du Toit's Kloof to Langeberg and Waboomsberg, Warmwaterberg, Little Karoo hills west of Anysberg, Rooiberg, and western Little Karoo to Gamka Mountains. HABITAT: Hot, dry, northern slopes at fynbos/karoo ecotone, 450-1200 m. STATUS: A social species growing in dense stands which dominate plant communities. FLOWERS: July to September, mainly August. FRUITS: Retained.

*Protea decurrens* E. Phillips                                    Linear-leaf Sugarbush     **Plate 1**

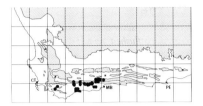

An erect shrublet 0.4-0.6 m tall, up to 0.5 m across, arising from a woody base. *Stems erect, hairless. Leaves curved upwards, fused to stem at base, with the blade continuous down the stem on one side, linear, 35-90 mm long, 2-5 mm wide, flat to slightly grooved, tip pointed.* Flowerhead axillary on basal branches, cup-shaped, 30-50 mm across, with a yeasty odour; stalked. Involucral bracts pinkish brown, with silver to rusty hairs, margin fringed with brown or silver hairs; outer series ovate, tip rounded, 4-10 mm long, 4-8 mm wide, overlapping; inner series oblong-spatulate, 20-30 mm long, 6-12 mm wide, splayed, curved inwards. Perianth 20-30 mm long, tube indistinct, tips red, hairless or with delicate hairs. Style sharply curved inwards, 30-35 mm long, cream. Pollen presenter 5 mm long, linear, tip pointed, slightly knee-bent at base.
DISTRIBUTION: Northern and southern slopes of Langeberg, with outlying populations at Shaw's Pass and Potberg. HABITAT: Arid silcrete or ferricrete gravels at the fynbos/renosterveld ecotone, 150-700 m. STATUS: Probably far more common than currently known because of its cryptic nature. *Red Data Book* status: Vulnerable, because of agriculture. Small clumps of a few dozen plants have been recorded over its distribution range. FLOWERS: July to October, mainly July and August. FRUITS: Retained.
□ VARIATION: Eastern forms tend to have broader leaves.

*Protea subulifolia* (Salisb. ex Knight) Rourke                    Awl-leaf Sugarbush     **Plate 1**

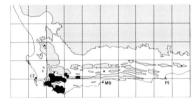

A low shrublet 0.3-0.7 m tall, up to 0.5 m across, with a woody base. Stems erect, hairless. *Leaves very variable, needle-like to grooved-round,* 5-85 mm long, 0.5-2 mm wide, hairless, tip with a fine, black point. Flowerhead axillary, cup-shaped, 45-60 mm across, with a yeasty odour; stalk 10-25 mm long. *Involucral bracts brown or pink, soft, papery,* densely covered with silver or brown velvety hairs on outer surface; outer series ovate, tip rounded, 5-10 mm long, 5-8 mm wide, tightly overlapping; inner series oblong-spatulate, 25-35 mm long, 8-16 mm wide, curved inwards. Perianth 20-25 mm long, tube 10 mm long, tips red and hairless but occasionally bristled. Style straight at base, 25-30 mm long, strongly curved inwards at tip, pale. Pollen presenter 4 mm long, linear, tip rounded, not distinct from style.
DISTRIBUTION: Stettyns to Riviersonderend Mountains and central Langeberg; Bot River (Rûens) to the Elim Flats. HABITAT: Varied, sandy to heavy clay soils, 60-1300 m.
STATUS: Typically in small groups of scattered plants. Lowland populations of the small-leaved form are threatened by agriculture and in some areas are largely confined to road verges.
FLOWERS: July to October, mainly July to September. FRUITS: Retained.
□ VARIATIONS: In the south at low elevations leaves are 5-15 mm long; at intermediate elevations leaves are 15-45 mm long, and at high elevations they are up to 85 mm long. Involucral bracts vary from pale pinkish brown in lowland forms to dark brown in montane forms.

## *Protea* The Grassland Sugarbushes

The Grassland Sugarbushes (section *Leiocephalae)* are among the most 'primitive' of the sugarbushes found in southern Africa and are best distinguished from the Mountain and Savanna Sugarbushes by their *hairless or nearly hairless involucral bracts*, although some species do have hairs. It is difficult to rigorously define the group, but the following characters are helpful: young stems are hairless, as are the involucral bracts (except in *P. caffra);* flowerheads tend to be shorter than 50 mm (except in *P. caffra)*, or to have a long, scaly stalk; flowers may either protrude or be contained within the involucral bracts; and the perianth may be hairless or hairy, occasionally with a tuft of hairs at the tip. Styles are usually strongly curved. The leaves are hairless.

### *Protea caffra* Meisn.

A very variable species, ranging in habit from erect shrubs or *small trees 3-8 m tall with a single main stem (old plants) to erect, multi-stemmed, branched shrubs 1-3 m tall, with a rootstock (young or frequently burned plants)*. Trunk up to 400 mm in diameter. Bark black, brown or grey, with a network of cracks when mature. *Branches 4-12 mm in diameter, hairless. Leaves variable, 70-250 mm long, 4-45 mm wide, hairless*, often glaucous, pale green to silvery. *Flowerhead globose to ovoid, 45-80 mm across*, solitary or in clusters of 3 or 4, with a sweet, sulphurous odour; stalk 0-25 mm long. *Involucral bracts pink to carmine or cream, hairless or densely covered with rust-brown or silvery silky hairs that are shed rapidly after flowering*; outer series ovate to triangular, 5-7 mm long, 10-20 mm wide, tightly overlapping; *inner series oblong to oblong-spatulate, 30-50 mm long*, 10-20 mm wide. Perianth 45-60 mm long, tube 7-14 mm long, with pink-brown to white hairs (even on the tube) which are soon shed. *Style 40-60 mm long*, curved inwards. Pollen presenter 7-12 mm long, linear and thread-like, knee-bent at base.

□ VARIATIONS: Several subspecies have been recognized, of which the 3 that occur in southern Africa are described below. The other 2 occur further north: *P. caffra* subsp. *mafingensis* Chisumpa & Brummitt (Mafingo Sugarbush) in northern Malawi and Zambia; and *P. caffra* subsp. *kilimandscharica* (Engl.) Chisumpa & Brummitt (Kilimanjaro Sugarbush) in the Rift Valley Mountains.

### *Protea caffra* subsp. *caffra*                                  Common Sugarbush    **Plate 2**

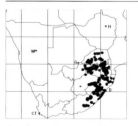

Similar to *P. caffra*, but: *Leaves 13-30 mm wide*, 70-170 mm long, linear-oblanceolate to elliptic, sometimes sickle-shaped, margin not wavy. *Flowerhead 40-70 mm across. Perianth tube 10-14 mm long.* DISTRIBUTION: Highlands of Free State, North-West Province, Gauteng, Northern Province, Mpumalanga and Lesotho; escarpment of Northern Province, Mpumalanga, Swaziland, KwaZulu-Natal and Eastern Cape; and coastal plains of KwaZulu-Natal and Eastern Cape. HABITAT: Varied, 0-2100 m. STATUS: Common as solitary plants or gregarious, dominating landscapes. FLOWERS: Locally variable, October to January, with a December peak. FRUITS: Released 9-12 months after flowering.

***Protea caffra*** subsp. ***nyasae*** (Rendle) Chisumpa & Brummit ⠀⠀⠀Malawi Sugarbush

Similar to *P. caffra*, but: *Leaves 17-30 mm wide*, linear-elliptic to linear-oblanceolate, 70-130 mm long, rounded below, with a wavy margin. *Flowerhead 50-70 mm across. Perianth tube 14-21 mm long.*
DISTRIBUTION: Mt Milanje, Malawi. HABITAT: Proteaceous-ericaceous moorland, 1800-2500 m. STATUS: Scattered plants on shallow soils. FLOWERS: December to January.
FRUITS: Released 9-12 months after flowering.

***Protea caffra*** subsp. ***gazensis*** (Beard) Chisumpa & Brummit ⠀⠀⠀Manica Sugarbush ⠀⠀**Plate 2**

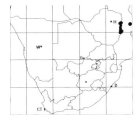

Similar to *P. caffra*, but: *Leaves 20-40 mm wide*, linear-oblanceolate, slightly sickle-shaped, 100-190 mm long, margin not wavy. *Flowerhead 60-100 mm across. Perianth tube 16-21 mm long.*
DISTRIBUTION: Eastern highlands, Zimbabwe and Mozambique. HABITAT: Mountain grassland, 800-2000 m. STATUS: Locally abundant, solitary or gregarious. FLOWERS: December to March.
FRUITS: Released 9-12 months after flowering.

***Protea petiolaris*** (Hiern) Baker & Wright subsp. ***elegans*** Chisumpa & Brummitt
⠀⠀⠀⠀⠀⠀⠀⠀⠀⠀⠀⠀⠀⠀⠀⠀⠀⠀⠀⠀Sickle-leaf Sugarbush ⠀⠀**Plate 2**

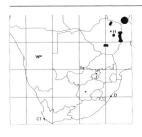

A *straggling tree up to 8 m tall.* Trunk to 400 mm in diameter. Bark black and fissured. Young branches hairless. *Leaves drooping*, blade oblanceolate, 50-140 mm long, 10-30 mm wide, green, hairless; *stalk 0-20 mm long.* Flowerhead solitary, turban-shaped, 55-70 mm long, 60-120 mm across. *Involucral bracts green to red; outer series with a whitish bloom to hairless*, margin with white hairs; inner series 40-50 mm long, 10-15 mm wide. *Perianth hairless inside, pink or white*, 40-50 mm long, tube 14-20 mm long. Style white, 50 mm long. Pollen presenter 5 mm long, linear and thread-like, knee-bent at base.
DISTRIBUTION: Zimbabwe and Malawi. Extralimitally to Burundi. HABITAT: High-altitude *Brachystegia* woodland and montane grassland. STATUS: Locally common.
FLOWERS: November to March. FRUITS: Not known.
NOTE: *Protea petiolaris* subsp. *petiolaris* (with young branches hairy; leafstalk 10-40 mm long; flowers 30-40 mm long; perianth tube 10-15 mm long) occurs west of the Rift Valley in Angola, Zambia and Democratic Republic of Congo, with intermediates in Democratic Republic of Congo. It is suspected that in *P. petiolaris* subsp. *elegans* the flowerhead develops from the bud of the previous year's growth, whereas in *P. petiolaris* subsp. *petiolaris* it occurs on a short, leafless branch.

***Protea simplex*** E. Phillips                                      Dwarf Grassland Sugarbush     **Plate 3**

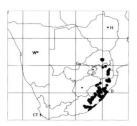

A dwarf shrub 0.3-1 m tall, with a *woody rootstock and multiple stems. Stems erect, not branching, 2-5 mm in diameter*, hairless, green with red or pink flush, withering and dying after 2-5 years without fire. Leaves oblong to oblanceolate, 60-120 mm long, 7-30 mm wide, hairless. Flowerhead solitary, obconic to globose, 30-60 mm across. *Involucral bracts hairless*, green to cream to pink to carmine; outer series broadly ovate, 5-10 mm long, 10-15 mm wide; inner series oblong, tips rounded, 25-30 mm long, 5-10 mm wide. Perianth 20-40 mm long, tube 4-8 mm long, with white to rusty brown hairs. Style straight or slightly curved, 20-40 mm long. Pollen presenter 3-10 mm long, linear and thread-like, almost indistinct from style.

DISTRIBUTION: Northern Province and Mpumalanga, Swaziland, KwaZulu-Natal to Eastern Cape. HABITAT: Grassland and escarpment, 0-2000 m. STATUS: Sometimes in dense isolated stands, more usually as scattered plants. FLOWERS: After fires, November to December. FRUITS: November to December.

***Protea parvula*** Beard                                               Dainty Sugarbush     **Plate 3**

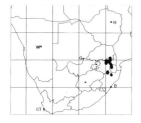

*A low, sprawling shrub 0.08-0.16 m tall, with a rootstock producing numerous sparsely branched stems up to 1 m long. Stems hairless, 2-4 mm in diameter. Leaves pointing vertically from a horizontal stem*, variable, linear to oblanceolate, 60-140 mm long, 5-20 mm wide, margin flushed with red. Flowerhead cup-shaped, 35-60 mm across, green to cream to pink, opening flat, *with a 0-25 mm long stalk. Involucral bracts hairless*; outer series ovate, 5-8 mm long, 7-10 mm wide; inner series oblong, 25-30 mm long, 5-15 mm wide, often fringed. Perianth 25-35 mm long, tube 5-7 mm long, white, hairless or with rusty brown hairs. Style straight or slightly bent, 30-35 mm long, white. Pollen presenter 5 mm long, linear and thread-like, not distinct from style.

DISTRIBUTION: Escarpment of Northern Province, Mpumalanga, Swaziland and KwaZulu-Natal, from Mariepskop to Vryheid. HABITAT: Rocky, exposed grassland on acid soils, 1300-2150 m. STATUS: Locally abundant. FLOWERS: December to March. FRUITS: April to July.

*Protea dracomontana* Beard — Drakensberg Sugarbush — **Plate 3**

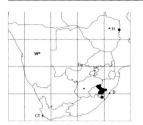

*A low shrub 0.5-1.5 m tall, up to 1 m across, with rarely branched, erect stems arising from a rootstock. Stems stout, 5-10 mm in diameter*, hairless. Bark thick, red. Leaves oblong to oblanceolate, 80-140 mm long, 25-45 mm wide, leathery, glaucous. Flowerhead cup-shaped, 40-60 mm across, solitary or in clusters of 3 or 4. *Involucral bracts hairless*, cream to carmine, margin hairy; outer series ovate, tip rounded, 7-10 mm long, 10-15 mm wide; inner series oblong, 30-40 mm long, 7-15 mm wide. Perianth 40-45 mm long, *tube 10 mm long, hairless at base*, tips with tufts of white to pink hairs. Style 45-60 mm long, white. Pollen presenter 8-10 mm long, thread-like, not distinct from style.
DISTRIBUTION: Eastern Cape, Lesotho, KwaZulu-Natal and Free State escarpment; Zimbabwe at Mt Inyangani. HABITAT: Subalpine *Themeda* grassland, on basalt, 1600-2600 m. STATUS: Typically in dense isolated stands. On Mt Inyangani it is known from a single population at the summit. FLOWERS: January to March. FRUITS: Released 9-12 months after flowering.
NOTE: The Mt Inyangani population (Rhodes Sugarbush) was regarded as a separate species, *P. inyanganiensis*, by Beard (1993). The plants are smaller in all their features than those of *P. dracomontana* from the Drakensberg. They also flower at a different time, from August to October.

*Protea nubigena* Rourke — Cloud Sugarbush — **Plate 3**

An erect shrub *with numerous stems arising from a rootstock*, 0.5-0.7 m tall, up to 0.5 m across. *Stems much-branched*, 2-5 mm in diameter, leaf scars prominent. *Leaves erect, oblanceolate-elliptic, small, 40-60 mm long, 7-13 mm wide*, hairless, glaucous. *Flowerhead globose, 40-50 mm across, with a sweet scent. Involucral bracts hairless*, green to pink, margin brown; outer series ovate, 10-15 mm long, 10 mm wide; inner series linear-oblong, 25-30 mm long, 3-7 mm wide. Perianth 30-35 mm long, tube 10 mm long, with rusty brown hairs. *Style 35-40 mm long*, curved inwards, white. Pollen presenter 10 mm long, linear, not distinct from style, pink.
DISTRIBUTION: KwaZulu-Natal Drakensberg at Policeman's Helmet. HABITAT: Cliffs, 2300 m. STATUS: Extremely localized, and known from a single population of about 50 plants. *Red Data Book* status: Endangered. FLOWERS: March to April. FRUITS: March to April.

## *Protea* **The Shaving-brush Sugarbushes**

The Shaving-brush Sugarbushes are the Cape Floral Kingdom representatives of the section *Leiocephalae*. All are readily distinguished in that they *resemble shaving brushes when in late bud stage. Flowerheads are open and bowl-shaped, and the styles are more conspicuous than the involucral bracts.* Most species rarely store their seeds for more than 2 flowering seasons. Plants of all 4 species are very long-lived, typically surviving for more than a century, either by resprouting after a fire or by growing in arid regions and on rocky outcrops, thus avoiding fires.

---

***Protea inopina*** Rourke                                             Large-nut Sugarbush    **Plate 4**

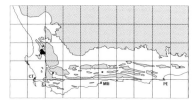

*A low, multi-stemmed shrub 0.5-1 m tall, with a root-stock.* Leaves elliptic to oblanceolate, 120-180 mm long, 25-50 mm wide, leathery, hairless, glaucous. Flowerhead ovoid, 100-120 mm across, flowers protruding in late bud stage; stalk up to 30 mm long. *Involucral bracts with red-brown velvety hairs,* base glaucous and green; outer series ovate, tip pointed, 10-20 mm long, 10-15 mm wide; inner series ovate to oblong, 20-25 mm long, 15-25 mm wide. Perianth 80-90 mm long, tube 10 mm long. *Style 80-90 mm long,* curved inwards, white. Pollen presenter 15-20 mm long, linear, not distinct from style. *Fruits large, 10-12 mm long, 6-8 mm in diameter.*
DISTRIBUTION: Olifants River Mountains southeast of Paleisheuwel. HABITAT: Sandstone soils, 600-650 m. STATUS: Extremely isolated, inconspicuous. *Red Data Book* status: Rare.
FLOWERS: September to December. FRUITS: Released 1-2 years after flowering.

---

***Protea glabra*** Thunb.                                             Clanwilliam Sugarbush    **Plate 4**

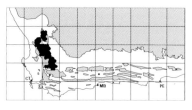

*A conical shrub up to 5 m tall, with many thick stems arising from a large rootstock up to 300 mm in diameter. Leaves curved upwards, elliptic to ovate, 40-75 mm long, 15-30 mm wide,* leathery, hairless, glaucous; stalk 0-7 mm long. Flowerhead ovoid to globose, 70-120 mm across, flowers protruding beyond involucral bracts in late bud stage. *Involucral bracts hairless or with brown downy hairs,* margin often densely fringed with brown hairs, collapsing after opening; outer series ovate, tip pointed, 6-10 mm long, 8-10 mm wide, overlapping; inner series oblong, 25-35 mm long, 6-15 mm wide. Perianth 35-50 mm long, tube 5-8 mm long. *Style 40-50 mm long,* straight, cream. Pollen presenter 10 mm long, thread-like, not distinct from style. *Old seedheads, after releasing seeds, form untidy brown masses.*
DISTRIBUTION: Bokkeveld escarpment to Olifants River Mountains and Koue Bokkeveld. HABITAT: Shallow sandstone soils or in cracks in rock slabs, 500-1500 m. STATUS: Typically in isolated populations of about a dozen plants, or often solitary. FLOWERS: July to November, mainly August and September. FRUITS: November to February.

***Protea rupicola*** Mund ex Meisn.                                    Krantz Sugarbush    **Plate 4**

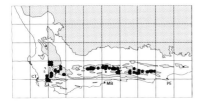

A much-branched shrub 0.5-2 m tall. Trunk up to 100 mm in diameter. *Leaves curved upwards, linear-spatulate to oblanceolate, 35-60 mm long, 5-20 mm wide, leathery, hairless, occasionally glaucous.* Flowerhead variable in size, ovoid, 40-100 mm across. *Involucral bracts reddish brown with sparse hairs, relatively inconspicuous* (and thus superficially more like a *Leucospermum* than a *Protea* species), margin with white or reddish hairs; outer series ovate-oblong, 8-10 mm long, 6-8 mm wide, overlapping; inner series 20-35 mm long, 3-10 mm wide, widely spread. Perianth 35-45 mm long, tube 5-10 mm long. *Style 45-55 mm long,* curved inwards, pink. Pollen presenter 5-10 mm long, linear, swollen at base, tip linear (western forms) or knobbed (eastern forms, which were once known as *P. dykei* E. Phillips).

DISTRIBUTION: Groot Winterhoek to Hottentots-Holland Mountains; along Langeberg and Swartberg to Winterhoek Mountains. HABITAT: High-altitude, sandstone summit ridges and rocky outcrops protected from too-frequent fires, 1300-2000 m. STATUS: Extremely localized near tops of mountains; isolated plants or small populations at about 40 known locations. FLOWERS: September to February. FRUITS: Released 9-12 months after flowering.

***Protea nitida*** Mill.                                                   Wagon Tree    **Plate 5**

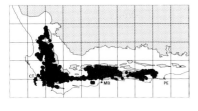

Variable in habit, a tree up to 5 m (occasionally 10 m) tall with a trunk up to 400 mm (occasionally 1 m) in diameter, or – in young plants and some populations – a multi-stemmed shrub to 1 m tall, with a rootstock. Bark thick, white-grey. Stems 6-10 mm in diameter, hairless. *Leaves oblong to elliptic, 80-180 mm long, 15-60 mm wide, hairless, leathery, olive- to silver-grey, glaucous.* Flowerhead globose, 80-160 mm across, flowers projecting beyond involucral bracts in bud. Involucral bracts cream to pink, hairless or with silky hairs; outer series ovate, 10-15 mm long, 10-15 mm wide, overlapping; inner series widely spread, oblong, 30-45 mm long, 10-20 mm wide. Perianth 60-75 mm long, tube 10-15 mm long. *Style 60-80 mm long,* curved inwards, cream. Pollen presenter 10-12 mm long, thread-like, not distinct from style.

DISTRIBUTION: Widespread from the Bokkeveld escarpment to Cape Peninsula to Winterhoek Mountains. HABITAT: Varied on drier, lower slopes, especially talus, 0-1200 m. STATUS: Locally abundant, forming open woodlands. FLOWERS: All year, with local peaks from May to August. FRUITS: Released 9-12 months after flowering.

□ VARIATIONS: A dwarf, multi-stemmed form with narrow green leaves has been recorded at Red Hill (Cape Peninsula), Kanonkop (Cape Flats), Olifantsberg (Riversdale Flats) and the western Langeberg. It was once regarded as a separate species, *P. reticulata* Thunb. Individual plants with deep pink flowerheads occur occasionally in the erect form.

NOTE: In the past, the leaves of this species were used to make ink, the bark was used for tanning leather (20 000 trees were killed annually in the late 19th century), and the wood was made into wheel rim pieces and brake blocks for wagons. Other important uses were firewood, charcoal burning and ornamental furniture.

### *Protea* **The Red Sugarbush**

The Red Sugarbush (section *Paludosae*) is a small prostrate to semi-erect species. The leaves tend to be narrow and shiny, and are hairless when mature. *The flowerheads are conical to turban-shaped after flowering. Involucral bracts are pointed, usually red and hairless.* The perianth is hairy.

*Protea enervis* Wild                                    Chimanimani Sugarbush    **Plate 5**

*A small, woody plant with creeping stems arising from a rootstock. Leaves linear, sickle-shaped, 40-50 mm long, 1-5 mm wide, erect, hairless, no venation visible, margin red. Flowerhead solitary, terminal, 50 mm long, 30 mm across; stalk 10 mm long.* Involucral bracts hairless except along the margin; outer series green; inner series red, 35 mm long, 5 mm wide. *Perianth 30-35 mm long, tube 9 mm long, white tinged with pink, base hairless,* tip with long, white hairs. Style white, hairless, 30 mm long. Pollen presenter 6 mm long, slender, not distinct from style.

DISTRIBUTION: Chimanimani Mountains in Zimbabwe and Mozambique. HABITAT: Ericaceous moorland on deeper sands and among rocks, 1700-2000 m. STATUS: Restricted to 2 areas of a few square kilometres, inconspicuous. FLOWERS: February to May. FRUITS: Not known.
NOTE: Very closely related to *P. paludosa* (Hiern) Engl. of Angola, Democratic Republic of Congo and Zambia, especially *P. paludosa* subsp. *secundifolia* (Hauman) Chisumpa & Brummitt.

### *Protea* **The Mountain Sugarbushes**

The Mountain Sugarbushes (section *Patentiflorae*) *tend to have the largest flowerheads (more than 70 mm long) outside the Cape. Their leaves are also large (100-200 mm long)* and either hairy or hairless. The involucral bracts may be either hairy or hairless, and in the tropics they are usually slightly longer than the flowers. *The perianth is longer than 45 mm.* The involucral bracts tend not to close after flowering, thus functioning to protect only the developing buds, not the developing fruits. It has been suggested that this feature indicates that Mountain Sugarbushes are among the most primitive of all sugarbushes, but this may be a derived feature in a group not often exposed to snowfalls. Three of the species – *P. rubropilosa*, *P. comptonii* and *P. curvata* – have a large, dome-shaped receptacle, which is also considered to be an extremely primitive feature in sugarbushes.

***Protea angolensis*** Welw.                                           Northern Sugarbush

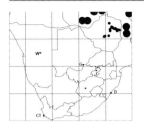

Variable in habit from a dwarf, multi-stemmed shrub up to 0.5 m tall with a rootstock and unbranched stems, to a shrub up to 3 m tall with a single, 100 mm-diameter trunk. Bark black and fissured. Stems 4-8 mm in diameter, hairless. Leaves very variable, oblanceolate to elliptic, 100-160 mm long, 20-80 mm wide, green to bluish green, leathery. *Flowerhead solitary, 70-100 mm long, 90-120 mm across; stalk 10-15 mm long, scaly.* Involucral bracts pale green, occasionally flushed red to carmine; outer series woody; *inner series with white hairs varying from sparse and silky to dense and velvety, margin soft and membranous*, tip rounded, 50-70 mm long (barely longer than styles), 10-20 mm wide. *Perianth 50-60 mm long, tube densely covered with short white hairs*, 25 mm long. Style 60-70 mm long, hairy below, white to pink. Pollen presenter 10-12 mm long, linear, not distinct from style. FLOWERS: April to July. FRUITS: June to July.

☐ VARIATIONS: Several varieties have been recognized, of which the 2 that occur in southern Africa are described below.

***Protea angolensis*** var. ***angolensis***            Dwarf Northern-woodland Sugarbush   **Plate 6**

Similar to *P. angolensis*, but: A dwarf plant up to 1 m tall, with many unbranched stems that arise from a *rootstock*, are covered with leaves and terminate in a flowerhead. *Leaves 20-60 mm wide*, oblanceolate, 100-200 mm long, tapering to the base, occasionally elliptic to circular. Flowerhead 60-120 mm across. *Involucral bracts rapidly maturing to hairless. Perianth tips usually hairy*, white. DISTRIBUTION: Zimbabwe and Mozambique. Extralimitally to Democratic Republic of Congo and Tanzania. HABITAT: Treeless grassland and dambo margins, 1200-2135 m. STATUS: Scattered plants.

***Protea angolensis*** var. ***divaricata*** (Engl. & Gilg) Beard      Northern Woodland Sugarbush   **Plate 6**

Similar to *P. angolensis,* but: A *small tree* up to 4 m (rarely to 7 m) tall. Trunk up to 100 mm in diameter. Bark thick, black, fissured. *Leaves 30-100 mm wide*, oblanceolate, 90-190 mm long, dark green. Flowerhead 90-160 mm across, borne on old, leafless stems. *Involucral bracts with silky hairs. Perianth tips hairless*, white. DISTRIBUTION: Zimbabwe and Mozambique. Extralimitally to Democratic Republic of Congo and Tanzania. HABITAT: Open wooded grassland and *Brachystegia* woodland, 1200-2000 m. STATUS: Scattered plants.

***Protea rupestris*** R.E. Fr.                                        Regal Sugarbush   **Plate 6**

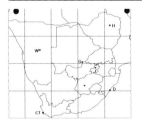

*A sparsely branched tree* up to 10 m tall. Bark smooth, grey, with horizontal cracks. Stems grey and hairless. *Leaves linear-oblancelate, sometimes sickle-shaped, 70-190 mm long, 10-33 mm wide, stalkless,* base either long and wedge-shaped or rounded, hairless when mature, glaucous. Flowerhead solitary, 120-180 mm across. *Involucral bracts collapse on opening to point downwards, do not close again, pink to crimson at tips,* occasionally with adpressed hairs at base; inner series linear-oblong to spatulate, 50-90 mm long, 7-15 mm wide, longer than flowers. Perianth 50-60 mm long, tips with shaggy hairs, tube 17-31 mm long. Style 70 mm long, pale. Pollen presenter 17 mm long, linear, knee-bent at base. DISTRIBUTION: Malawi and Mozambique. Extralimitally to Angola and Tanzania. HABITAT: Open *Brachystegia* woodland and montane grassland, 1200-1950 m. STATUS: Uncommon, although widely distributed; relatively unknown. FLOWERS: May to December. FRUITS: Not known.

**Protea madiensis** Oliv. subsp. *madiensis*        Tall Woodland Sugarbush    **Plate 6**

Shrub or tree up to 6 m tall, occasionally resprouting from a root-stock. Trunk up to 100 mm in diameter. Bark black, fissured. *Leaves variable, lanceolate to elliptic, 100-200 mm long, 30-100 mm wide, hairless when mature, semi-glaucous, veins prominent, red. Flowerhead 80 mm long, 100-150 mm across, stalk shorter than 10 mm.* Involucral bracts often hairless, inner surface pale, outer surface pale green and tipped red or pink; outer series with silky hairs; inner series 70 mm long, 20 mm wide, hairless when mature, longer than flowers. *Perianth 45 mm long, tube 15-20 mm long, tip 10-13 mm long, hairless. Style 50 mm long, flattened and grooved.* Pollen presenter 10 mm long, knee-bent at base.
DISTRIBUTION: Mozambique and Malawi. Extralimitally to Nigeria and Ethiopia.
HABITAT: Varied, miombo woodland to grassland, 900-2150 m. STATUS: Widespread, locally common. FLOWERS: April to May. FRUITS: Not known.

**Protea rubropilosa** Beard        Transvaal Sugarbush    **Plate 7**

A gnarled, spreading tree 1-8 m tall. Trunk up to 450 mm in diameter. Branches stout, 10-15 mm in diameter, hairless. Bark 3-5 mm thick, black and flaking. Leaves elliptic-oblanceolate, 120-220 mm long, 30-65 mm wide, leathery, dark green. Flowerhead solitary, 70-90 mm across, oblong with bracts opening to saucer-shaped. *Involucral bracts with outer surface densely covered with thick, brown, velvety hairs,* inner surface red; outer series ovate, tip pointed, 10-15 mm long, 10 mm wide; inner series oblong, tip rounded, 50 mm long, 10 mm wide. *Perianth with shaggy white hairs at the tip,* 50-80 mm long, tube 18 mm long, hairless below. Style 60-70 mm long, slightly curved, red. Pollen presenter 15 mm long, thread-like, minutely knee-bent at base.
DISTRIBUTION: Escarpment from Wolkberg to Lydenburg in Northern Province and Mpumalanga.
HABITAT: Sandstones and quartzites on south-facing slopes, 1400-2300 m. STATUS: Locally abundant, forming open woodlands with *P. roupelliae.* FLOWERS: September to December, mainly October. FRUITS: Released 12-24 months after flowering.

**Protea comptonii** Beard        Saddleback Sugarbush    **Plate 7**

*A tree 4-8 m tall, with a rounded and open crown. Trunk up to 500 mm in diameter. Bark grey, corky, up to 20 mm thick,* deeply fissured longitudinally. Stems stout, 10-20 mm in diameter, hairless, leaves crowded on current year's growth. Leaves oblanceolate to elliptic, 120-250 mm long, 25-50 mm wide, hairless, deep green, thick, leathery, midrib and margin red. Flowerhead ovate, 80-120 mm across; stalkless. *Involucral bracts cream, hairless;* outer series triangular, 15 mm long, 15-20 mm wide, overlapping; inner series oblong-spatulate, 50-60 mm long, 10-20 mm wide, loosely spreading, forming a flat saucer when open. Perianth 65-70 mm long, tube 15 mm long, tip with white shaggy hairs. *Style 65-80 mm long,* curved inwards, white. Pollen presenter 10 mm long, thread-like, knee-bent at base.
DISTRIBUTION: Mpumalanga, Swaziland and KwaZulu-Natal escarpment. HABITAT: Quartzite outcrops, steep southern slopes, 1200-1600 m. STATUS: Localized but abundant, forming a component of *Protea* woodland. *Red Data Book* status: Vulnerable. FLOWERS: May to September, mainly May to July. FRUITS: October to January.

**Protea curvata** N.E. Br.                                     Barberton Sugarbush     **Plate 7**

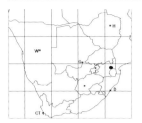

A small, erect tree up to 8 m tall, with a sparse crown, young plants with a rootstock. Trunk 100-300 mm in diameter. Bark black, scaly and fissured. Stems erect, 5-10 mm in diameter, hairless, leaves on current year's growth. *Leaves narrowly oblong-lanceolate, sickle-shaped, 110-200 mm long, 8-16 mm wide, base tapering*, leathery, hairless, glaucous. Flowerhead globose, 50-70 mm across. *Involucral bracts with deep red-black, silky to velvety hairs on the margin, hairless below*; outer series ovate, 7-15 mm long, 10-15 mm wide; inner series ovate-oblong, 20-30 mm long, 8-16 mm wide, widely separated. Perianth 50-60 mm long, tube 15 mm long, with short, pale hairs. Style 60-65 mm long, pink. Pollen presenter 15 mm long, thread-like, slightly knee-bent at base. *Seedhead shears off when fruits are mature.*
DISTRIBUTION: Claremont Vale on the Drakensberg escarpment near Barberton, Mpumalanga.
HABITAT: Serpentine soils, 850 m. STATUS: Known from a single population. *Red Data Book* status: Vulnerable. FLOWERS: June to October, mainly June and July. FRUITS: October to December.
NOTE: *Protea caffra* from east of Claremont Vale – a form previously known as *P. rhodantha* var. *falcata* – also has a sickle-shaped leaf and resembles *P. curvata* in general appearance. However, it has a typical *P. caffra* flowerhead.

**Protea laetans** L.E. Davidson                                  Blyde Sugarbush     **Plate 7**

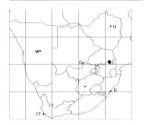

*A slender tree up to 5 m tall, with 2-6 stems arising from a rootstock*, occasionally with a single main trunk 50-150 mm in diameter. Bark grey turning black with age, with rectangular fissures. *Stems hairless*, 7-10 mm in diameter, leaves clustered on previous 2 years' growth. Leaves narrowly oblanceolate to lanceolate, occasionally sickle-shaped, 100-200 mm long, 15-35 mm wide, base tapering, leathery, hairless, glaucous, margin yellow. Flowerhead cup-shaped, 80-100 mm across; *stalk robust,* 10-25 mm long. *Involucral bracts with inner surface deep carmine, outer surface densely covered with silver or brown-red silky hairs*; outer series ovate, tip pointed, 7-12 mm long, 8-15 mm wide, tightly overlapping; inner series oblong, 15-20 mm long, 8-15 mm wide, margin dry and membranous. *Perianth with tawny brown silky hairs at the tip*, 50-60 mm long, tube 15-20 mm long, hairless below. Style 50-55 mm long, slightly curved inwards, red. Pollen presenter 10 mm long, thread-like, grooved, not distinct from style.
DISTRIBUTION: Drakensberg escarpment of Northern Province and Mpumalanga from Mogologolo to Bourke's Luck. HABITAT: Quartzite soils, 1000-1400 m. STATUS: Known from a few stands of several thousand plants, with scattered plants to the south. FLOWERS: March to September, mainly April and May. FRUITS: Not known.
NOTE: Beard (1993) considered this a subspecies of *P. gaguedi,* but this view is not upheld here, as the hairless stems and crimson flowerheads in *P. laetans* contrast with the densely hairy young stems and silvery white flowerheads in *P. gaguedi.* Moreover, the 2 species occur together without any records of hybrids or intermediate forms.

## *Protea* **The Savanna Sugarbushes**

The Savanna Sugarbushes (section *Lasiocephalae*) have *hairy young stems. Flowerheads are medium-sized (about 50 mm across). The involucral bracts are generally covered with silky hairs. The perianth is hairy on the outer surface, 20-50 mm long.* Styles are longer than 30 mm, usually straight or very slightly curved, and *as long as or longer than the involucral bracts.* Clusters of flowerheads are borne at the ends of branches, although in *P. gaguedi* the flowerhead is usually solitary.

The 2 species of Savanna Sugarbushes in southern Africa are closely related, although *P. gaguedi* is the larger in most features. The most reliable distinguishing feature is that *P. gaguedi* rapidly loses the hairs on its leaves, whereas *P. welwitschii* usually retains the brown hairs on its mature leaves. The involucral bracts are silver in *P. gaguedi*, whereas those of *P. welwitschii* are brown. The leaves of *P. gaguedi* are 5-9 times longer than broad, compared to 2-5 times in *P. welwitschii*. All distinctions between the species appear to break down in Angola.

*Protea laetans* is considered by Beard (1993) to belong to this group, but it has hairless leaves, hairless stems and crimson flowerheads, and it is larger in all its features (compared to *P. gaguedi* from Mpumalanga). In many respects *P. laetans* is intermediate between *P. rubropilosa* and *P. gaguedi*, but it fits more comfortably with the Mountain Sugarbushes.

*Protea welwitschii* Engl.                         Dwarf Savanna Sugarbush     **Plate 8**

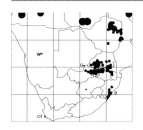

A shrub 0.5-1.5 m tall with numerous stems arising from a rootstock, occasionally up to 4 m tall with a single trunk up to 150 mm in diameter. Bark grey to grey-brown. *Stems densely covered with long white or brown hairs, glaucous when mature,* 5-8 mm in diameter, with leaves not clustered at tips, occasionally with leaves deciduous. *Leaves densely covered with white or brown hairs, tending to be hairless when mature except at bases,* elliptic to broadly oblanceolate, 50-120 mm long, 15-95 mm wide. *Flowerheads in clusters of 3 or 4,* globose opening to saucer-shaped, 30-60 mm across, *with a strong, sickly-sweet, honey-like smell; stalk up to 10 mm long. Involucral bracts sparsely to densely covered with white to brown silky hairs;* outer series ovate, tip rounded, 10 mm long, 10-12 mm wide; inner series oblong, 20-50 mm long, 5-15 mm wide. *Perianth 20-50 mm long,* tube 5-20 mm long, with white, cream or brown hairs. Style 30-50 mm long, curved inwards. Pollen presenter 6-8 mm long, linear and thread-like, knee-bent at base.
DISTRIBUTION: North-West Province, Gauteng, Northern Province, Mpumalanga, KwaZulu-Natal, Zimbabwe, Malawi and Mozambique. Extralimitally to Uganda. HABITAT: Varied, from subtropical KwaZulu-Natal coast at 300 m to cool mountain grassland at 2000 m. STATUS: Widespread in many isolated populations in South Africa, but continuous and widespread in Zimbabwe. FLOWERS: December to May, mainly January and February. FRUITS: Not known.
□ VARIATIONS: Extremely variable throughout its range. Although many varieties have been recognized in the past, some of which were geographically distinct, none is currently upheld by most taxonomists. Montane populations have large, solitary flowerheads and broad

leaves, whereas those at lower altitudes have narrow leaves and smaller flowerheads, often in clusters of up to six. Northernmost populations have hairless leaves.

*Protea welwitschii* subsp. *hirta* Beard (Plate 8), now no longer recognized by most taxonomists, has a low, unbranched, multi-stemmed habit and is confined to KwaZulu-Natal lowlands.

***Protea gaguedi*** J.F. Gmel.    African Sugarbush    **Plate 8**

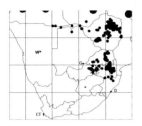

An erect to gnarled shrub, 2-3 m tall (occasionally up to 10 m), much branched, 2-3 m across. Trunk 100-150 mm in diameter. Bark thick, grey, corky, flaking. Stems 5-8 mm in diameter, initially densely covered with hairs but hairless when mature, leaves often deciduous, especially after frost. *Leaves sparsely covered with silky hairs, hairless and glaucous when mature, elliptic to oblong to sickle-shaped, 12-36 mm wide, 80-200 mm long. Flowerhead depressed-globose, 50-110 mm across,* usually solitary but occasionally in clusters; with a slight sweet or unpleasant odour. *Involucral bracts with silvery, silky hairs, occasionally with a rusty brown margin*; outer series ovate to triangular, 10-15 mm long, 10-20 mm wide, tightly overlapping; inner series oblong, tip curved inward, 30-50 mm long, 5-10 mm wide, widely separated. *Perianth 35-65 mm long,* tube 10-25 mm long, densely covered with shaggy hairs, silvery. Style straight, 40-65 mm long, white. Pollen presenter 10-12 mm long, thread-like, tip bilobed, swollen at base. DISTRIBUTION: The second-most widespread of all sugarbushes, occurring in North-West Province, Gauteng, Northern Province, Mpumalanga, Swaziland, KwaZulu-Natal, Malawi, Zimbabwe, Botswana and Namibia. Extralimitally to Ethiopia. HABITAT: Varied, usually in drier sites and on rocky outcrops, 600-2500 m. STATUS: Usually in isolated groves or as scattered plants, but also locally common, forming a dwarf woodland. FLOWERS: August to February, mainly December to February. FRUITS: Not known.
☐ VARIATIONS: Flowers tend to be smaller towards the southern end of this species' distribution and at lower altitudes. In tropical Africa the sizes in general are larger than in southern Africa.
NOTE: The roots have been recorded as being used as an aphrodisiac in Namibia, where the species is now thought to be extinct.

## *Protea* **The Moorland Sugarbushes**

The Moorland Sugarbushes (section *Cristatae*) are shrubs which tend to occur in high mountain areas. Their leaves are hairy, often becoming hairless when mature. *The perianth tube is slender, and on opening the segments recoil to the base of the style.*

---

***Protea asymmetrica*** Beard                                             Inyanga Sugarbush     **Plate 9**

A shrub up to 1.6 m tall, with numerous unbranched stems arising from a rootstock. Stems 5-9 mm in diameter, red, with long hairs, hairless when mature, with leaves along entire length. Bark smooth, yellow-brown. Leaves obovate, 80-120 mm long, 25-35 mm wide, base tapering, with scattered, long grey hairs. Flowerhead solitary, globose, 70-90 mm long, 80-100 mm across. *Involucral bracts pale green to pink, densely covered with long, reddish to pink hairs*, up to 65 mm long, 20 mm wide, shorter than flowers. *Perianth densely covered with long, white hairs, 60-70 mm long*, tube 25-30 mm long. Style 60-70 mm long, white. Pollen presenter 10 mm long, linear, knee-bent at base, pink. DISTRIBUTION: Inyangani Mountain and Chingamwe Plateau, Zimbabwe. HABITAT: Afro-alpine grassland at 2000 m. STATUS: Known from only 2 populations. FLOWERS: June to August. FRUITS: Not known.

---

***Protea wentzeliana*** Engl.                                           Wentzel's Sugarbush     **Plate 9**

Shrub 0.6-1.5 m tall, with numerous unbranched stems arising from a rootstock. Stems slender, 2-5 mm in diameter, with woolly hairs, hairless when mature. Bark red. Leaves elliptic to obovate, 60-120 mm long, 15-55 mm wide, woolly, hairless when mature, twisted, leathery; stalk 3 mm long. Flowerhead solitary, turban-shaped, 60-70 mm long, 60-110 mm across; stalkless. *Involucral bracts pale brown with pink tips, with silky hairs collapsing on flowering*, up to 50 mm long and 12-15 mm wide, shorter than flowers. *Perianth hairless at the base, with tufts of white hairs at the tip*, 30-55 mm long, tube 10-20 mm long. Style 50-60 mm long, white. Pollen presenter 8 mm long, thread-like, not distinct from style, pink. DISTRIBUTION: Chimanimani Mountains between Zimbabwe and Mozambique. Extralimitally to Tanzania and Democratic Republic of Congo. HABITAT: Grassland and ericaceous-proteaceous moorland and grassland at 1800-2700 m. STATUS: Within southern Africa it is locally abundant at its single known site. FLOWERS: May to December. FRUITS: Not known.

□ VARIATION: There is much variation in forms to the north of southern Africa. Although Beard (1993) considers the forms in southern Africa to be *P. neocrinita,* other authors do not recognize even subspecies.

## *Protea* The King Sugarbush

The King Sugarbush is the South African national flower, and is unmistakable with its *large flowerheads and distinctly stalked leaves.* It is also distinguished by the *short, pink, velvety hairs on the numerous involucral bracts.* The sole member of section *Cynaroideae,* it is most closely related to the Snow Sugarbushes.

*Protea cynaroides* (L.) L.                                                   King Protea     **Plate 10**

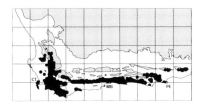

An upright shrub 0.3-2 m tall, with erect, sparsely branching, *hairless stems arising from an underground rootstock. Leaves round, ovate or elliptic,* 120-300 mm long, 20-130 mm wide, leathery, hairless; *stalk 40-180 mm long.* Flowerhead conical to bowl-shaped, 120-200 mm long, 120-300 mm across. Involucral bracts overlapping, hairless or with silky to velvety hairs, pink to crimson or cream; outer series lanceolate to ovate, 20-40 mm long, 7-25 mm wide; inner series lanceolate, 80-120 mm long, 10-35 mm wide. Perianth 70-100 mm long, yellow, limbs with terminal white awns. Style 80-95 mm long, curved inwards, sparsely covered with hairs below. Pollen presenter 10-15 mm long, linear to awl-shaped, quadrangular, knee-bent at base, yellow. Ovary with black hairs in old seedheads. HABITAT: Extremely varied, growing in a wide range of situations, perhaps favouring rocky areas, 0-1500 m. STATUS: Common in most areas, typically as scattered plants, rarely in dense clumps. FLOWERS: All year round, locally variable. FRUITS: Retained.
□ VARIATIONS: Perhaps the most variable of all sugarbushes. A gradual reduction in the size of leaves and flowerheads occurs towards the east. Involucral bracts vary from pointed to rounded in outline and the shape of the flowerheads varies from conical to bowl-shaped. With altitude, involucral bracts become more hairy and their colour also changes. Flowering season varies considerably, depending on altitude, habitat and locality, and is genetically fixed, so that it does not change if plants are translocated.
    Three broad groups are recognized, comprising some 80 natural 'horticultural variants' which are grouped into 10 'trade variants'. However, these enjoy no formal botanical recognition; a detailed taxonomic study of the variants is required.
□ The oval-leaf variant has *ovate to round* leaves and occurs from the Cederberg to the Cape Peninsula and western Langeberg, and on the Potberg.
□ The elliptic-leaf variant has *broad elliptic* leaves and may be found from the western Langeberg to the Tsitsikamma Mountains and Elandsberg.
□ The small-leaf variant has *small elliptic* leaves and occurs on the Garden Route Flats from George to Port Elizabeth, mostly below 150 m.

## *Protea* The Snow Sugarbushes

The Snow Sugarbushes (section *Paracynaroides*) are characterized by their rhizomatous or prostrate growth form; *involucral bracts that have a long thin tip and are covered or edged, like the awns, with thick, white, woolly hairs*; a reddish colour to the insides of the involucral bracts; flowerheads that are borne at ground level and produce a strong yeasty odour; and *fruit with white hairs*. All grow at high altitudes on mountain tops, above or near the snowline.

The 4 species can readily be distinguished by leaf shape, style length and the colour of the involucral bracts.

### *Protea scolopendriifolia* (Salisb. ex Knight) Rourke          Harts-tongue-fern Sugarbush    **Plate 11**

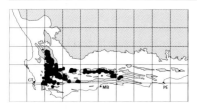

*A rhizomatous shrub forming clumps 0.5-1.0 m across, regenerating from subterranean stems. Leaves oblanceolate to spatulate, 20-85 mm wide, 200-600 mm long, blade flat*, rough, leathery, hairless when mature, midrib prominent; *stalk 10-100 mm long*, hairy. Flowerhead shallowly cup-shaped, 60-120 mm across, surrounded by dark brown, lanceolate basal bracts. Involucral bracts lanceolate, tip pointed, carmine, loosely overlapping; outer series 15-25 mm long, 5-15 mm wide, hairless with a hairy margin; inner series 35-50 mm long, 5-7 mm wide, densely covered with woolly or velvety hairs. Perianth 35-45 mm long, tube 10 mm long, hairless or with shaggy hairs, white. Style 30-45 mm long, curved inwards, carmine. Pollen presenter 10 mm long, linear, not distinct from style. DISTRIBUTION: Cederberg to Kogelberg and along the Riviersonderend Mountains, Langeberg and Swartberg to the Kouga Mountains. HABITAT: Cederberg shale, rarely sandstone soils, 450-1800 m. STATUS: Scattered plants can predictably be found where the habitat is suitable over the distribution range. FLOWERS: September to December. FRUITS: Retained.
□ VARIATION: In dry localities the leaves and flowerheads tend to be smaller, the involucral bracts are more densely covered with woolly hairs, and the plants are less compact in habit.

### *Protea scabriuscula* E. Phillips          Hoary Sugarbush    **Plate 11**

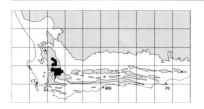

*A prostrate shrub resembling a cushion plant, 0.5-0.7 m across, up to 0.5 m tall, with a single main stem and branches above ground, so that it is killed by fire. Leaves linear to linear-lanceolate, 150-250 mm long, 5-20 mm wide*, hairless when mature, rough, margin wavy and horny, midrib prominent. *Flowerhead obconic to bell-shaped, 40-60 mm long*, 30-40 mm across, with dark brown, lanceolate basal scales, never opening fully, concealed among leaves. Involucral bracts lanceolate, tightly overlapping, densely covered with white, woolly hairs, hairless at tip, flushed carmine; outer series 10-15 mm long, 5 mm wide; inner series 20 mm long, 2-3 mm wide. Perianth 40-45 mm long, tube 8 mm long, woolly, white. Style 30-35 mm long, straight. Pollen presenter 6-7 mm long, linear to thread-like, scarcely distinct from style, carmine.
DISTRIBUTION: Hex River Mountains and Koue Bokkeveld. HABITAT: Rocky, east-facing sandstone slopes, 1100-2100 m. STATUS: Known from a handful of small, isolated populations.
FLOWERS: October to January, mainly December. FRUITS: Retained.

***Protea cryophila*** Bolus                                    Snowball Protea    **Plate 11**

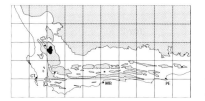

A prostrate shrub forming dense, tufted clumps, 1-3 m across, 0.5 m tall, with a single main stem and inter-locked, creeping branches. *Leaves 300-500 mm long, 50-70 mm wide, blade elliptic, folded lengthwise,* leathery to gristly, margin horny, midrib prominent, clustered at branch tips; stalk 200-250 mm long. *Flowerhead shallowly cup-shaped, 120-140 mm long,* 130-160 mm across, with basal bracts reddish brown and narrowing to a point. *Involucral bracts lanceolate, tip tapering to a narrow point,* outside white and densely covered with woolly hairs, inside carmine; outer series 60-70 mm long, 10-15 mm wide; *inner series 90-100 mm long, 5-7 mm wide.* Perianth 85-90 mm long, tube 10-15 mm long, creamy white to pink. *Style straight, 65-90 mm long,* red. Pollen presenter 15 mm long, linear, not distinct from style.

DISTRIBUTION: Central Cederberg peaks. HABITAT: Rocky ledges and screes, 1750-1900 m. STATUS: Locally frequent on half a dozen high peaks. *Red Data Book* status: Rare. FLOWERS: January to April, mainly February. FRUITS: Retained.

***Protea pruinosa*** Rourke                                    Frosted Sugarbush    **Plate 11**

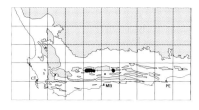

*A dense, prostrate shrub 0.5-1.5 m across, up to 0.5 m tall, formed by a single main stem with creeping branches. Leaves 200-450 mm long, 40-80 mm wide, blade elliptic to oblanceolate, folded lengthwise,* leathery to gristly, margin horny, midrib prominent, clustered at branch tips; *stalk 100-200 mm long. Flowerhead deeply cup-shaped, 100-120 mm long,* 80-120 mm across, with brown, lanceolate basal bracts. Involucral bracts densely covered externally with woolly hairs and white at tips, carmine and hairless at base, inner surface hairless and deep carmine; outer series ovate, tip pointed, 20-35 mm long, 5-20 mm wide; *inner series linear-lanceolate, 40-45 mm long, 4-6 mm wide.* Perianth 55-65 mm long, tube 38-40 mm long, white. *Style 55-60 mm long,* slightly curved, white. Pollen presenter 10 mm long, linear, not distinct from style.

DISTRIBUTION: Klein Swartberg, with a single population on the Groot Swartberg at Blesberg (east of Meiringspoort). HABITAT: Ridges and summits, 1800-2100 m. STATUS: Known only from a few isolated populations containing several (rarely up to 25) scattered plants. *Red Data Book* status: Rare. FLOWERS: January and February. FRUITS: Retained.

## *Protea* The Spoon-bract Sugarbushes

The Spoon-bract Sugarbushes (section *Ligulatae*) are characterized by *long, spoon- or tongue-shaped (spatulate) inner involucral bracts*, with a slightly hairy margin. *These equal or exceed the flowers in length.* The perianth usually has 3 awns. Both the perianth and the inner involucral bracts collapse after flowering, resulting in an untidy, spiky seedhead.

---

*Protea roupelliae* Meisn. subsp. *roupelliae*                     Silver Sugarbush     **Plate 12**

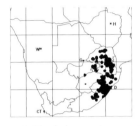

A small, upright tree 3-8 m tall, with a rounded crown. Trunk short, 200-500 mm in diameter. Bark grey to black, thick, fissured. Stems hairless when mature. Leaves curved upwards, linear-lanceolate to obovate, 60-170 mm long, 15-50 mm wide, hairless or with shaggy to silky hairs, tip rounded to pointed; almost stalkless. *Flowerhead oblong-obconic to bowl-shaped*, 80-120 mm long, 80-100 mm across. Involucral bracts pink or ruddy to brown, sparsely to densely covered with silver, silky hairs; outer series overlapping, ovate-oblong, 10-15 mm long, 8-12 mm wide, margin papery, curled back, brown; *inner series spatulate, tip pointed*, 50-100 mm long, 6-10 mm wide. Perianth 60-80 mm long, tube 15 mm long, limbs with gristly awns with short, cream, brown, red or purple-black hairs. Style curved inwards, 50-65 mm long, downy at base. Pollen presenter linear, awl-shaped, knee-bent at base.
DISTRIBUTION: North-West Province, Gauteng, Northern Province and Mpumalanga, Swaziland, KwaZulu-Natal, Lesotho and Eastern Cape. HABITAT: Varied, found in many vegetation and soil types, 0-2400 m. STATUS: Usually social, a dominant element in open protea woodland.
FLOWERS: All year round, but mainly February to April. FRUITS: Not known.
□ VARIATION: *Protea roupelliae* subsp. *hamiltonii* Beard ex Rourke (Dwarf Silver Sugarbush) is similar to *P. roupelliae* subsp. *roupelliae* but is a low, sprawling shrublet forming mats up to 0.3 m tall and 1 m across. It occurs in the Barberton region at Nelshoogte in bare, leached clay on quartzite, at 1300 m. Classified as Endangered in the *Red Data Book*, it is extremely localized, occurring in populations scattered over a few square kilometres. Flowers are borne from February to April.

---

*Protea eximia* (Salisb. ex Knight) Fourc.                     Broad-leaf Sugarbush     **Plate 12**

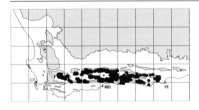

An erect shrub 2-5 m tall, sparsely branched. Trunk up to 300 mm in diameter. Stems glaucous when mature. *Leaves horizontal, ovate to oblong, heart-shaped at base, hairless*, 60-100 mm long, 30-65 mm wide, leathery, glaucous. Flowerhead obconic, 100-140 mm long, 80-120 mm across. Involucral bracts with silky hairs externally, margin hairy; outer series overlapping, ovate, 10-15 mm long, 10-15 mm wide, margin brown; *inner series widely splayed, oblong to spatulate*, 40-100 mm long, 8-15 mm wide, pink to

orange-brown. Perianth 85-100 mm long, tube 10 mm long, *awns extended with purple-black, velvety hairs.* Style straight, 60-75 mm long, downy below. Pollen presenter 6-8 mm long, linear, knee-bent at base.
DISTRIBUTION: From Keeromsberg along the Langeberg and Swartberg to Kouga Mountains and Elandsberg. HABITAT: Sandstone and quartzite soils, 200-1600 m. STATUS: Highly social, forming dense, extensive stands. FLOWERS: July to December, mainly August to October. FRUITS: Retained.
☐ VARIATIONS: In wetter habitats leaves tend to be green and less glaucous; in drier inland areas they may acquire a pink blush in winter.

*Protea compacta* R. Br.                                           Bot River Sugarbush   **Plate 12**

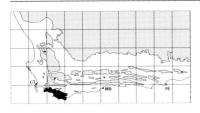

*An erect, lanky shrub 2-3.5 m tall, sparsely branched. Stems hairless when mature. Leaves curved upwards, ovate to lanceolate, heart-shaped at base, 50-130 mm long, 20-55 mm wide*, hairless and leathery when mature. Flowerhead oblong-obconic, 90-120 mm long, 70-100 mm across. Involucral bracts pink or white, downy, margin hairy; outer series overlapping, ovate, tip pointed, 10-20 mm long, 10-15 mm wide; inner series splayed, oblong-spatulate, 70-100 mm long, 5-15 mm wide. Perianth 60-80 mm long, tube 15 mm long, awns wavy, with downy hairs. Style slightly bent inwards, 60-70 mm long, hairless. Pollen presenter 10-12 mm long, linear with swelling at tip, knee-bent at base.
DISTRIBUTION: Kleinmond, Klein River and Bredasdorp Mountains and the flats between these and the sea. HABITAT: Sandy soils, 0-200 m. STATUS: Highly social, occurring in large, dense stands. FLOWERS: April to September, mainly May and June. FRUITS: Retained.

*Protea obtusifolia* H. Buek ex Meisn.                              Limestone Sugarbush   **Plate 12**

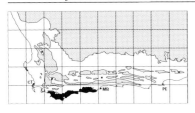

An erect shrub 2-4 m tall, rounded or spreading. Trunk up to 600 mm in diameter. Stems downy, hairless when mature. *Leaves curved upwards, oblanceolate-elliptic, base tapering, hairless when mature*, 100-150 mm long, 20-40 mm wide, tip rounded, leathery. Flowerhead oblong-obconic, 90-120 mm long, 50-80 mm across. Involucral bracts overlapping, cream to red; *outer series edged brown*, with silky hairs, 10-20 mm long, 10-15 mm wide; *inner series hairless, shiny*, lanceolate to spatulate, 40-100 mm long, 5-18 mm wide, margin densely fringed. Perianth 70-80 mm long, tube 15 mm long, awns 10 mm long, with silky-shaggy hairs. Style straight, 60-70 mm long. Pollen presenter 8 mm long, linear, knee-bent at base.
DISTRIBUTION: Elim, Bredasdorp and Riversdale Flats. HABITAT: Limestone hills and flats, 0-200 m. STATUS: Social, occurring in dense stands. FLOWERS: April to September, mainly June and July. FRUITS: Retained.

***Protea susannae*** E. Phillips                                   Stink-leaf Sugarbush     **Plate 13**

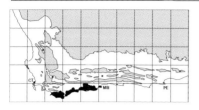

An erect shrub 2-3 m tall, 3-4 m across. Trunk up to 150 mm in diameter. Stems hairless and glaucous when mature. *Leaves with a sulphurous odour, margin undulating,* curved upwards, oblong to oblanceolate-elliptic, tapering at base, 80-160 mm long, 15-30 mm wide. Flowerhead obconic, 80-100 mm long, 70-110 mm across. *Involucral bracts with dark brown, sticky, varnish-like coating,* pink-brown, with short,
delicate hairs at base; outer series ovate, tip pointed, 10-20 mm long, 10-15 mm wide, margin often hairy; inner series oblong to spatulate, 60-80 mm long, 8-20 mm wide, tip rounded. Perianth 65-80 mm long, tube inflated, 15-20 mm long, awns 5-10 mm long, densely covered with long, white hairs interspersed with black ones. Style straight, 60-70 mm long, hairy at base. Pollen presenter 8-10 mm long, linear, curved inwards above, knee-bent at base.
DISTRIBUTION: Elim, Bredasdorp and Riversdale Flats. HABITAT: Calcareous and neutral sandy soils, 0-200 m. STATUS: Social in dense, isolated stands, especially common in the Albertinia-Still Bay region. FLOWERS: April to September, mainly May to July. FRUITS: Retained.
NOTE: A promiscuous species, but all hybrids known to date inherit the leaves' offensive odour, making them unsuitable as vase subjects.

***Protea burchellii*** Stapf                                   Burchell's Sugarbush     **Plate 13**

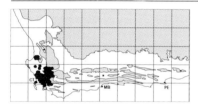

An erect, spreading shrub 1-2 m tall, up to 3 m across. Trunk 300 mm in diameter. Stems hairless when mature. *Leaves linear to narrowly oblong, olive-green, with a fine black point,* 70-170 mm long, 7-20 mm wide, hairless and rough when mature, margin and midrib horny and prominent. Flowerhead obconic, 90-100 mm long, 50-70 mm across, with short flowers sunken within the long involucral bracts. *Involucral bracts shiny,* cream to pink to carmine; *outer series hairless,* overlapping, ovate to oblong, 15-25 mm long, 10 mm wide; *inner series one-third longer than flowers, margin densely covered with hairs,* oblong to linear-spatulate, 70-90 mm long, 5-8 mm wide, tip with a black or white beard. Perianth 60-70 mm long, tube 10 mm long, awns with white hairs interspersed with black ones. *Style 55-65 mm long, lower two-thirds hairy,* straight. Pollen presenter 5-10 mm long, thread-like, knee-bent at base, tip pointed, often minutely hooked.
DISTRIBUTION: Hottentots-Holland to Olifants River Mountains; Cape to Hopefield Flats; isolated populations at Witzenbergvlakte, Piketberg and the upper Breede River Valley. HABITAT: Varied but favouring richer soils, 100-850 m. STATUS: Large populations on lower mountain slopes with isolated populations on flats: extinct (but re-established) on the Cape Peninsula. FLOWERS: Mainly June and July, but also August. FRUITS: Retained.
☐ VARIATION: The colour of the beard on the inner involucral bracts varies considerably. The beard's density also varies, from being non-existent to dense.
NOTE: Where this species' distribution overlaps with that of *P. laurifolia,* a small proportion of hybrid plants may be found.

*Protea longifolia* Andrews                              Long-leaf Sugarbush    **Plate 13**

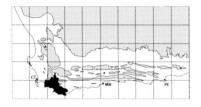

An almost erect to sprawling shrub, 0.5-1.5 m tall, up to 2 m across. Trunk up to 40 mm in diameter. Stems hairless when mature. *Leaves curved upwards, linear to linear-spatulate*, 90-200 mm long, 5-17 mm wide, tapering at base. Flowerhead oblong-obconic, *awns forming a pointed, black, woolly cone*, size variable, 80-160 mm long, 40-90 mm across. Involucral bracts green to white to pink, hairless; outer series over-lapping, ovate, tip pointed, 12-15 mm long, 10-15 mm wide; inner series ovate to lanceolate, 70-120 mm long, 5-15 mm wide, tip pointed; innermost bracts linear, densely fringed. Perianth 45-100 mm long excluding awns, tube 10 mm long, *awns 20-55 mm long, inner much longer, with dense, black, woolly hairs.* Style 40-65 mm long, lower three-quarters hairy. Pollen presenter 7-10 mm long, linear, knee-bent at base.

DISTRIBUTION: Du Toit's Kloof to Riviersonderend and Bredasdorp Mountains and Elim Flats. HABITAT: Sandstone and ironstone soils, 0-150 m, but rarely up to 1000 m. STATUS: Common, but sparsely distributed, seldom forming dense stands. FLOWERS: May to September, mainly June and July. FRUITS: Retained.

□ VARIATION: The form on the Elim Flats, *P. longifolia* var. *minor* E. Phillips, has short (80-120 mm) flowerheads and green involucral bracts and is small (up to 0.5 m); in these respects it is similar to *P. pudens.*

NOTE: Records of natural hybrids between this and many other *Protea* species indicate that this is a promiscuous species. These hybrids are easily recognized by their intermediate characters, and may form a large proportion of plants at some sites.

*Protea pudens* Rourke                              Bashful Sugarbush    **Plate 13**

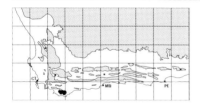

A sprawling, prostrate shrub up to 1 m across, 0.4 m tall, with a single main stem. *Stems trailing*, hairless when mature. *Leaves pointing vertically from a hori-zontal stem, linear to linear-spatulate, 2-5 mm wide*, 60-140 mm long, hairless, margin often hairy. Flowerhead bell-shaped, 50-80 mm long, 30-60 mm across, *awns forming a pointed, woolly cone.* Involucral bracts deep rusty pink, ovate, tip rounded, hairless, margin hairy; outer series 6-10 mm long, 6-10 mm wide; inner series 30-50 mm long, innermost bracts often with silky hairs. Perianth 40-60 mm long, tube 5-8 mm long; *awns 10-18 mm long, with feathery hairs, white at base and black at tip. Style 30-45 mm long*, straight, hairy below. Pollen presenter 5-7 mm long, curved, knee-bent at base.

DISTRIBUTION: Elim Flats. HABITAT: Heavy sandy-clay soils, 30-40 m. STATUS: Locally abundant, but not conspicuous. *Red Data Book* status: Endangered, due to agriculture. FLOWERS: May to September, mainly July and August. FRUITS: Retained.

### *Protea* **The 'True' Sugarbushes**

The 'True' Sugarbushes (section *Melliferae*) are characterized by their *large obconic flowerheads with linear-oblong to oblong inner involucral bracts.* Other features useful for identification include the hairless styles, involucral bracts and perianth (except for the tip which has a pale beard).

*Protea repens* (L.) L.                    Common Sugarbush    **Plate 14**

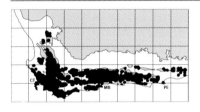

An erect, branched shrub up to 4.5 m tall. Trunk up to 300 mm in diameter. *Stems hairless. Leaves upright, linear-spatulate to oblanceolate, hairless,* 50-150 mm long, 5-18 mm wide. Flowerhead oblong to obconic, 100-160 mm long, 70-90 mm across. *Involucral bracts with outer surface with a gum-like, sticky substance,* tightly overlapping, cream to green to red, hairless, tip pointed; outer series ovate, 10-20 mm long, 10-12 mm wide; inner series lanceolate, 80-110 mm long, 6-20 mm wide. Perianth 70-100 mm long, 3 limbs with awns and a beard, 1 limb and awn hairless. Style slightly bent, 70-90 mm long. Pollen presenter 20 mm long, linear, not distinct from style. *Seedhead a pointed, brown, inverted 'ice-cream cone'.*

DISTRIBUTION: From the Bokkeveld escarpment to Cape Peninsula to Soetwaterberg, east of Grahamstown. HABITAT: Extremely varied, 0-1500 m. STATUS: Almost ubiquitous, either as scattered plants or in dense stands. FLOWERS: All year round, mainly May to October in the west and September to March in the east. FRUITS: Retained.

□ VARIATIONS: Fairly uniform in leaf and flowerhead features, but varies considerably in flowering season and colour of involucral bracts, with a tendency for redder forms to occur in the eastern part of its range.

NOTE: This species was the unofficial South African national flower until *P. cynaroides* was made the official flower in 1976. It is by far the most abundant sugarbush in the Cape flora, and is heavily used in the cut-flower trade. One of the staple plants for the Cape sugarbird, it has prolific nectar (hence the old name *P. mellifera* Thunb. which described the plant as honey-bearing) which used to be collected and boiled to make *bossiestroop,* an essential component of 19th-century medicine chests in the Cape.

**Protea aristata** E. Phillips                                    Ladismith Sugarbush          **Plate 14**

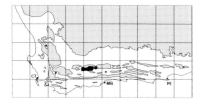

An erect, stocky shrub up to 2.5 m tall, 3 m across. Trunk up to 250 mm in diameter. Stems hairless. *Leaves erect, linear, 70-110 mm, long, 2-3 mm wide, flattened, hairless, tip with black point*, producing a sulphurous odour when picked. Flowerhead obconic to bell-shaped, 110-140 mm long, 100-120 mm across. *Involucral bracts crimson*; outer series ovate, tip rounded, 10 mm long, 10-15 mm wide; inner series spatulate, 100-120 mm long, 10-15 mm wide, tip pointed and curved inward, downy. Perianth 90-100 mm long, tube 20 mm long, limbs crimson, hairless except for a beard on the 15 mm-long awn. Style 70-75 mm long, crimson. Pollen presenter 7-10 mm long, linear, slightly knee-bent at base.

DISTRIBUTION: Klein Swartberg between Buffelspoort and Seweweekspoort.
HABITAT: Krantzes and rocky sandstone slopes, 750-2000 m. STATUS: Scattered plants in large, diffuse stands create an impression of rarity. FLOWERS: October to February, mainly December. FRUITS: April to August, but retained in cultivation.

**Protea lanceolata** E. Mey. ex Meisn.                              Lance-leaf Sugarbush          **Plate 14**

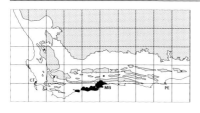

An erect shrub 2-4 m tall. Trunk up to 100 mm in diameter. *Stems hairless. Leaves erect, lanceolate, hairless*, 50-75 mm long, 5-15 mm wide, tip round-pointed. Flowerhead obconic, 70-80 mm long, 50-70 mm across, untidy when open. Involucral bracts green with a brown margin; *outer series hairless*, tightly overlapping, ovate, tip pointed, 8-14 mm long, 8-10 mm wide; *inner series widely splayed*, ovate to lanceolate, 25-40 mm long, 5-15 mm wide, hairless or fringed with minute, red hairs at the base. Perianth 55-65 mm long, tube 15 mm long, white, claws with red hairs at tip. Style 55-60 mm long, curved inwards. Pollen presenter 15-18 mm long, thread-like, straight, not distinct from style. *Seedhead a globose cone with a concave receptacle*, 50-70 mm across, tufted with protruding brown perianth.

DISTRIBUTION: Potberg and Riversdale Flats to Robinson Pass. HABITAT: Calcareous white sands, often at the fynbos/thicket ecotone, at Mossel Bay on gravels, 0-200 m. STATUS: Typically in dense, isolated stands. *Red Data Book* status: Vulnerable, due to invasion of its habitat by Rooikrans. FLOWERS: April to October, mainly May to July. FRUITS: Retained.
NOTE: This species should perhaps be considered more closely allied to the White Sugarbushes, but it lacks the diagnostic feature of the perianth coiling down into the base of the flowerhead. The seedhead is often mistaken for a conebush cone, but it should be apparent that all the plants bear the seedheads.

## *Protea* The Bearded Sugarbushes

The Bearded Sugarbushes (section *Speciosae*) are most easily distinguished by a *conspicuous fringe of long, dense hairs (the beard) on the incurved involucral bracts*. The inner involucral bracts may be spatulate. The perianth also has 3 awns with hairs or a beard. It does not collapse into the flowerhead, but *remains erect, concealing the style even after the flower has finished opening.*

*Protea laurifolia* Thunb.                                   Grey-leaf Sugarbush   **Plate 15**

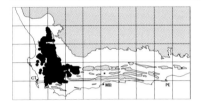

An erect shrub up to 8 m tall, branching from 0.2 m above ground. Trunk up to 300 mm in diameter. Stems with dense, grey hairs. *Leaves elliptic, midrib and horny margin prominent, glaucous*, 80-140 mm long, 10-55 mm wide, tips sometimes with a fine point, hairless when mature; *stalk 3-20 mm long, formed by the leaf gradually tapering to the base.* Flowerhead oblong, 100-130 mm long, 40-60 mm across. Involucral bracts cream to silvery pink, with dense, silky hairs; outer series with *brown horny margin when mature*, ovate, 10-20 mm long, 10-12 mm wide, tip pointed, becoming *recurved and splitting when mature*; inner series oblong to spatulate, 80-100 mm long, 3-15 mm wide, with a purple-black or white beard 5-10 mm long. Perianth 75-90 mm long, tube 10-12 mm long, awns 15 mm long and densely covered with purple-black or white hairs. Style straight, 65-70 mm long, with very sparse hairs. Pollen presenter 8-10 mm long, linear, tip pointed, knee-bent at base.

DISTRIBUTION: Bokkeveld escarpment to Hottentots-Holland and Riviersonderend Mountains, extending eastwards to the Witteberg and Anysberg. HABITAT: Dry, sandy or granite soils, 400-1200 m. STATUS: Gregarious, typically forming an open woodland over vast areas. FLOWERS: April to November, mainly May to July. FRUITS: Retained.

□ VARIATIONS: Southwestern forms lack the strongly glaucous leaves, having instead green ones which cause confusion with *P. neriifolia.* The tree-like stature with a short trunk becomes less obvious in these forms.

*Protea neriifolia* R. Br.                              Narrow-leaf Sugarbush    **Plate 15**

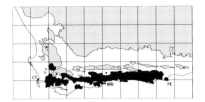

An erect shrub 1.5-3 m tall, 2 m across. Trunk 110-400 mm in diameter. Stems hairless when mature. *Leaves curved upwards, oblong with parallel margin not horny, hairless when mature, green, tapering abruptly at base, 100-180 mm long, 14-30 mm wide.* Flowerhead oblong to obconic, 100-130 mm long, 60-80 mm across. Involucral bracts cream to pink to carmine; outer series *with margin horny, brown and recurved when mature*, ovate-oblong, 10-15 mm long, 10-12 mm wide, glaucous, with sparse hairs; inner series oblong to spatulate, 90-110 mm long, with silky hairs, tips rounded with a white or black beard 8-10 mm long, *fine silver hairs below beard.* Perianth 70-100 mm long, tube 8-10 mm long, tipped with woolly, brown awns 15-25 mm long. Style straight, 55-70 mm long, base hairy. Pollen presenter 7-10 mm long, linear to thread-like, knee-bent at base. DISTRIBUTION: Hottentots-Holland to Riviersonderend Mountains and Langeberg to Winterhoek Mountains and Elandsberg; also on the Rooiberg, Kammanassie Mountains and Potberg, with an isolated population near Tulbagh and Ceres. HABITAT: Sandstone, occasionally granite soils, 0-1300 m. STATUS: Typically forming dense stands over vast areas. FLOWERS: February to November. FRUITS: Retained.
☐ VARIATIONS: The colour of the involucral bracts and beard varies considerably. Some northern forms have blue-grey leaves and might be confused with *P. laurifolia.* Western forms peak flowering in autumn, eastern forms in spring.
NOTE: Although this species does not occur naturally on the Cape Peninsula, it has been extensively planted there. Confusion with *P. lepidocarpodendron* can be avoided by looking for the silver hairs below the beard.

*Protea lepidocarpodendron* (L.) L.                     Black-beard Sugarbush    **Plate 15**

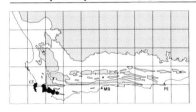

An erect shrub 2-3 m tall, with a single basal stem. Stems hairless when mature. *Leaves curved upwards, narrowly oblong, 80-130 mm long, 10-20 mm wide,* hairless when mature, tip with a fine point, base tapering abruptly to a heart shape, horny margin prominent; stalkless. Flowerhead oblong, 90-110 mm long, 50-60 mm across. Involucral bracts cream to pink, with silky hairs; outer series ovate, tips pointed, margin densely covered with hairs, *brown and contrasting with the inner involucral bracts*, tips recurved when mature, 10-15 mm long, 8-10 mm wide; inner series oblong to spatulate, *tips curved inwards and upper 20-30 mm densely covered with a purple-black beard, short hairs below the beard black*, margin with white hairs. Perianth 70-80 mm long, tube 7-9 mm long, awns densely covered with white hairs. Style straight, 60-65 mm long, hairy at base. Pollen presenter 8-10 mm long, tip minutely hooked, knee-bent at base.
DISTRIBUTION: Cape Peninsula and Kogelberg, Groenland, Kleinmond and Klein River Mountains. HABITAT: Sandstone, ferricrete and granite soils, 0-600 m. STATUS: Locally forming dense stands over large areas. FLOWERS: April to August, mainly July. FRUITS: Retained.
☐ VARIATION: The involucral bracts vary from cream to pink. When pink, they often lead to confusion with *P. neriifolia*, but the black hairs below the beard are diagnostic.

***Protea lorifolia*** (Salisb. ex Knight) Fourc.                    Strap-leaf Sugarbush      **Plate 16**

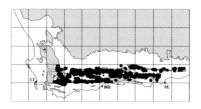

A compact, rounded shrub 1.5-3 m (rarely 5 m) tall. Trunk 100-400 mm in diameter. Stems glaucous when mature. *Leaves erect, broadly oblanceolate, glaucous, blue-grey, margin yellow to red, thickened and horny,* 120-250 mm long, 20-50 mm wide, tip rounded, hairless when mature, leathery; *stalk 10-15 mm long, formed by the leaf gradually tapering to the base.* Flowerhead oblong-obconic, 70-130 mm long, 25-50 mm across. Involucral bracts with silky hairs, tips with a white or purple-brown beard, margin densely covered with cream to pink to beige hairs; *outer series erect,* ovate, tip pointed, 10-30 mm long; inner series oblong, 60-100 mm long, 3-10 mm wide, tip rounded to spatulate. Perianth 65-90 mm long, tube 12 mm long, awns densely covered with short, mixed white and purple-black hairs. Style straight, 55-65 mm long, lower half hairy. Pollen presenter 7-12 mm long, thread-like to linear, knee-bent at base.
DISTRIBUTION: Koue Bokkeveld to Swartberg, Riviersonderend Mountains and Langeberg to Kouga, Baviaanskloof and Grootrivier Mountains; outlying populations between Grahamstown and Riebeek East; also a curious herbarium record from the Bosberg at Somerset East which cannot be relocated. HABITAT: Dry slopes, sandstone soils, 450-1400 m. STATUS: Locally abundant in diffuse populations, often dominating the vegetation. FLOWERS: April to October, mainly April to June. FRUITS: Retained.
☐ VARIATIONS: Western forms are smaller plants (1.5-2 m tall) with flowerheads 70-100 mm long, cream-beige involucral bracts and awns projecting beyond the involucral bracts.
Progressing eastward, they gradually become taller trees, with involucral bracts that lack the beige-brown tints, are covered in white hairs and extend well beyond the flowers.

***Protea coronata*** Lam.                                          Green Sugarbush      **Plate 16**

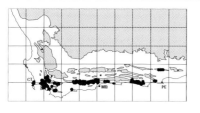

An erect shrub 2-3 m tall, occasionally up to 5 m. Trunk up to 150 mm in diameter. *Stems with dense, long hairs.* Leaves curved upwards, lanceolate, tip pointed, 60-90 mm long, 8-28 mm wide, green turning purplish around the flowerhead, hairless or with silvery, silky hairs; stalkless. Flowerhead oblong, 90-100 mm long, 50-60 mm across. *Involucral bracts bright green,* hairless, glaucous; outer series ovate, 15-20 mm long, 15 mm wide, *tips elongated to long-haired appendages 50-100 mm long*; inner series oblong to spatulate, 60-70 mm long, 10-20 mm wide, tips curved inwards, with a silky-haired margin. Perianth 70-90 mm long, tube 40-45 mm long, awns black, with *white, woolly-cobwebby hairs,* protruding above involucral bracts. *Style hairless,* straight, 60-65 mm long. Pollen presenter 10 mm long, thread-like, straight.
DISTRIBUTION: A curious distribution with 2 major gaps. Cape Peninsula and Du Toit's Kloof to Kogelberg, Riviersonderend and Bredasdorp Mountains and Potberg; then a gap in the western Langeberg; eastern Langeberg and Outeniqua Mountains; then another gap; eastern Tsitsikamma Mountains and Suurberg. HABITAT: Heavy clay soils with high rainfall, 200-750 m. STATUS: Typically forming dense stands, 'weedy' in places. FLOWERS: April to September, mainly May and June. FRUITS: Retained.
☐ VARIATION: The leaves of western forms have sparse hairs, whereas those of eastern forms have silvery downy hairs.

*Protea speciosa* (L.) L.                                                    Brown-beard Sugarbush     **Plate 16**

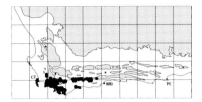

A low shrub 0.5-1.2 m tall, *with a rootstock.* Stems short, erect, seldom branched, hairless when mature. *Leaves obovate to oblanceolate*, 90-160 mm long, 10-60 mm wide, leathery, thickened margin horny, hairless when mature, tip rounded to pointed. Flowerhead oblong, 90-140 mm long, 60-80 mm across. Involucral bracts green to cream to pink to brown, tightly overlapping, with dense, silky hairs, *tip with a dense, rusty brown beard 10-15 mm long*; outer series ovate, tip rounded, 15-20 mm long, 10 mm wide; inner series oblong to oblong-spatulate, 50-90 mm long, 5-20 mm wide, tip rounded. Perianth 75-90 mm long, tube 10 mm long; *awns 3 in number, straight, white, with silky hairs.* Style straight, hairy below, 65-75 mm long. Pollen presenter 8 mm long, straight, slightly knee-bent at base.

DISTRIBUTION: Cape Peninsula; Hottentots-Holland to Riviersonderend Mountains and Langeberg; Klein River and Bredasdorp Mountains and seaward flats; Potberg. HABITAT: Montane, cool, southern slopes, typically 300-600 m, but also from 0-1300 m. STATUS: Widely scattered individuals occur throughout the distribution range, with local, dense stands in the southeast. FLOWERS: June to January, mainly September and October. FRUITS: Retained.

□ VARIATIONS: Forms on the Klein River Mountains tend to have narrow leaves (10-20 mm wide), with lime-yellow involucral bracts, while on the Cape Peninsula leaves may be so broad as to be confused with those of *P. grandiceps*. Beard colour is usually chocolate-brown or tawny, but tends to be white in the Hottentots-Holland Mountains.

*Protea stokoei* E. Phillips                                                    Pink Sugarbush     **Plate 16**

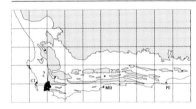

An erect shrub up to 2 m tall, sparsely branched. Trunk up to 150 mm in diameter. Stems hairless when mature. *Leaves curved upwards, obovate to ovate*, 70-120 mm long, 30-50 mm wide, tips rounded, hairless when mature. Flowerhead oblong, 90-130 mm long, 50-70 mm across. Involucral bracts densely covered with silky hairs, tips with a dense brown beard 5-7 mm long; outer series ovate, tip rounded, 20-30 mm long, 15-25 mm wide; inner series oblong to oblong-spatulate, 70-90 mm long, 15-25 mm wide, upper tips curved inwards. Perianth 80-90 mm long, tube 20 mm long; *awns 10-12 mm long, curling outwards, densely covered with white, silky hairs. Style 65-70 mm long, with minute hairs below*, slightly curved inwards. Pollen presenter 6 mm long, linear, not distinct from style.

DISTRIBUTION: Kogelberg, Hottentots-Holland and Groenland Mountains. HABITAT: Highly specific, in montane, moist, peaty soils, 900-1200 m. STATUS: Locally dense stands of a few dozen plants, rarely several hundred, in suitable habitats. FLOWERS: May to October, mainly May and June. FRUITS: Retained.

***Protea grandiceps*** Tratt.                                    Red Sugarbush    **Plate 17**

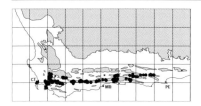

A rounded shrub up to 2 m tall, 3 m across. Trunk 120 mm in diameter. Stem hairless. *Leaves curved upwards, ovate to obovate*, 80-130 mm long, 30-85 mm wide, leathery, glaucous, hairless, tips rounded, margin wavy. Flowerhead broadly oblong, 100-140 mm long, 60-80 mm across. *Involucral bracts coral-pink*, hairless to downy, overlapping; outer series ovate, 15-25 mm long, 15-20 mm wide, margin with minute hairs; inner series oblong-spatulate, 70-80 mm long, 15-20 mm wide, rounded and curved inwards at tip, margin with a white or purple beard 10-15 mm long. Perianth 75-85 mm long, tube 10 mm long, awns 10-15 mm long. Style slightly curved, 65-75 mm long, hairless. Pollen presenter linear to thread-like, curved, knee-bent at base.

DISTRIBUTION: Cape Peninsula; Hottentots-Holland to Riviersonderend Mountains, Langeberg, Outeniqua, Winterhoek and Kammanassie Mountains. HABITAT: Dry (occasionally moist) upper-most slopes, 1200-1700 m. Tends to favour rocky outcrops and steep slopes where it is relatively safe from too-frequent fires. STATUS: Although widespread, it is known from only about a dozen isolated sites with very few to several thousand plants. Almost extinct on Table Mountain.
FLOWERS: September to January, mainly December and January. FRUITS: Retained.
☐ VARIATIONS: The size and colour of flowerheads vary locally. Eastern forms tend to have deep maroon rather than white beards.

***Protea magnifica*** Link                                    Queen Sugarbush    **Plate 17**

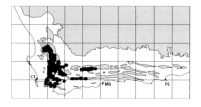

An erect to sprawling shrub 0.5-2.5 m tall, 2-4 m across. Trunk single. Stems glaucous when mature. *Leaves variable, oblong to oblanceolate, 100-210 mm long, 30-60 mm wide*, leathery, hairless when mature, glaucous, margin horny, undulating and red to yellow, midrib prominent; *stalk indistinct.* Flowerhead cup-shaped, 90-140 mm long, 50-80 mm opening to 150 mm across, with the awns forming a cone.
*Involucral bracts with silky hairs, recurved, tipped with a dense beard*; outer series ovate, 10-12 mm long, 10-20 mm wide; inner series oblong-spatulate, 80-100 mm long, 15-20 mm wide. Perianth 70-120 mm long, tube 14 mm long; *awns 3 per flower*, densely covered with woolly white hairs peripherally and with white, black or brown hairs on cone tip. *Style 60-70 mm long*, straight, lower two-thirds hairy. Pollen presenter 7-10 mm long, linear, tip pointed, prominently knee-bent at base.

DISTRIBUTION: Skimmelberg, Koue Bokkeveld to Hottentots-Holland Mountains, Klein Swartberg, Riviersonderend Mountains and central Langeberg. HABITAT: Montane, hot, dry slopes near the snow line, typically 1200-2700 m, rarely to 600 m. Tends to favour rocky outcrops and steep slopes where it is relatively safe from too-frequent fires. STATUS: Locally common in isolated dense stands, occasionally as scattered plants. FLOWERS: June to January. FRUITS: Retained.
☐ VARIATIONS: Highly variable, with countless undocumented variants. Habit varies from sprawl-ing and prostrate to erect, rounded shrubs. Flowerhead size varies considerably, with larger flower-heads in drier regions. Shape of flowerheads varies from cup- to bell- to bowl-shaped. Involucral bracts may be green, cream, pink or carmine. Beards and the cone may be white, brown, purple-black or black.
NOTE: The most sought-after cut flower among proteas.

***Protea holosericea*** (Salisb. ex Knight) Rourke      Sawedge Sugarbush      **Plate 17**

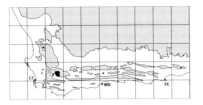

An almost erect to sprawling shrub up to 1.2 m tall, up to 2 m across. Trunk up to 120 mm in diameter. Stems hairless when mature. Leaves elliptic, 90-150 mm long, 15-30 mm wide, glaucous when mature, leathery, margin horny and wavy, tip pointed. Flowerhead ovoid to obconic, 60-80 mm across. Involucral bracts pale cream, with silky hairs, *tip rounded, margin with a very dense, black beard*; outer series ovate, 10-15 mm long, 10 mm wide, outermost bracts with a brown beard; inner series oblong, 20-50 mm long, 10-15 mm wide. Perianth 45-55 mm long, tube 7 mm long; *awns 10 mm long, 2 per flower*, with white to purple hairs at the base and black hairs at the tip. *Style 45-50 mm long, lower two-thirds hairy*, curved inwards. Pollen presenter 8 mm long, slender, curved, knee-bent at base.

DISTRIBUTION: Sawedge Peak and Rabiesberg in the Keeromsberg. HABITAT: Arid rocky slopes, 1200-1300 m. Tends to favour rocky outcrops and steep slopes where it is relatively safe from too-frequent fires. STATUS: Almost picked to extinction during the 1970s, but further picking prohibited timeously. Known only from 2 adjacent peaks, populations totalling a few thousand plants. *Red Data Book* status: Rare. FLOWERS: September and October. FRUITS: Retained.

## *Protea* The Dwarf-tufted Sugarbushes

> The Dwarf-tufted Sugarbushes are a group of largely lowland sugarbushes. They tend to be more *colourful* than the other *Protea* species that bear their flowers near ground level, and are therefore most probably bird-pollinated. They are characterized by their *rough, sandpapery leaves* and include all the ground-flowering *Protea* species with *straight styles*. Most species have underground stems.

The various species within this group can best be distinguished by the size of their flowerheads (or styles); the shape and size of the leaves; and whether the leaves emerge directly from the ground or are borne on short emergent stems.

### *Protea lorea* R. Br.        Thong-leaf Sugarbush    **Plate 18**

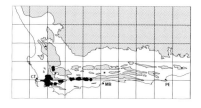

A rhizomatous shrublet forming mats up to 1 m across. Stems underground, scale-covered, terminating in a tuft of leaves at ground level. *Leaves needle-like, 150-450 mm long, tip with a fine point, hairless. Flowerhead obconic, 80-120 mm long, 50-80 mm across. Involucral bracts overlapping, yellow, with dense, silky hairs*; outer series ovate to lanceolate; inner series lanceolate, tip pointed, 60-100 mm long, 7-16 mm wide. *Perianth densely covered with woolly, white hairs at tip, hairs ending abruptly below the anthers*, 75-85 mm long, tube 10 mm long. Style straight, 75-90 mm long. Pollen presenter 10 mm long, linear, tip pointed, distinctly knee-bent at base.
DISTRIBUTION: Wemmershoek Mountains to Kogelberg; Riviersonderend Mountains and Langeberg; outlying populations near Ceres and Caledon. HABITAT: Grassy, lower mountain slopes, 450-650 m. STATUS: Typically occurring locally as scattered plants. Probably more common than we are aware of because of its cryptic nature. FLOWERS: Mainly 1-2 years after fire, January and February. FRUITS: Released 1-2 years after flowering.

### *Protea scorzonerifolia* (Salisb. ex Knight) Rycroft     Channel-leaf Sugarbush    **Plate 18**

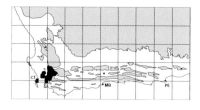

A rhizomatous shrublet forming mats to 1 m across. Stems underground, covered with black scales, with 150-mm *upright stems ending in tufts of leaves. Leaves needle-shaped to linear-channelled, 150-350 mm long*, 2-5 mm wide, tip with a fine point, hairless when mature, margin rough. Flowerhead obconic, 90-110 mm long, 50-80 mm across. Involucral bracts cream-yellow to pink, with silky hairs; outer series ovate, tip rounded, 10-20 mm long, 8-12 mm wide; inner series oblong-lanceolate, 50-70 mm long, 5-15 mm wide. Perianth 70-85 mm long, tube 8-10 mm long, tips with long white hairs. *Style straight, 60-75 mm long.* Pollen presenter 10-12 mm long, linear, tip pointed, slightly knee-bent at base.
DISTRIBUTION: Upper Breede River Valley and Du Toit's Kloof to Hottentots-Holland Mountains, and the Cape Flats at Constantia. HABITAT: Varied on lower mountain foothills, 150-450 m. STATUS: Locally common as sparsely scattered plants. *Red Data Book* status: Vulnerable,

due to agriculture. It is already extinct on the Cape Peninsula. FLOWERS: Mostly 2-3 years after fire, August to December, mainly September and October. FRUITS: Released 1-2 years after flowering. NOTE: A dwarf form occurs around the Nuwekloof Pass.

***Protea aspera*** E. Phillips                                    Rough-leaf Sugarbush      **Plate 18**

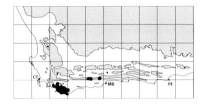

A rhizomatous shrublet up to 0.5 m across. Stems underground, covered with black scales, *aerial shoots emerging 100-200 mm above soil. Leaves linear, flat, 70-200 mm long, 3-14 mm wide, rough*, tapering at base, tip with a fine point, hairless when mature. *Flowerhead borne on short, aerial shoots, ovoid-oblong*, 65-95 mm long, 40-60 mm across. Involucral bracts golden brown to beige, occasionally pink, with silvery to rusty silky hairs, tip rounded; outer series ovate-oblong, 10-18 mm long, 8-12 mm wide; inner series oblong, 30-75 mm long, 5-12 mm wide, tips velvety. Perianth 55-70 mm long, tube 10-12 mm long, tips with silver or rusty hairs. *Style 50-70 mm long*, slightly curved inwards. Pollen presenter 10 mm long, linear, not distinct from style.

DISTRIBUTION: Klein River and Bredasdorp Mountains and flats seaward of these, with an outlying population on the eastern Langeberg at Garcia's and Cloete's Passes. HABITAT: Lowlands on shales and sandy soils, 0-200 m. STATUS: Widely scattered plants occur over much of the range. FLOWERS: Mostly after fire, September to December, mainly September and October. FRUITS: Released 1-2 years after flowering.

***Protea scabra*** R. Br.                                    Sandpaper-leaf Sugarbush      **Plate 19**

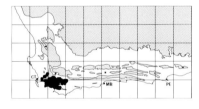

A rhizomatous shrublet, forming clumps up to 0.5 m across. *Stems underground*, covered with black scales, with *tufts of leaves at ground level.* Leaves needle-like to linear to oblanceolate-channelled, 100-300 mm long, 2-25 mm wide, rolled back or flat, hairless when mature, sandpapery rough. *Flowerhead turban-shaped, 30-50 mm across, borne at ground level; stalkless. Involucral bracts cream, with rusty, velvety hairs*, margin often with rusty hairs; outer series overlapping, ovate, tip pointed, 5-8 mm long, 5-7 mm wide; inner series oblong, tips rounded, 15-20 mm long, 4-10 mm wide. Perianth 35-40 mm long, tube 10 mm long with a swollen region, *tips densely covered with rusty hairs. Style cream, 30-35 mm long*, strongly curved inwards. Pollen presenter 6 mm long, linear, not distinct from style.

DISTRIBUTION: Hottentots-Holland to Riviersonderend and Klein River Mountains and the Caledon Swartberg. HABITAT: Montane, especially on Cederberg shales, 50-900 m. STATUS: Locally common as scattered plants over large areas. Extinct on flats at Eerste River. FLOWERS: Usually 2 years after fire, April to October, mainly July to October. FRUITS: Released 1-2 years after flowering.

□ VARIATIONS: Leaves are extremely variable in shape, from 25 mm wide and flat to 2 mm wide with the margin rolled inwards.

***Protea piscina*** Rourke                           Visgat Sugarbush    **Plate 19**

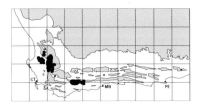

A rhizomatous shrublet, forming mats up to 1 m across. Stems underground, with black scales, leaves in tufts at ground level. *Leaves needle-shaped with a channel to linear and flat, margin horny, 150-300 mm long, 2-5 mm wide*, rough, tip with a fine point, often hooked, hairless when mature. Flowerhead obconic to turban-shaped, 35-50 mm long, 40-50 mm across. *Involucral bracts pale yellow (occasionally pink), margin with white, silky hairs*, tips rounded; outer series ovate, tip pointed, 7-10 mm long, 5-7 mm wide; inner series oblong-linear, 20-35 mm long, 2-5 mm wide. Perianth 30-35 mm long, tube 8-10 mm long, tips with shaggy, white hairs. *Style 30-35 mm long*, slightly curved. Pollen presenter 5-7 mm long, linear, not distinct from style.
DISTRIBUTION: Cederberg and Piketberg to Ceres; central and eastern Langeberg and foothills from Swellendam to Heidelberg. HABITAT: Sandstone soils, 400-1200 m. STATUS: Abundant as scattered individuals in local populations. Probably more common than we are aware owing to its cryptic habit. FLOWERS: Mostly 2-3 years after fire, June to January. FRUITS: Released 1-2 years after flowering.

***Protea restionifolia*** (Salisb. ex Knight) Rycroft          Reed-leaf Sugarbush    **Plate 19**

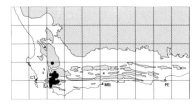

A rhizomatous shrublet up to 1 m across. Stems underground, covered with peg-like leaf scars, with tufts of leaves borne at ground level. *Leaves needle-shaped, sparsely covered with long white hairs, each arising from a minute knob, 190-300 mm long, 1-2 mm wide*, tip with a fine point, rough. Flowerhead ovoid, 30-70 mm long, 30-60 mm across. Involucral bracts with outer series overlapping, ovate, 10-15 mm long, 10 mm wide, margin with rusty hairs; inner series splayed, oblong to spatulate, 30-50 mm long, 3-10 mm wide, *tips densely covered with velvety, red to dark brown hairs.* Perianth 35-55 mm long, tube 8-10 mm long, tips with white hairs. *Style curved, 45-60 mm long*, yellow or pink. Pollen presenter 6-8 mm long, linear to thread-like, not distinct from style.
DISTRIBUTION: Upper Breede River Valley to Bot River Valley (Rûens); an outlying population at Kleinvlei in the Koue Bokkeveld. HABITAT: Dry areas at fynbos/karoo or fynbos/renosterveld ecotones, 150-300 m. STATUS: Frequent as scattered plants in local populations. *Red Data Book* status: Vulnerable, due to agriculture. FLOWERS: Mainly after fire, August to October, mostly September. FRUITS: Released 1-2 years after flowering.
□ VARIATION: Southern populations have flowerheads twice the size (60-70 mm long) of those of northern populations (30-40 mm long).

*Protea denticulata* Rourke                Tooth-leaf Sugarbush     **Plate 19**

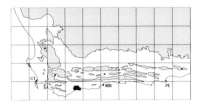

A dense shrub up to 1 m tall and 2 m across, *with an underground rootstock. Stems short, erect. Leaves curved upwards, hard and wiry with horny denticles, linear-channelled,* 150-250 mm long, 5-8 mm wide, tip pointed and often hooked, base often cylindrical, nearly hairless when mature. Flowerhead ovoid, 40-50 mm long, 35-40 mm across. *Involucral bracts dull reddish carmine, densely covered with velvety hairs, margin prominent and chestnut-brown,* tip rounded; outer series oblong to ovate, 13-15 mm long, 6-7 mm wide; inner series oblong to linear, 30-40 mm long, 4-6 mm wide. Perianth 25-35 mm long, tube 8-10 mm long, tips with chestnut hairs. *Style dull red,* curved inwards, 25-35 mm long. Pollen presenter 6 mm long, linear to thread-like, not distinct from style.
DISTRIBUTION: Potberg. HABITAT: Sandstone midslopes, 120-300 m. STATUS: Common as scattered individuals. FLOWERS: August to October. FRUITS: Released after a few years.

## *Protea* The White Sugarbushes

The White Sugarbushes (section *Exsertae*) have *hairless styles longer than the inner involucral bracts,* which have a short fringe of silky hairs. *The perianth is slender at the base, and on opening coils up into the base of the flowerhead away from the styles,* giving the flowerheads a neat appearance. It has 3 tips and is hairless except at the tips.

The species of White Sugarbushes are best distinguished from one another by observing the tip of the pollen presenter, the leaf shape and the degree to and manner in which the involucral bracts spread during flowering. Hybrids readily occur under cultivation.

*Protea subvestita* N.E. Br.             Waterlily Sugarbush     **Plate 20**

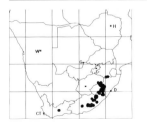

*A large, upright shrub, killed by fire,* 2-5 m tall, with a single main stem. Trunk up to 300 mm in diameter. Stems densely covered with grey hairs, hairless when mature. *Leaves curved upwards, elliptic to lanceolate, base tapering,* 50-110 mm long, 15-35 mm wide, densely covered with shaggy to woolly hairs, hairless when mature. Flowerhead oblong, 55-70 mm long, 30-40 mm across. Involucral bracts carmine or pink or creamy white, with silky hairs or hairless, margin with long, white silky hairs; *outer series ovate, tip pointed,* 10-15 mm long, 7-10 mm wide, tightly overlapping; inner series *with tips bending outwards* and even downwards, oblong, loosely overlapping, 35-40 mm long, 8-12 mm wide. Perianth 50-60 mm long, tube 8-10 mm long, tips with white, wavy, silky hairs. *Style with tip bending outwards when open,* straight, 55-60 mm long, pink. *Pollen presenter linear to thread-like,* 8-10 mm long, knee-bent at base, tip minutely knobbed.
DISTRIBUTION: Mpumalanga, KwaZulu-Natal, Lesotho, Eastern Cape escarpment from Wakkerstroom to Somerset East, and a curious population in the Klein Swartberg.

HABITAT: Montane, highland sourveld and fynbos, 1200-2300 m. STATUS: A social species, often forming open woodland, rarely dense thickets. Many populations have been exterminated by too-frequent fires. FLOWERS: Decem-ber to June, mainly January to March. FRUITS: Retained.
□ VARIATION: At higher altitudes, especially above the snow line, the leaves retain their hairs for longer periods.

*Protea lacticolor* Salisb.                                   Hottentot Sugarbush    **Plate 20**

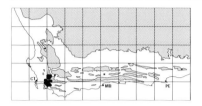

An erect shrub 2-6 m tall, with a single main stem. Trunk 80-300 mm in diameter. Bark grey. Stems with downy hairs, hairless when mature. *Leaves curved upwards, lanceolate to ovate, 70-110 mm long, 25-50 mm wide, base heart-shaped, with downy hairs, hair-less when mature, dark blue-green.* Flowerhead oblong, 60-80 mm long, 50-60 mm across. Involucral bracts cream or pink, densely covered with silky hairs, margin with long, silky, white or brown hairs; outer series ovate, 6-10 mm long, 8-14 mm wide; inner series oblong, 35-50 mm long, 6-12 mm wide. Perianth 55-70 mm long, tube 6-8 mm long, tips hairless except for a fringe of pale brown hairs. Style straight, 65-70 mm long, cream or pink. *Pollen presenter thread-like, with a minute, skew knob,* knee-bent at base and curved inwards.
DISTRIBUTION: Slanghoek to Hottentots-Holland and Groenland Mountains. HABITAT: Stream-banks or moist Cederberg shale, 600-1500 m. STATUS: Highly social, occurring in dense, almost impenetrable thickets. FLOWERS: February to June, mainly March and April. FRUITS: Retained.

*Protea punctata* Meisn.                                    Water Sugarbush    **Plate 20**

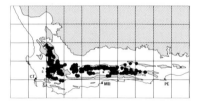

An erect shrub 2-4 m tall, with a single main stem. Trunk up to 300 mm in diameter. Bark smooth, grey. Stems with velvety hairs, hairless when mature. Leaves curved upwards, ovate to obovate to elliptic, tip pointed, 35-80 mm long, 20-45 mm wide, with shaggy, silky hairs, hairless when mature, glaucous. Flowerhead obconic, 35-60 mm long, 20-25 mm across. *Involucral bracts spreading outwards horizontally at flowering,* pink to white, with silky hairs; outer series ovate, tip pointed, 8-10 mm long, 10-12 mm wide, tightly overlapping; inner series oblong, 25-40 mm long, 10-15 mm wide, widely spread. Perianth 35-55 mm long, tube 10 mm long, tips hairless, occasionally with tawny hairs. Style straight, 45-50 mm long. *Pollen presenter uniformly thread-like, curling over after flowering,* 10-15 mm long, merging with style.
DISTRIBUTION: Cederberg to Riviersonderend Mountains and to the Swartberg, Kammanassie, Kouga and Grootrivier Mountains. HABITAT: Dry rocky or Cederberg shale slopes, 1200-2000 m. STATUS: Locally dense stands forming thickets. FLOWERS: December to June, mainly March and April. FRUITS: Retained.
□ VARIATION: Forms from moister sites produce larger leaves, approaching those of *P. lacticolor* in size.

***Protea mundii*** Klotzsch                                    Forest Sugarbush    **Plate 20**

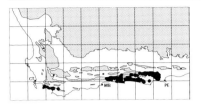

An upright shrub 3-8 m (occasionally 12 m) tall, with a single main stem. Trunk 150-250 mm in diameter. Bark smooth, grey. Stems downy, hairless when mature. *Leaves elliptic to elliptic-lanceolate,* 60-120 mm long, 18-40 mm wide, with sparse hairs, hairless when mature, bright green. *Flowerhead oblong-obconic,* 65-80 mm long, 40-65 mm across. Involucral bracts green-cream or pink, sparsely to densely covered with silky hairs, tips with white to tawny silky fringes; outer series ovate, tips pointed, 8-10 mm long, 10-12 mm wide; inner series oblong (occasionally spatulate), 35-40 mm long, 8-15 mm wide. Perianth 50-70 mm long, tube 12-15 mm long, tips wavy with silky white-tawny hairs. Style straight, 55-65 mm long, cream or pink. *Pollen presenter linear to thread-like, 8-10 mm long, tip a large knob.* DISTRIBUTION: Kogelberg to Klein River Mountains, Outeniqua and Kouga Mountains to Tsitsikamma and Winterhoek Mountains. Curiously absent from the Langeberg, where it is replaced by *P. aurea.* HABITAT: Moist slopes and forest margins, 200-1300 m. STATUS: Common in dense, local stands. FLOWERS: January to September, mainly February to April. FRUITS: Retained.

***Protea aurea*** (Burm. f.) Rourke subsp. ***aurea***            Common Shuttlecock Sugarbush    **Plate 21**

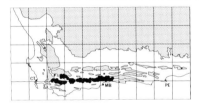

A large, erect shrub 3-5 m tall, with a single main trunk. Stems hairy to hairless. *Leaves oblong to ovate, 40-90 mm long, 15-40 mm wide, base heart-shaped, hairless. Flowerhead obconic, 90-120 mm long, resembling a shuttlecock on opening.* Involucral bracts creamy green to crimson, outer surface with silky hairs, margin with long silky hairs; outer series ovate, tip pointed, 15 mm long, 15 mm wide; inner series oblong, 40-90 mm long, 5-14 mm wide. Perianth 90-110 mm long, tube 10 mm long, tips with white hairs. Style straight, 85-105 mm long. Pollen presenter 17 mm long, thread-like, slightly knee-bent at base. DISTRIBUTION: Riviersonderend Mountains, Langeberg and Outeniqua Mountains. HABITAT: Cool, moist southern slopes, 150-800 m. STATUS: A social species, forming dense, impenetrable, isolated stands. FLOWERS: All year round, mainly January to June. FRUITS: Retained.

***Protea aurea*** subsp. ***potbergensis*** (Rourke) Rourke            Potberg Sugarbush    **Plate 21**

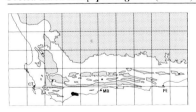

Similiar to *P. aurea* subsp. *aurea,* but: *Leaves ovate, 60-90 mm long, 45-65 mm wide, decreasing up the stem to 35 mm long and 25 mm wide below flowerhead, base heart-shaped, with velvety hairs, hairless when mature, margin densely covered with hairs.* Flowerhead 90-130 mm long. Involucral bracts creamy green. Style straight, 110-130 mm long. DISTRIBUTION: Potberg. HABITAT: Upper slopes, 360 m. STATUS: A social species forming sparse to dense isolated stands. *Red Data Book* status: Vulnerable. FLOWERS: April to July, mainly May and June. FRUITS: Retained.

***Protea venusta*** Compton                                Cascade Sugarbush    **Plate 21**

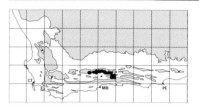

*A prostrate shrub up to 0.7 m tall, 3 m across, with a single main stem* and many trailing stems. Stems with downy hairs, hairless when mature. Leaves curved upwards or pointing vertically from a horizontal stem, oblanceolate, 25-60 mm long, 8-20 mm wide, base tapering, with downy hairs, hairless when mature, glaucous. Flowerhead bell-shaped, 50-70 mm long, 80-100 mm across, *with a honey-like scent.* Involucral bracts ivory; outer series ovate, 7-15 mm long, 7-12 mm wide, with downy hairs, overlapping, margin brown; *inner series pink-tipped, oblong to oblong-spatulate, 40-50 mm long, 8-18 mm wide*, with silky hairs or hairless, margin with white hairs. Perianth 55-65 mm long, tube 8-10 mm long, tips with long, silvery hairs. Style straight, 55 mm long, pale. Pollen presenter 8 mm long, thread-like, barely distinct from style.
DISTRIBUTION: Swartberg and Kammanassie Mountains. HABITAT: Cool, rocky, southern slopes and summit, 1700-2000 m. STATUS: Scattered, isolated populations of a few dozen plants. *Red Data Book* status: Rare. FLOWERS: January to March, mainly January and February. FRUITS: Retained.

### *Protea* The Bishop Sugarbush

The Bishop Sugarbush is the only species in the section *Obvallatae.* Easily identified by the *ovate, brown, papery leaves which clasp the base of the flowerhead*, it appears to be intermediate between the Bearded Sugarbushes, whose flowerhead it shares, and the Snow Sugarbushes, which have brown leaves narrowing to a point and clasping the flowerhead, and which also occur at high altitudes. A highly variable species, the Bishop Sugarbush occurs only at elevations above 1000 m.

***Protea caespitosa*** Andrews                               Bishop Sugarbush    **Plate 22**

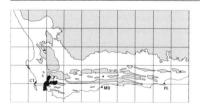

*A compact, rounded shrub* 0.2-0.7 m tall, up to 1 m across, with interlocking branches. Trunk up to 40 mm in diameter. Stem hairless when mature, covered by old leaf bases. Leaves oblanceolate to broadly ovate, 150-300 mm long, 20-95 mm wide, clustered at stem tip, tapering and winged at base, tip pointed, hairless when mature although the wavy margin may remain fringed with white hairs, midrib prominent. Flowerhead obconic to ovoid, 45-60 mm across, *clasped below by ovate leaves, with a pointed tip, 20-75 mm long, 15-30 mm wide, turning brown and papery with age.* Involucral bracts with silky hairs, margin with a silky white or tawny beard; outer series ovate to oblong, tip rounded, 10-20 mm long, 10 mm wide; inner series oblong to linear-spatulate, 30-35 mm long, 3-8 mm wide. Perianth 40-45 mm long, tube 8-10 mm long, *awns 15 mm long, with a white base and tawny tip and densely covered with woolly hairs.* Style straight, 40-45 mm long, often hairy at base. Pollen presenter 6 mm long, linear to thread-like, not distinct from style.

HABITAT: Summits on Cederberg shales, 1000-1800 m. STATUS: Locally dominant, forming dense, isolated stands. FLOWERS: July to November. FRUITS: Retained for a few years.
□ VARIATIONS: There are 3 variants of this species:
□ The Riviersonderend variant is *up to 0.3 m tall and has narrowly oblanceolate leaves that are 20-33 mm wide*; it occurs on the Olifantsberg in the Riviersonderend Mountains.
□ The Hottentots-Holland variant is *up to 0.7 to tall and has broadly oblanceolate leaves that are 40-70 mm wide*; it occurs in the Hottentots-Holland and Du Toit's Kloof Mountains.
□ The cabbage-leaf variant is *up to 0.7 m tall and has broadly ovate leaves that are 70-90 mm wide*; it occurs on the Kogelberg.

## *Protea* The Eastern Ground Sugarbushes

The Eastern Ground Sugarbushes form a distinct group that can be linked with the Western Ground Sugarbushes. In both groups *the flowerheads are inclined to be long –* 20-50 mm in the case of the Eastern Ground Sugarbushes – *with styles 25-35 mm long and curved inwards.* In the Eastern Ground Sugarbushes, however, the *leaves tend to be slightly horny or sandpapery to the touch.* Their geographical restriction to the mountains east of Riversdale readily prevents confusion with the Western Ground Sugarbushes.

Species of Eastern Ground Sugarbushes can be relatively easily distinguished by the habit of the stems.

*Protea tenax* (Salisb.) R. Br.                    Tenacious Sugarbush    **Plate 22**

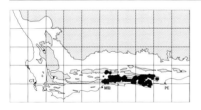

A low trailing shrub up to 4 m across. *Stems trailing, arising from a rootstock, sparsely branched*, with downy hairs, hairless when mature. *Leaves pointing vertically from a horizontal stem, linear to lanceolate to oblanceolate, 80-180 mm long, 2-28 mm wide, midrib prominent. Flowerhead 40-60 mm across, bowl-shaped*, with a yeasty odour. Involucral bracts greenish yellow, occasionally flushed with carmine, with silky hairs, hairless when mature, margin with minute hairs; outer series ovate, 10-20 mm long, 10-20 mm wide; inner series oblong, 35-40 mm long, 10-15 mm wide. Perianth 25-30 mm long, tube 8 mm long, tips densely covered with white hairs. Style straight to curved, 25-30 mm long. Pollen presenter 5 mm long, linear, tip pointed, not distinct from style.
DISTRIBUTION: Outeniqua, Tsitsikamma, eastern Groot Swartberg, Kammanassie, Kouga, Baviaanskloof and Winterhoek Mountains. HABITAT: Varied, 1250-1750 m. STATUS: Isolated populations with scattered plants. FLOWERS: All year round, mainly May to September.
FRUITS: Released 1-2 years after flowering.
□ VARIATIONS: Leaves vary in width from narrow in the east to broad in the west. Occasionally they may curve upwards rather than point vertically from a horizontal stem.

***Protea foliosa*** Rourke                                    Leafy Sugarbush    **Plate 23**

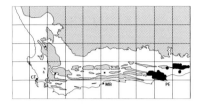

A rounded shrub up to 1.5 m tall, with many erect stems arising from a rootstock. Stems seldom branched, hairless. *Leaves lanceolate to elliptic, 90-160 mm long, 15-70 mm wide, flat, margin wavy,* base narrowed, leathery, slightly sandpapery, with downy hairs, hairless when mature. *Flowerhead upright, hidden by enfolding leaves,* ovoid to globose, 30-40 mm across, often in clusters of 2 to 5. Involucral bracts green-yellow, occasionally flushed carmine, margin fringed; outer series ovate, tip rounded, 7-15 mm long, 7-12 mm wide; inner series oblong-spatulate, 30-35 mm long, 10 mm wide. Perianth 25-30 mm long, tube 8-10 mm long, tip with white or brown woolly hairs. Style straight or curved inwards, 25 mm long. Pollen presenter 5 mm long, linear, tip pointed, not distinct from style.
DISTRIBUTION: Elandsberg to Port Elizabeth, Riebeek East to Bushmans River Poort.
HABITAT: Sandstone and quartzitic soils, 150-600 m. STATUS: Scattered plants, becoming locally abundant on moist sites. FLOWERS: March to September, mainly May and June.
FRUITS: Released 1-2 years after flowering.

***Protea vogtsiae*** Rourke                                    Kouga Sugarbush    **Plate 23**

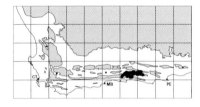

A dwarf shrublet up to 0.25 m tall, 0.2-0.5 m across. *Stems underground, scaled, with leaves in a terminal tuft. Leaves oblanceolate to spatulate, 120-250 mm long, 8-30 mm wide, glaucous, base tapering,* slightly sandpapery. Flowerhead ovoid to globose, 35-40 mm across. Involucral bracts yellow-green to carmine, with silky hairs, hairless when mature, margin with minute hairs; outer series ovate, 7-15 mm long, 7-10 mm wide; inner series oblong-spatulate, 30-35 mm long, 5-10 mm wide. *Perianth 30-35 mm long, tips with white, woolly hairs.* Style curved inwards, 25-30 mm long. Pollen presenter 5-6 mm long, linear to thread-like, grooved, flattened and thinner than style.
DISTRIBUTION: Outeniqua, Kouga and Baviaanskloof Mountains. HABITAT: Steep, rocky southern slopes, sandstone soils, 1000-1500 m. STATUS: Small, isolated populations. Probably far more common than reported because of its inconspicuous habit. FLOWERS: August to November.
FRUITS: Released 1-2 years after flowering.

***Protea intonsa*** Rourke                                    Tufted Sugarbush    **Plate 23**

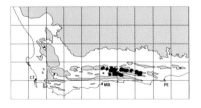

A dense, dwarf shrub up to 0.3 m tall, 0.3-0.6 m across. *Stems underground, scaled, with leaves in tufts. Leaves needle-like to linear, 150-400 mm long, 2-5 mm wide, hairless,* occasionally glaucous, smooth to slightly sandpapery. Flowerhead globose, 20-50 mm across. Involucral bracts greenish, with silky hairs, hairless and carmine when mature, margin with minute hairs; outer series ovate, 10-15 mm long, 10-15 mm wide; inner series oblong-spatulate, 20-25 mm long, 5-10 mm wide. *Perianth 25-30 mm long, tips with white, woolly hairs.* Style curved inwards, 25-30 mm long. Pollen presenter 5-6 mm long, linear to thread-like, grooved, flattened, thinner than style.
DISTRIBUTION: Eastern Swartberg, Kammanassie and Baviaanskloof Mountains, Uniondale.
HABITAT: Dry, exposed mountain slopes, 1000-1600 m. STATUS: Scattered plants in isolated populations. Probably far more common than reported. FLOWERS: September to November.
FRUITS: Released 1-2 years after flowering.

***Protea montana*** E. Mey. ex Meisn.                    Swartberg Sugarbush    **Plate 23**

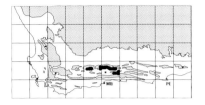

*A low shrub forming dense, prostrate mats 0.5-4 m across*, up to 0.2 m tall, with a single trunk. *Stems numerous, much-branched*, spreading, with silky hairs, hairless when mature. *Leaves pointing vertically from a horizontal stem, needle-like to linear-spatulate, 40-100 mm long, 1-4 mm wide*, with minute silky hairs, hairless when mature. Flowerhead bowl-shaped, 30-50 mm across. Involucral bracts green flushed with carmine, with silky hairs; outer series oblong to ovate, 10-20 mm long, 10-15 mm wide, *outermost bracts with leaf-like extension*; inner series oblong-spatulate, 35-40 mm long, 6-10 mm wide. Perianth 30-40 mm long, tube 7-10 mm long, *tips densely covered with white, woolly hairs.* Style straight to curved, 25-35 mm long. Pollen presenter 5-6 mm long, linear, tip pointed, not distinct from style.
DISTRIBUTION: Swartberg and Kammanassie Mountains. HABITAT: Steep upper slopes and summits, 1600-2000 m. STATUS: Solitary plants are encountered sporadically.
FLOWERS: February to June. FRUITS: Released 1-2 years after flowering.
□ VARIATION: Forms with needle-like leaves tend to be hairless, but forms with wider leaves, which tend to occur in the east, often have sparse, downy hairs.

## *Protea* The Western Ground Sugarbushes

The Western Ground Sugarbushes (section *Microgeantae*) form a distinct group that may be linked with the Eastern Ground Sugarbushes. *Flowerheads tend to be 20-70 mm long*, slightly larger than in the Eastern Ground Sugarbushes. They also have *sharply inward-curving styles* that are 25-35 mm long. *The leaves are usually silky smooth* and tend to be less horny than those of the Eastern Ground Sugarbushes.

Western Ground Sugarbushes are confined to the western plains and the mountains west of Grootberg at Barrydale along the coast, although inland they extend eastwards to the Klein Swartberg.

Western Ground Sugarbush species can be distinguished by stem habit and leaf shape.

***Protea acaulos*** (L.) Reichard                    Common Ground Sugarbush    **Plate 24**

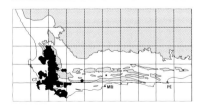

*A low shrub up to 1 m across, with underground branches and a rootstock. Stems trailing, hairless, without soft scale leaves. Leaves variable, base tapering gradually or abruptly to a stalk, hard, leathery*, pointing vertically from a horizontal stem (rarely curved upwards), oblanceolate-linear to broadly ovate, 60-250 mm long, 6-70 mm wide, hairless, occasionally glaucous. Flowerhead cup-shaped, 30-60 mm across. Involucral bracts green with red tips, hairless; outer series ovate, tip pointed, 5-8 mm long, 4-8 mm wide, tightly overlapping; inner series oblong to spatulate, tips rounded, 20-25 mm long, 5-8 mm wide, margin occasionally with minute hairs, widely spread. Perianth 22-28 mm long, tube 8-10 mm long, tips densely covered with woolly to shaggy hairs. Style strongly curved inwards, 25-35 mm long, hairless. Pollen presenter 5-7 mm long, linear, tip pointed, not distinct from style.

DISTRIBUTION: Cape Peninsula and flats to the Cederberg and to the Riviersonderend Mountains, Elim Flats and the Langeberg at Barrydale. HABITAT: Varied, usually on sandy soils, 0-1500 m. STATUS: Scattered to solitary plants are typically encountered. Probably more common than appreciated. FLOWERS: June to November, mainly August and September. FRUITS: Released 1-2 years after flowering.

□ VARIATIONS: The leaf shape is very variable, with different shapes often occurring within a population. A form with flat, broadly ovate leaves, a long-tapering leafstalk and a rounded tip occurs in the southwest; southeastern forms have narrowly obovate leaves, 6-10 mm wide; and northern forms have a short leafstalk abruptly expanding into the leaf blade, which has a pointed tip and wavy margin.

*Protea angustata* R. Br.　　　　　　　　　　　Kleinmond Sugarbush　**Plate 24**

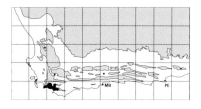

A dwarf shrublet up to 0.35 m tall, forming a *sparse, tufted mat up to 1.5 m across, with underground branches giving rise to many short, erect, leafy stems.* Stems hairless. *Leaves curved upwards, linear, 120-250 mm long, 2-8 mm wide,* flat or occasionally with margin rolled back, tapering at base, tip pointed, hairless, smooth. Flowerhead cup-shaped, 30-45 mm across, overtopped by leaves, with a strong yeasty odour. *Involucral bracts hairless,* yellow with red blush, margin occasionally with minute, brown hairs; outer series ovate, tip pointed, 6-10 mm long, 5-8 mm wide, overlapping; inner series oblong, 15-25 mm long, 5-8 mm wide. Perianth 22-28 mm long, tube 6-8 mm long, tips with brown velvety hairs. Style curved to almost right angles, 25-28 mm long, sparsely bristled at middle. Pollen presenter 5 mm long, linear to thread-like, not distinct from style.
DISTRIBUTION: Kogelberg to Groenland and Klein River Mountains and to Caledon Swartberg. HABITAT: Seaward-facing slopes and flats, sands and clays, 0-180 m. STATUS: Known from several isolated localities of a few scattered plants. *Red Data Book* status: Vulnerable.
FLOWERS: July to October, mainly September. FRUITS: Released 1-2 years after flowering.

*Protea laevis* R. Br.　　　　　　　　　　　Smooth-leaf Sugarbush　**Plate 24**

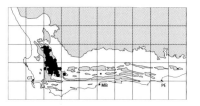

A prostrate shrublet forming mats up to 0.8 m across, *without a rootstock,* killed by fire. *Stems lying on ground, hairless, with long, brown, pointed, soft scale leaves. Leaves pointing vertically from a horizontal stem, flat, soft (fleshy),* variable, oblanceolate to oblong, 70-300 mm long, 6-35 mm wide, base tapering, tip pointed, hairless, glaucous. Flowerhead globose opening to cup-shaped, 40-70 mm across. Involucral bracts glaucous, yellow-green, inner surface flushed with carmine, margin occasionally fringed with minute brown hairs; outer series ovate, tip rounded, 5-10 mm long, 5-10 mm wide, overlapping; inner series 25-35 mm long, 5-12 mm wide, widely separated when open. Perianth 20-30 mm long, tube 8-10 mm long, with a fringe of silver hairs. Style curved almost at right angles, 28-35 mm long, hairless. Pollen presenter 7-8 mm long, linear, tip pointed, not distinct from style.
DISTRIBUTION: Cederberg to Hex River Mountains, with outlying populations on Waboomsberg and the Riviersonderend Mountains. HABITAT: Dry, rocky, mountain ledges, 1000-1800 m. STATUS: Solitary or sparse, isolated groups of fewer than two dozen plants. FLOWERS: September to February, mainly September to November. FRUITS: Released 1-2 years after flowering.

□ VARIATION: Forms on moist sites have large, flaccid leaves, whereas on dry sites leaves are shorter and leathery.

NOTE: Plants may accumulate sand around the prostrate stems and thus survive fire, appearing to have underground stems. Can be distinguished from *P. acaulos* most easily by the reduced (scale) leaves on the stem.

*Protea convexa* E. Phillips                          Large-leaf Sugarbush    **Plate 24**

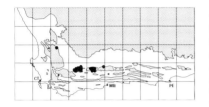

A prostrate shrub with a single main stem and many sprawling, branched stems forming a mat 1-2 m across. Trunk up to 50 mm in diameter. *Stems red-brown with a sticky, varnish-like substance, hairless. Leaves pointing vertically from a horizontal stem, obovate, 180-250 mm long, 60-100 mm wide,* tapered at base, pink-tinged, glaucous, hairless. Flowerhead cup-shaped, 60-80 mm across.

Involucral bracts greenish yellow tinged with carmine, thin, margin with short hairs, tip rounded; outer series ovate, 7-10 mm long, 7-10 mm wide; inner series oblong, 20-30 mm long, 7-15 mm wide. Perianth 25-30 mm long, tube 10 mm long, carmine, tips with silver, silky hairs. Style strongly curved inwards, 25-30 mm long, base with minute hairs. Pollen presenter 5 mm long, linear, not distinct from style.

DISTRIBUTION: Witteberg, Elandsberg and Klein Swartberg, and Tratra Mountains northwest of Wuppertal. HABITAT: Arid, rocky northern kloofs, 1100-1500 m. STATUS: Known from very few populations of a few dozen plants, but probably much more common than realized. *Red Data Book* status: Rare. FLOWERS: August to November, mainly October. FRUITS: Released 1-2 years after flowering.

*Protea revoluta* R. Br.                             Rolled-leaf Sugarbush    **Plate 25**

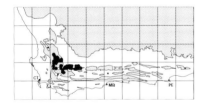

A prostrate shrublet up to 2 m across, 0.2 m tall. Stems underground, hairless. *Leaves rolled, linear, 150-250 mm long, 2-3 mm wide (rarely to 13 mm), pointing vertically from a horizontal stem, tips curved,* glaucous, hairless, flushed pink when young; *stalk cylindrical.* Flowerhead cup-shaped, 40-60 mm across. Involucral bracts greenish yellow flushed with carmine, thin, margin fringed; outer series ovate, tip pointed, 7-10 mm long, 5-8 mm wide; inner series oblong-spatulate, 30-35 mm long, 5-8 mm wide. Perianth 25-30 mm long, tube 10 mm long, with shaggy or woolly silver hairs. Style curved inwards, 30 mm long, yellow. Pollen presenter 3-4 mm long, linear to thread-like, not distinct from style.

DISTRIBUTION: Cederberg to Witteberg. HABITAT: Mountainous restioveld, 900-1600 m. STATUS: Locally abundant as scattered plants; it may dominate plant communities in the Swartruggens. FLOWERS: November to January, mainly November and December. FRUITS: Released 1-2 years after flowering.

### *Protea* The Shale Sugarbushes

The Shale Sugarbushes are largely confined to soils derived from shales of the Klipheuwel and Malmesbury Formations. They are characterized by their *very small flowerheads (less than 50 mm across) and short styles (shorter than 20 mm)*. Only 2 species are in this group, both of which have ivory involucral bracts with pink tips. The flowers have a faint sweet scent and are pollinated by wasps.

---

**Protea mucronifolia** Salisb.                                    Dagger-leaf Sugarbush    **Plate 25**

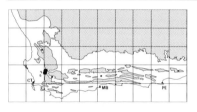

A small, erect shrub 0.5-1 m tall, up to 1 m across. Trunk 10-20 mm in diameter. Stems hairless. *Leaves curved upwards, lanceolate, 20-40 mm long, 2-4 mm wide, flat, tip a 2 mm-long black spine*, hairless, glaucous; stalkless. *Flowerhead bell-shaped, 25 mm long, 50 mm across.* Involucral bracts ivory, tips flushed with pink; inner series lanceolate, 20-25 mm long, 2-5 mm wide. Perianth 20-22 mm long, tube absent, pink, tips densely covered with white hairs. *Style 15-17 mm long*, straight, ivory. Pollen presenter 4 mm long, thread-like, not distinct from style.
DISTRIBUTION: Malmesbury Flats, mostly east of the Berg River from Hermon to Saron.
HABITAT: Gravelly Klipheuwel soils, 80 m. STATUS: *Red Data Book* status: Vulnerable, having been reduced by agriculture to 2 populations of a few thousand plants, mostly on a private nature reserve south of the Voëlvlei Dam. FLOWERS: October to January, mainly November and December.
FRUITS: Retained.

---

**Protea odorata** Thunb.                                    Swartland Sugarbush    **Plate 25**

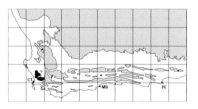

A small, erect shrub 0.7-1.2 m tall. Trunk up to 20 mm in diameter. Stems hairless. *Leaves curved upwards, linear, 25-65 mm long, 1.5-2 mm wide, undersurface grooved, tip a bent spine*, hairless. *Flowerhead bell-shaped, 20-30 mm across.* Involucral bracts creamy white, tips flushed with pink; inner series 10-20 mm long, 2-5 mm wide. Perianth 15-17 mm long, tube 5 mm long, pink, tips with white bristles. *Style 15-17 mm long*, straight, pink. Pollen presenter 4 mm long, thread-like, not distinct from style.
DISTRIBUTION: Malmesbury Flats from Klapmuts to Riverlands. HABITAT: Flatlands, slightly saline Klipheuwel gravels mixed with sands, 120-150 m. STATUS: Almost extinct. *Red Data Book* status: Endangered, as a result of agriculture, invasion of its habitat by alien acacias, grazing and too-frequent fires. In 1985 fewer than 1000 plants remained in a handful of small, dense populations at the northern end of its range. Ten years later, fewer than a dozen plants were known to survive in the wild. The last remaining population was ploughed up in August 1996 but, following conservation action, is recovering well. FLOWERS: February to June, mainly March and April.
FRUITS: Retained.

## *Protea* The Rose Sugarbushes

The Rose Sugarbushes (section *Pinifoliae*) tend to be smaller than other sugarbushes, with *flowerheads 25-50 mm long.* The *involucral bracts are hairless*, the inner series being longer than the flowers. In most species the *leaves are narrowly linear or needle-like*, and for this reason the group is also known as Needle-leaf Sugarbushes.

*Protea scolymocephala* (L.) Reichard                    Thistle Sugarbush    **Plate 26**

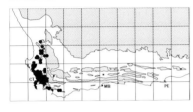

A small, erect shrub 0.5-1.5 m tall. Trunk up to 15 mm in diameter. Stems hairless. *Leaves curved upwards, linear-spatulate, 35-90 mm long, 3-6 mm wide*, hairless, tapering at base, tips pointed. *Flowerhead 35-45 mm across. Involucral bracts creamy green, hairless, margin fringed*; outer series ovate, 6-8 mm long, 5-8 mm wide; inner series oblong-spatulate, 15-25 mm long, 3-7 mm wide, widely spreading when open. Perianth 15-25 mm long, tube 6-8 mm long, hairless or occasionally with bristles, cream. Style strongly curved inwards, 12-25 mm long. Pollen presenter 2 mm long, linear, knee-bent at base.
DISTRIBUTION: Gifberg and Sandveld Flats to the Cape Peninsula and the Cape Flats, with an outlying population between Kleinmond and Hawston, near Hermanus. HABITAT: Sandy flats and coastal lowlands, often near drainage lines, 0-400 m. STATUS: Once abundant on Cape Flats, now virtually extinct due to urbanization. Typically occurring as isolated dense stands of thousands of plants, but reduced to a few plants where alien acacias are abundant. FLOWERS: July to November, mainly August and September. FRUITS: Retained.

*Protea acuminata* Sims                    Black-rim Sugarbush    **Plate 26**

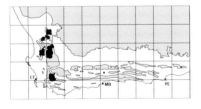

An erect, rounded shrub 1-2 m tall, up to 1.5 m across. Trunk up to 30 mm in diameter. Stems hairless, reddish. *Leaves curved upwards, linear to sputulate, 60-120 mm long, 5-8 mm wide, tip with a fine point, flat, hairless*, glaucous. Flowerhead globose, 25-35 mm across, overtopped by leaves. *Involucral bracts wine-red, margin dark*, hairless; outer series 5-10 mm long, 5-8 mm wide, tightly overlapping; inner series oblong-spatulate, 15-25 mm long, 4-10 mm wide, curved inwards. Perianth 20-25 mm long, tube 8 mm long, tips with brown bristles. Style strongly curved inwards, 20 mm long, red. Pollen presenter 4 mm long, linear, distinct from style.
DISTRIBUTION: Three isolated populations: the Bokkeveld escarpment near Nieuwoudtville; Cederberg and Olifants River Mountains; Du Toit's Kloof, Stettyns and Riviersonderend Mountains. HABITAT: Varied on dry sandstone soils, 300-1500 m. STATUS: Regularly and sparsely dispersed plants occur in isolated stands. FLOWERS: June to September, mainly July and August. FRUITS: Retained.

***Protea canaliculata*** Andrews                                     Groove-leaf Sugarbush     **Plate 26**

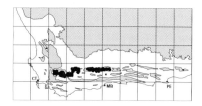

An erect, compact, rounded shrub up to 1.2 m tall and
1 m across, with a single trunk branching from near
ground level. Stems hairless when mature. *Leaves
channelled on undersurface, tip a recurved black spine,
curved upwards, linear to spatulate, 45-80 mm long,*
2-7 mm wide, green to glaucous, hairless when
mature. Flowerhead shallowly cup-shaped, 35-60 mm
across. Involucral bracts wine-red to pink-red, occa-
sionally with silky hairs, margin hairless; outer series ovate, tip pointed, 10 mm long, 10 mm wide,
tightly overlapping; inner series oblong, 20-30 mm long, 7-14 mm wide, curved inwards. Perianth
20-25 mm long, tube 10 mm long, tips with brown hairs. Style 20-30 mm long, yellow. Pollen
presenter 4 mm long, linear, not distinct from style.
DISTRIBUTION: Hex River Mountains to Waboomsberg and Swartberg. HABITAT: Rocky,
exposed sandstone or quartzitic soils, 800-1500 m. STATUS: Widely dispersed as scattered plants,
occasionally forming dense clumps. FLOWERS: March to June, mainly May. FRUITS: Retained.
☐ VARIATIONS: Western forms have narrow, needle-like leaves which are green and hairless,
and involucral bracts which are dark wine-red and hairless. Eastern forms have broad leaves
which are often sparsely covered with hairs, and pinkish red bracts which have a sparse covering
of downy hairs.

***Protea nana*** (P.J. Bergius) Thunb.                               Mountain-rose Sugarbush     **Plate 26**

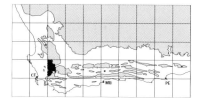

An erect, rounded shrub up to 1.3 m tall. Trunk up to
30 mm in diameter. *Stems hairless. Leaves dense,
curved upwards, needle-shaped, 18-30 mm long,
1-1.5 mm wide, bright green, hairless, tip with a soft
brown spine. Flowerhead pendulous, 30-45 mm
across,* cup-shaped. Involucral bracts scarlet to green,
hairless, margin fringed with short hairs; outer series
ovate, tip rounded, 10-15 mm long, 6-8 mm wide;
inner series elliptic, 25-30 mm long, 10-12 mm wide. Perianth 20-22 mm long, tube 8 mm long, tip
with brown bristles. Style curved inwards, 20-25 mm long, hairless. Pollen presenter 2-3 mm long,
linear, tip pointed, knee-bent at base.
DISTRIBUTION: Du Toit's Kloof to Groot Winterhoek Mountains and Skurweberg. HABITAT:
Varied, montane, 400-900 m. STATUS: Typically in dense, isolated stands, but scattered plants are
frequently encountered. FLOWERS: July to October. FRUITS: Retained for a few years.
☐ VARIATION: The colour of involucral bracts varies from dark red to bright red to dirty-faded red,
occasionally pale green.

***Protea witzenbergiana*** E. Phillips                               Swan Sugarbush     **Plate 27**

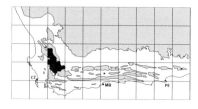

*A sprawling to prostrate shrub* 0.15-0.5 m tall, forming
mats up to 3 m across, single trunk. *Stems hairy, hairless when mature. Leaves blue-grey to carmine,
pointing vertically from a horizontal stem, needle-
like, 15-55 mm long, 1-2 mm wide, sparsely covered
with delicate hairs, hairless when mature, glaucous,*
grooved, tips with a backward-curving spine.
Flowerhead cup-shaped, 40-70 mm across, facing down-
wards on a stem curved like a swan's neck. Involucral bracts brown-red, hairless, margin with short
hairs; *outer series 5-30 mm long, outermost bracts leaf-like,* ovate, tip pointed, 8-10 mm long,
8-10 mm wide; inner series oblong, 20-30 mm long, 8-15 mm wide, curved inwards. Perianth

20-22 mm long, tube 8 mm long, tip with brown bristles. Style curved inwards, 25-30 mm long. Pollen presenter 3-4 mm long, thread-like, slightly knee-bent at base.
DISTRIBUTION: Cederberg to Hex River and Bokkerivier Mountains. HABITAT: Varied, mountain slopes, 750-1800 m. STATUS: Locally dominant, a prominent, if mat-like, feature of plant communities. FLOWERS: March to June, mainly April and May. FRUITS: Retained for a few years.
□ VARIATIONS: At high elevations a low, dense prostrate habit (up to 0.2 m tall) is assumed, with leaves as short as 15 mm. At lower elevations a lax, sparsely branched habit (up to 0.5 m tall) prevails, with leaves 55-90 mm long: these resemble leaves of *P. pityphylla,* but are blue-grey, not green.

***Protea pityphylla*** E. Phillips                    Ceres Sugarbush    **Plate 27**

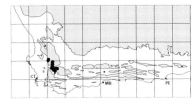

An almost erect to sprawling lax shrub up to 1 m tall, 2 m across, with a single trunk. *Stems hairless. Leaves bright green, curved upwards to pointing vertically from a horizontal stem, needle-like, 40-90 mm long, 1 mm wide, slightly grooved, hairless,* tip a sharp spine. *Flowerhead cup-shaped, 50-80 mm across,* nodding or on a stem curved like a swan's neck, with a yeasty odour. Involucral bracts wine-red, hairless, margin occasionally with hairs; *outer series 15-20 mm long, outermost bracts leaf-like,* ovate, tip pointed, 10-15 mm long, 10-12 mm wide; inner series ovate to oblong, 30 mm long, 10-15 mm wide, curved inwards. Perianth 25 mm long, tube 8-10 mm long, tip with brown bristles. Style strongly curved inwards, 30-35 mm long, pale. Pollen presenter 6-8 mm long, linear to thread-like, slightly knee-bent at base.
DISTRIBUTION: Skurweberg and Hex River Mountains, with a population in the Olifants River Mountains near the Dasklip Pass. HABITAT: Montane among large boulders, 500-1500 m. STATUS: Locally frequent in small, isolated stands of a few dozen plants. FLOWERS: May to September, mainly May to July. FRUITS: Retained for a few years.
NOTE: Very similar to *P. witzenbergiana,* but young stems hairless, not hairy, and leaves green, not blue-grey.

### *Protea* The Penduline Sugarbushes

The Penduline Sugarbushes tend to be *sprawling or rounded plants with flowerheads which face downwards or horizontally at the ends of sinuous branches. Flowerheads are large, 50-130 mm across.* Leaves are hairless. A high-altitude group, Penduline Sugarbushes grow above 1000 m.

***Protea recondita*** H. Buek ex Meisn.                    Hidden Sugarbush    **Plate 27**

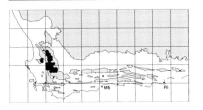

A sprawling shrub 0.5-1 m tall, up to 3 m across, with a single trunk. *Stems hairless. Leaves curved upwards, oblanceolate to ovate, 75-160 mm long, 25-55 mm wide, hairless, glaucous grey to purple* (prominently so in winter); stalk 20 mm long, formed by a tapering leaf base. *Flowerhead enclosed by leaves,* cup-shaped, 70-90 mm across, with a yeasty odour. *Involucral bracts hairless,*

green-yellow (occasionally with bright red edges), tips minutely fringed; outer series ovate, tip pointed, 10 mm long, 10 mm wide; inner series oblong, 30-45 mm long, 5-15 mm wide, curved inwards. Perianth 25-30 mm long, tube 10 mm long, tips with delicate brown hairs. Style strongly curved inwards, 30-35 mm long. Pollen presenter 10 mm long, linear, not distinct from style. DISTRIBUTION: Piketberg and Cederberg to Groot Winterhoek Mountains. HABITAT: Uppermost rocky slopes, 1000-2000 m. STATUS: Scattered plants occur in rocky habitats, but in open habitat isolated clumps of dense plants may dominate the vegetation. FLOWERS: May to September, mainly May to July. FRUITS: Retained for a few years.

### *Protea effusa* E. Mey. ex Meisn.           Scarlet Sugarbush   **Plate 28**

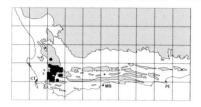

Variable in habit, an erect, sprawling or prostrate shrub up to 1.5 m tall and 3 m across. Stems hairless. *Leaves elliptic, 45-90 mm long, 5-30 mm wide, curved upwards to pointing vertically from a horizontal stem,* hairless, usually glaucous. *Flowerhead erect,* cup-shaped, 60-100 mm across, with a yeasty odour. Involucral bracts deep red (occasionally green-yellow tinged with red), hairless; outer series ovate, tip pointed, 10-15 mm long, 15-20 mm wide; inner series oblong to oblong-spatulate, 30-40 mm long, 5-15 mm wide, curved inwards. Perianth 25 mm long, tube 10 mm long, tips hairless to sparsely covered with brown bristles. Style strongly curved inwards, 30-35 mm long. Pollen presenter 5-7 mm long, linear to thread-like, not distinct from style.

DISTRIBUTION: Koue Bokkeveld to Du Toit's Kloof and Riviersonderend Mountains. HABITAT: Exposed rocky ridges, 1200-1800 m. STATUS: Low numbers of plants occur in isolated populations, most of which are found in the north. FLOWERS: May to September, mainly June and July. FRUITS: Retained for a few years.

☐ VARIATIONS: Northern forms are upright, rounded shrubs up to 1.5 m tall, with broad leaves (20-30 mm wide) and erect to pendant flowerheads. Southern forms are sprawling, up to 0.5 m tall, with trailing stems and leaves 10-15 mm wide. Eastern forms are prostrate, 0.2 m tall, forming dense mats up to 3 m across, with upward-facing flowerheads produced at the perimeter.

### *Protea sulphurea* E. Phillips           Sulphur Sugarbush   **Plate 28**

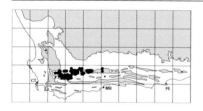

A low, dense, spreading shrub up to 0.5 m tall, 7 m across, with a single trunk. Stems hairless, flushed pink. *Leaves curved upwards, elliptic to oblanceolate, 10-40 mm long, 4-12 mm wide, green to glaucous,* tips with a fine black point. *Flowerhead pendulous on a short shoot,* cup-shaped, 90-130 mm across, with a yeasty odour. Involucral bracts green with red tips outside, sulphur-yellow inside; outer series ovate, tip rounded, 10-15 mm long, 10-15 mm wide; inner series oblong, 40-50 mm long, 7-15 mm wide. Perianth 30-35 mm long, tube 10 mm long, tips with downy, golden brown hairs. Style strongly curved inwards, 30-38 mm long. Pollen presenter 10 mm long, linear, tip pointed, clearly distinct from style.

DISTRIBUTION: Hex River Mountains to Swartberg and Waboomsberg. HABITAT: Dry, arid, sandstone soils, 1000-1550 m. STATUS: Small, isolated populations occur in the west, but populations around the Little Karoo may consist of thousands of regularly spaced plants. FLOWERS: April to August, mainly May and June. FRUITS: Retained for a few years.

☐ VARIATION: Eastern forms tend to have uniformly red involucral bracts.

*Protea namaquana* Rourke                                    Kamiesberg Sugarbush     **Plate 28**

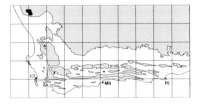

An erect shrub 1-2 m tall, up to 2 m across, with a single trunk. Stems hairless. *Leaves curved upwards, oblanceolate to linear-spatulate, 30-60 mm long, 4-10 mm wide, green,* hairless, tips with a fine black point. *Flowerhead pendulous,* cup-shaped, 90-100 mm across, with a yeasty odour. Involucral bracts dull carmine outside; outer series ovate, tip rounded, 8-10 mm long, 10-15 mm wide; inner series oblong, 20-25 mm long, 15-20 mm wide. Perianth 25-35 mm long, tube 10 mm long, tips with downy, golden brown hairs. Style strongly curved inwards, 30-35 mm long. Pollen presenter 8 mm long, cylindrical, clearly distinct from style.
DISTRIBUTION: Rooiberg and Ezelskop in the Kamiesberg. HABITAT: Upper granite slopes, 1200-1600 m. STATUS: Only a handful of populations of a few dozen plants are known. *Red Data Book* status: Endangered. FLOWERS: June to September. FRUITS: Retained for a few years.

*Protea pendula* R. Br.                                              Nodding Sugarbush     **Plate 28**

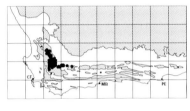

An erect, densely branched, rounded shrub 1-3 m tall, up to 3 m across. Trunk 100-150 mm in diameter. Stems hairless when mature. *Leaves curved upwards, oblanceolate, 30-55 mm long, 5-15 mm wide,* grey with downy hairs, hairless when mature, tip with a fine black point. *Flowerhead hanging from a short lateral shoot with leaves pointing backwards,* cup-shaped, 40-70 mm across, with a faint yeasty odour. Involucral bracts variable in colour within a single population (purple-red to pink or green with red tips), with brown or silver silky hairs, margin hairless; outer series ovate, tip pointed, 5-8 mm long, 10-12 mm wide; inner series oblong, 25-35 mm long, 5-14 mm wide. Perianth 25-30 mm long, tube 5-8 mm long, tips with shaggy, tawny hairs. Style curved inwards, 25-30 mm long, hairless. Pollen presenter 5 mm long, linear to thread-like, not distinct from style.
DISTRIBUTION: Cederberg to Koue Bokkeveld and east to Tweedside. HABITAT: Arid, rocky areas and krantzes, 1000-2000 m. STATUS: Usually scattered, isolated populations of a few plants that are cryptic, blending in with the surrounding vegetation. FLOWERS: May to August, mainly May and June. FRUITS: Retained for a few years.

## *AULAX* P.J. Bergius **The Featherbushes**

♀

♂

Featherbushes occur as either male or female plants. The female flowerhead comprises *a woody cup formed by short, inwardly curved, modified branches, inside which the flowers are borne on a conical central column. Male plants bear only male flowers in lax, terminal, spike-like racemes.* The female flowers have the perianth parts fused at the base around the ovary, all 4 perianth limbs free, and the anthers reduced to a linear thread. The male flowers have perianth limbs united into a basal tube with symmetrical free lobes, and a conspicuously thick style tip functioning as the pollen presenter. Floral nectaries are absent in both sexes. The fruit is a compressed obovoid achene, truncate at the base and densely covered with long white hairs which are largely confined to the edges and the median ridge. As in *Protea,* and unlike in *Leucadendron,* most fruits contained in a featherbush cup are non-viable – typically only about 20 per cent will germinate.

The species can be distinguished from one another by their leaves alone, although in the field the growth form is also a useful feature.

### *Aulax pallasia* Stapf                     Needle-leaf Featherbush     **Plate 29**

An erect, sparsely branched shrub up to 3 m tall, *arising from a large subterranean rootstock. Leaves needle-like to linear, 40-110 mm long, 1-5 mm wide, red when young.* Male flowerhead a lax, terminal, stalked raceme, 30-60 mm long, axillary, in clusters of 5-15. Style thread-like, 6-7 mm long, tip a club-shaped to cylindrical pollen presenter. Female flowerhead an open cup formed by 8-12 *inwardly curved lateral branches and containing stalked female flowers and sterile male flowers* on a central conical column; borne in flat-topped clusters. Style 5-8 mm long, tip club-shaped. Fruits with 6 prominent, hair-fringed ridges.
DISTRIBUTION: Piketberg and Koue Bokkeveld to Hottentots-Holland and Groenland Mountains and to the central Langeberg and Riviersonderend Mountains. HABITAT: Montane, sandstone soils, 800-2000 m. STATUS: Isolated clumps of several scattered plants are occasionally encountered. FLOWERS: January to April. FRUITS: Retained.

*Aulax cancellata* (L.) Druce                                           Channel-leaf Featherbush    **Plate 29**

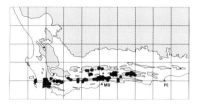

An erect to sprawling shrub 0.5-2.5 m tall, with a single main stem. *Leaves needle-like to spatulate, 45-100 mm long, 1-3 mm wide, with a channel on the upper surface.* Male flowerhead a lax, terminal, stalked raceme, 30-50 mm long, axillary, borne in clusters of 5-15. Style thread-like, 6-7 mm long, tip a club-shaped to cylindrical pollen presenter. Female flowerhead a terminal, globose, stalked cup formed by 8-15 inwardly curved bundles of axillary branches and bearing stalked female flowers on a short central axis. Style 6-8 mm long, tip bilobed. Fruits with 4 prominent vertical ridges, of which the *2 median ridges are fringed with long white hairs, and a network of smaller ridges connect them.*
DISTRIBUTION: Cape Peninsula and Hottentots-Holland Mountains to Langeberg and Kouga Mountains; Swartberg and Kammanassie Mountains. HABITAT: Sandstone soils, 0-1200 m.
STATUS: Extinct (but re-introduced) on Table Mountain, and a few plants in a single population at Silvermine. Small scattered, occasionally dense, groups of plants occur elsewhere.
FLOWERS: November to February. FRUITS: Retained.
□ VARIATIONS: Eastern populations have longer, straighter, narrower leaves. In exposed localities plants are usually sprawling (up to 0.5 m tall) and dense. In sheltered localities sparsely branched, erect plants (up to 2 m tall) may occur.
NOTE: The channel on the leaf may be apparent only in dried material.

*Aulax umbellata* (Thunb.) R. Br.                                          Broad-leaf Featherbush    **Plate 29**

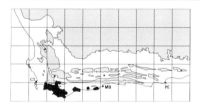

An erect shrub up to 2.5 m tall, with a single main stem. *Leaves linear to oblanceolate, 20-110 mm long, 2-15 mm wide.* Male flowerhead a lax terminal raceme, rarely compound, borne in clusters of 4-10. Style thread-like, 6-10 mm long, terminating in a club-shaped pollen presenter. Female flowerhead a globose cup formed by 8-15 inwardly curved bundles of axillary branches, covered externally with leaf-like bracts, and bearing stalked female flowers, some terminally, on a central conical column. Style 6-8 mm long, tip bilobed and with minute rounded projections. Fruits ovoid to obovoid, compressed, with 4 prominent ridges and dense, long, white hairs on the equatorial ridge.
DISTRIBUTION: Kogelberg to Riversdale Flats, mainly on coastal lowlands; an isolated population in the Riviersonderend Mountains near McGregor. HABITAT: Sandstone sands, 0-500 m.
STATUS: Highly social, often forming dense, usually extensive stands. FLOWERS: November to February. FRUITS: Retained.
□ VARIATIONS: Forms in the extreme west have narrow leaves like those of *A. cancellata*, but without the channel. In southern forms, especially on slightly calcareous soils, the broader leaves are strongly curved inwards.

## *FAUREA* Harv. **The Beechwoods**

The genus *Faurea is* characterized by flowerheads in which the *flowers are borne on spikes.* All species in southern Africa are trees and occur in savanna and forest habitats. The leaves are lanceolate, and vary in size from 1 species to another. *The perianth parts are fused into a tube at the base, but 1 remains free at the tip. The ovary is covered with long, silky hairs.* The fruits are hairy and have persistent styles.

There are about 15 species of *Faurea* in Africa and Madagascar, of which 6 occur in southern Africa.

*Faurea rubriflora* Marner         Manica Beechwood    **Plate 30**

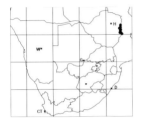

A large tree up to 25 m tall. Leaves 65-125 mm long, 13-20 mm wide, margin entire, wavy, glossy green; young leaves red; stalk up to 20 mm long. *Flowerhead red to bright crimson,* a robust spike 150-200 mm long. Fruits small, hairy, winged nuts.
DISTRIBUTION: Eastern Zimbabwe and Mozambique. HABITAT: Montane forest and forest fringe. STATUS: Common, encountered in isolated patches. FLOWERS: March and April. FRUITS: June to January.

*Faurea galpinii* E. Phillips         Forest Beechwood    **Plate 30**

Although it grows to a height of 10 m, this species generally has a shrub-like habit. Leaves up to 100 mm long, 25 mm wide, margin entire; stalk 10 mm long. *Flowerhead erect, not pendulous,* 80-100 mm long, greenish white, finely covered with velvety hairs. *Flowers stalked.* Fruits with long, hoary, whitish hairs.
DISTRIBUTION: Drakensberg escarpment of Northern Province, Mpumalanga and Swaziland. HABITAT: *Confined to high-altitude mist-belts* at forest edges and early seral forest succession.
STATUS: Common in isolated patches. FLOWERS: October to January. FRUITS: November to April.

*Faurea macnaughtonii* E. Phillips         Terblans Beechwood    **Plate 30**

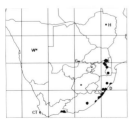

A tree up to 25 m tall. Wood sweet-smelling, with a beautiful dark brown grain. *Leaves variable, 25-30 mm wide,* up to 120 mm long; stalk 10 mm long. Flowerhead up to 160 mm long, 30 mm across, white or pale pink, with a sweet scent. Fruits with long, white-yellow hairs.
DISTRIBUTION: Unusual in that it occurs in small, isolated areas in Northern Province, Mpumalanga, KwaZulu-Natal, Eastern Cape, and southern Cape (Knysna to George). Extralimitally to Madagascar. HABITAT: *Forest and forest margin.* STATUS: *Red Data Book* status: Rare. Scattered in isolated patches. The Gouna population near Knysna is unusually large and vigorous. FLOWERS: December to February. FRUITS: February to June.

*Faurea rochetiana* (A. Rich.) Pic. Serm.         Broad-leaf Beechwood    **Plate 31**

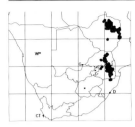

A small, spreading, crooked, leafy tree 4-7 m tall. *Leaves 25-60 mm wide, green above, grey below due to a dense covering of velvety hairs,* 70-170 mm long, margin entire and wavy, turning orange and red in autumn when the fiery colours may lead to confusion with *Combretum adenogonium*; stalk *short and thick, 5-12 mm long, hairy. Flowerhead 220-300 mm long, 30-40 mm across*, cream to pink. *Flowers 20-25 mm long,* densely covered with white hairs. DISTRIBUTION: Eastern Zimbabwe, western Mozambique, Northern Province to Swaziland, northern KwaZulu-Natal.
Extralimitally to Angola, Nigeria and Ethiopia. HABITAT: Hilly country in mist-belts, deciduous *Brachystegia* and related woodland and grassland, 900-2400 m. STATUS: Frequent, especially in scrub woodland. FLOWERS: March to September. FRUITS: June to January.
NOTE: Previously known as *F. speciosa,* this species is now recognized to be the same as *F. rochetiana* from eastern Africa. The status of the southern African variant as a subspecies or variety has still to be determined.

*Faurea saligna* Harv.         Transvaal Beechwood    **Plate 31**

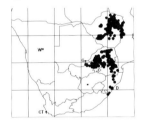

*A tree with a slender, straight trunk and a willow-like appearance,* normally 7-10 m tall but reaching 20 m in KwaZulu-Natal. *Bark dark grey to black.* Wood pale yellow to red, with a beautiful grain; soaking in water yields a red dye. *Leaves long and narrow, almost hairless,* 65-125 mm long, 13-20 mm wide, lanceolate-elliptic, slightly sickle-shaped, drooping, waxy, margin entire, green in summer and red in autumn; *stalk 20 mm long. Flowerheads in slender spikes 20-30 mm across*, 120-150 mm long, green to cream-white, borne at branch tip, with a honey- or coconut-like scent. *Flowers 12 mm long,* densely covered with adpressed, grey hairs when young.
DISTRIBUTION: Zimbabwe, Mozambique, North-West Province, Gauteng, Northern Province, Mpumalanga, Swaziland and KwaZulu-Natal. HABITAT: Low- to medium-altitude *Brachystegia* woodland or grassland. STATUS: Often common, usually as scattered trees. FLOWERS: August to February. FRUITS: October to April.
□ VARIATION: Leaves of plants in the north of the region appear to be larger than those of plants in the south.
NOTE: Resembles the Karee *(Rhus lancea),* but does not have trifoliate leaves.

*Faurea delevoyi* De Wild.         Delevoy's Beechwood    **Plate 31**

A spreading tree up to 30 m tall. *Leaves elliptic to broadly elliptic, 30-50 mm wide,* 130-190 mm long, glossy green, almost hairless but with a few long hairs above the base; *stalk absent or very short. Flowerhead dense,* up to 120 mm long, borne at branch tips, pale yellow-green, with a creamy-milk smell. *Flowers 10 mm long, strongly curved,* with white, adpressed, downy hairs.
DISTRIBUTION: Zimbabwe, Mozambique and Malawi. Extralimitally to Angola, Zambia. HABITAT: *Riverine forest,* to 2000 m. STATUS: Not known. FLOWERS: August to February. FRUITS: Not known.

## *SERRURIA* Salisb. **The Spiderheads**

Since *Serruria* was last revised in 1912, new species have been discovered and described, and several more await description. The classification of *Serruria* species in this book is based on Goldblatt & Manning, 2000 (see References and Further Reading).

Members of the genus *Serruria* can easily be recognized by their *dissected leaves which have cylindrical segments. Flowerheads may be solitary,* in which case they are always borne at the tip of the branch, or *they may be multiple* and are then also borne in the axils of the topmost leaves. The flowers each have a conspicuous floral bract, and consist of 4 free perianth segments united only at their bases. Involucral bracts seldom occur, but when they do they are loosely arranged on the stalk of the flowerhead. The fruit is a small hard nut, sparsely covered with hairs and containing an elaiosome at the base.

Spiderheads are largely confined to the winter-rainfall area and extend as far east as Mossel Bay along the coast.

Spiderheads can be divided into 2 major groups: one in which the flowerhead is simple, and the other in which the flowerhead consists of many headlets. At this stage the further division of these groups, as given in the following pages of this chapter, is based on convenience rather than to reflect relationships.

It is especially difficult to delimit the Curly Spiderheads, as the common stalk of the flowerhead may be so reduced as to appear absent (*S. nervosa* and *S. roxburghii*), or it may be 20-50 mm long. Another problem concerns species such as *S. inconspicua* (Pin Spiderheads) and *S. nervosa* (Curly Spiderheads), which have a solitary to many flower-heads linked to a common basal stalk. In these cases the form with a solitary flowerhead may easily be identified to the wrong group. The reverse applies to *S. aitonii* (Paw Spiderheads) and *S. aemula* (Skirted Spiderheads), which are here regarded as the most primitive of their groups. They may appear to have multiple flowerheads, but in fact usually bear many separate flowerheads at the branch tips.

## A QUICK KEY TO THE SPIDERHEADS

### FLOWERHEAD WITH MANY HEADLETS

**The Pin Spiderheads**
(Page 84, Plate 32)
Leaves fine and thin
Flowers straight in bud, clustered
in loose headlets on short stalks

**The Curly Spiderheads**
(Page 86, Plate 34)
Flowers curved in bud,
clustered in loose headlets
on short stalks

**The Stalked Spiderheads**
(Page 89, Plate 36)
Plant erect
Leaves large and stout
Flowerhead stalk longer
than 80 mm (rarely 20 mm)

**The Tulbagh Spiderhead**
(Page 89, Plate 36)
Flowerhead dense, untidy
and flat-topped, borne on
a short stalk

**The Whip-leaf Spiderheads**
(Page 104, Plate 46)
Stems creeping, with leaves arising vertically
Leaves with 1 to 4 tips
Flowerhead with 4 to 10 flowers
Floral bracts large

### FLOWERHEAD SIMPLE

**The Skirted Spiderheads**
(Page 99, Plate 43)
Flowers straight or slightly
kinked in bud
Involucral bracts form a 'skirt'
around the flowerhead, often
brightly coloured
Flowerhead stalk conspicuous

**The Stalkless Spiderheads**
(Page 96, Plate 41)
Flowerhead solitary
Flowerhead stalk absent or
hidden by dense leaves at base
of flowerhead

**The Paw Spiderheads**
(Page 92, Plate 38)
Flowers curved strongly in bud
Flowerhead stalk conspicuous
Involucral bracts inconspicuous
Style occasionally hairy

### *Serruria* The Pin Spiderheads

The Pin Spiderheads are characterized by *straight flowers borne in many loose headlets on short stalks* that together form a flowerhead. Within the group there is a progression from a flowerhead which comprises many lax headlets to one which comprises only 2 or 3 headlets. The headlets are generally few-flowered. The leaves of Pin Spiderheads tend to be fine and thin rather than robust.

---

***Serruria inconspicua*** L. Guthrie & T.M. Salter                 Cryptic Spiderhead     **Plate 32**

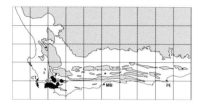

*A sprawling shrub 0.2-0.3 m tall*, 0.3 m across. Main stem 5 mm in diameter. *Leaves with crispy hairs, 15-25 mm long, 15-25 mm wide, erect, dissected, with 8-14 tips, often strongly curved inwards; stalk 5 mm long. Flowerhead 6-10 mm long, 7-9 mm across, inconspicuous and hidden by leaves, lax, comprising 1-5 headlets of 3-8 flowers each; flowerhead stalk short.* Involucral bracts absent. Perianth yellow. Style straight, 5 mm long. Pollen presenter 0.5 mm long, club-shaped, not distinct from style.
DISTRIBUTION: Cape Peninsula and Kogelberg to Groenland Mountains, with a record from the Stettyns Mountains. HABITAT: Dry slopes and flats, sandstone soils, 0-305 m. STATUS: Often occurring in dense stands as an understorey to sugarbushes. FLOWERS: July to December, mainly September and October. FRUITS: Released within 2 months of flowering.

---

***Serruria candicans*** R. Br.                 Shiny Spiderhead     **Plate 32**

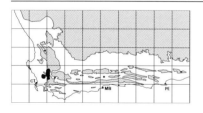

An erect shrub 0.4-0.8 m tall, 0.5 m across. Main stem 10 mm in diameter. *Leaves erect, 25-55 mm long, 2-15 mm wide, dissected, with 18-25 tips with sharp, fine points, covered with silver, woolly hairs; stalk 1-15 mm long.* Flowerhead 25 mm long, 30 mm across, comprising 10-25 headlets of 6-7 flowers each; flowerhead stalk 5 mm long, hairy. Involucral bracts absent. Perianth pink with dark tips, with spreading, silver hairs. Style straight, 6-9 mm long. Pollen presenter 0.5 mm long, club-shaped.
DISTRIBUTION: Elandskloof to Slanghoek Mountains and Paardeberg (Malmesbury). HABITAT: Granite and sandy soils, fynbos/renosterveld ecotone, 60-160 m. STATUS: Known from 3 locations in which very large populations comprising a few thousand plants are scattered. *Red Data Book* status: Rare. FLOWERS: July to December. FRUITS: Released within 2 months of flowering.

---

***Serruria fasciflora*** Salisb. ex Knight                 Common Pin Spiderhead     **Plate 32**

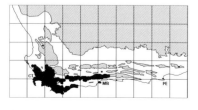

An erect to sprawling shrub 0.4-0.9 m tall, up to 0.5 m across, variable. *Leaves curved upwards, 30-70 mm long, 25-35 mm wide, dissected, with 10-15 thread-like tips, with straight hairs. Flowerhead flat-topped, 15-25 mm long, 15-50 mm across, comprising 10-15 headlets of 5-7 flowers each*, with a faint sweet scent; *flowerhead stalk short, hairy.* Involucral bracts lanceolate. Perianth pink to cream, hairy but occasionally hairless. Style straight, 5-7 mm long. Pollen presenter 0.5 mm long, linear to club-shaped, not distinct from style.

DISTRIBUTION: Flats and mountains from Hopefield Flats and Slanghoek Mountains to Potberg, Riviersonderend Mountains, Langeberg and Outeniqua Mountains.HABITAT: Varied, 0-610 m. STATUS: Variable from dense populations to scattered plants. FLOWERS: All year round, mainly May to December. FRUITS: Released within 2 months of flowering.
□ VARIATIONS: A very variable species; its previous treatment as 6 separate species was based primarily on differences in the hairiness of the leaves and perianth and the size of the flowerhead.

*Serruria kraussii* Meisn.                              Snowball Spiderhead      **Plate 33**

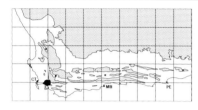

An erect shrub 0.3-1 m tall, 0.5 m across. Main stem 20 mm in diameter. *Leaves erect, 50-75 mm long, 30-65 mm wide, dissected, with 20-29 round, hairless tips; stalk 20 mm long. Flowerhead globose, 65-70 mm across, comprising 5-12 headlets of 15-30 flowers each*; flowerhead stalk short, hairy. *Involucral bracts lanceolate, almost hairless.* Perianth white, with spreading, silver hairs. Style straight, 5-9 mm long. Pollen presenter 1 mm long, tip forming a knob.
DISTRIBUTION: Hottentots-Holland Mountains from Jonkershoek to Sir Lowry's Pass. HABITAT: Granite and sandstone soils, 180-460 m. STATUS: Several populations totalling 2000 plants. *Red Data Book* status: Rare. FLOWERS: July to November. FRUITS: Released within 2 months of flowering.

*Serruria zeyheri* Meisn.                              Matchstick Spiderhead      **Plate 33**

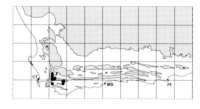

A rounded shrub 0.3-0.5 m tall, 0.5 m across. Main stem 10 mm in diameter. Leaves erect, 70-120 mm long, 40-80 mm wide, hairless when mature, dissected, with 15-25 tips with fine points; stalk 20-30 mm long. Flower-head flat-topped, 40-55 mm long, 60-70 mm across, comprising 15-30 headlets of 20-25 flowers each; flowerhead stalk short. Involucral bracts lanceolate. *Perianth white with shiny black, hairless tips, conspicuous while in bud.* Style straight, 10 mm long. Pollen presenter 1 mm long, tip forming a knob.
DISTRIBUTION: Du Toit's Kloof to Riviersonderend Mountains; possibly Groenland Mountains. HABITAT: Moist sandstone and peaty slopes, 760-1220 m. STATUS: Rarely encountered. FLOWERS: August to November. FRUITS: Released within 2 months of flowering.

*Serruria viridifolia* Rourke                              Mat Spiderhead      **Plate 33**

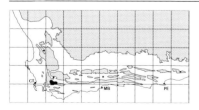

*A shrub forming mats up to 0.3 m tall and 2 m across, with creeping stems* from a single 15-mm main stem. *Leaves pointing vertically from a horizontal stem, 20-50 mm long, 15-40 mm wide, hairless, green, dissected, with 8-12 tips; stalk 10-20 mm long.* Flower-head globose, 10-15 mm across, up to 5 per branch, comprising 2 or 3 headlets of 10-14 flowers each; flowerhead stalk 0-8 mm long. Involucral bracts teardrop-shaped. *Perianth with minute hairs*, white. Style straight, 8-10 mm long. Pollen presenter 1 mm long, linear.
DISTRIBUTION: Jonaskop to Wolfieskop in the Riviersonderend Mountains; Stettyns Mountains. HABITAT: Deep sands on sandstone slopes, 800-1100 m. STATUS: Scattered plants beneath other shrubs. *Red Data Book* status: Rare. FLOWERS: September to December, mainly October and November. FRUITS: Released within 2 months of flowering.

## *Serruria* The Curly Spiderheads

The Curly Spiderheads are characterized by flowers which are slightly to markedly *curved in bud. The flowers are borne in loose headlets on a short common stalk.* There are 3 exceptions: *S. collina* has flowerhead stalks which are longer (20-50 mm); and *S. roxburghii* and *S. nervosa* have flowerheads which are crowded, and are united on a very short, inconspicuous flowerhead stalk. Like the Pin Spiderheads, to which they are closely related, the Curly Spiderheads tend to have fine rather than stout leaves.

*Serruria rubricaulis* R. Br.                    Red-stem Spiderhead    **Plate 34**

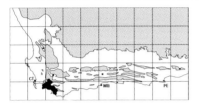

*A prostrate shrub 0.1-0.3 m tall, up to 0.5 m across, with a rootstock and creeping, red branches. Leaves curved upwards to pointing vertically from a horizontal stem, 35-45 mm long, 20-25 mm wide, hairless, dissected, with 12-18 rounded tips with fine points; stalk 20-25 mm long.* Flowerhead globose, 20-25 mm long, 25-30 mm across, lax, comprising 5-25 headlets of 6-10 flowers each; headlet stalk short and thick, hairy. Involucral bracts absent. Perianth pink, with adpressed, short, silky hairs. Style curved, 8 mm long. Pollen presenter 0.5 mm long, club-shaped.
DISTRIBUTION: Hottentots-Holland and Groenland Mountains to Klein River Mountains and hills to the south of Salmonsdam. HABITAT: Sandstone soils, on lower slopes and flats, 0-160 m. STATUS: Common as scattered plants over large areas. FLOWERS: September and October. FRUITS: Released within 2 months of flowering.

*Serruria adscendens* (Lam.) R. Br.                    Kleinmond Spiderhead    **Plate 34**

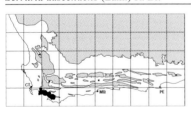

*A rounded shrub 0.5-1 m tall, up to 0.5 m across. Main stem 20 mm in diameter. Leaves erect, 25-65 mm long, 20-25 mm wide, hairless, dissected, with 10-17 rounded tips with fine points; stalk 15-25 mm long.* Flowerhead globose, 20-25 mm long, 25-30 mm across, comprising 5-25 headlets of 6-10 flowers each, with a strong sweet scent; headlet stalk short and thick, hairy. Involucral bracts absent.
Perianth pink, with adpressed, short, silver hairs. Style curved, 7-8 mm long. Pollen presenter 0.5 mm long, club-shaped.
DISTRIBUTION: Hottentots-Holland and Groenland Mountains to Klein River Mountains, and flats seawards of these. HABITAT: Sandstone soils, flats and lower slopes, 0-950 m. STATUS: A social species occurring in isolated clumps of a few hundred plants. FLOWERS: July to October. FRUITS: Released within 2 months of flowering.

*Serruria decipiens* R. Br.                              Sandveld Spiderhead     **Plate 34**

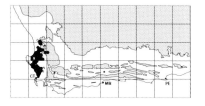

A rounded shrub 0.6-1 m tall, up to 0.5 m across. Main stem 10 mm in diameter. *Leaves curved upwards, 30-45 mm long, 15-20 mm wide, hairless when mature, dissected, with 12-15 rounded tips with fine points; stalk 15-20 mm long.* Flowerhead globose, 20-25 mm long, 25-30 mm across, up to 3 per branch, *lax, each comprising 5-10 headlets of 6-10 flowers each*, with a sweet scent; flowerhead stalk very short and thick. Involucral bracts absent. Perianth silver-pink. Style curved, 8-9 mm long. Pollen presenter 1 mm long, club-shaped.

DISTRIBUTION: Sandveld, Hopefield and Cape Flats; Piketberg and Olifants River Mountains. HABITAT: Sandstone and sandy soils, 0-250 m. STATUS: Still extremely common north of Cape Town as scattered to dense colonies. FLOWERS: July to October. FRUITS: Released within 2 months of flowering.

□ VARIATIONS: Incredibly variable in length, number and size of the flowerheads; probably many local races exist. A resprouting form with black floral bracts, from Piketberg and the Olifants River Mountains, may be a new species (Plate 34).

*Serruria collina* Salisb. ex Knight                     Lost Spiderhead     **Plate 35**

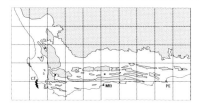

A sprawling shrub 0.1 m tall, up to 3 m across. Main stem 5 mm in diameter. *Leaves pointing vertically from a horizontal stem, 50-150 mm long, 40 mm wide, hairless, dissected, with 13-43 blunt tips; stalk 40-60 mm long.* Flowerhead globose, 40-80 mm long, 35-40 mm across, *comprising 8-15 headlets of 5-12 flowers each*, with a sweet scent; *flowerhead stalk 20-50 mm long.* Involucral bracts absent. *Perianth cream, with dense, long hairs.* Style straight, 8-10 mm long. Pollen presenter 3 mm long, linear to thread-like.

DISTRIBUTION: Southern Cape Peninsula. HABITAT: Sandstone soils, 150-500 m. STATUS: *Red Data Book* status: Vulnerable, as a result of invasion by alien acacias. Known from 4 populations totalling 500 scattered plants; a few more very small populations may exist. FLOWERS: July to October. FRUITS: Released within 2 months of flowering.

*Serruria glomerata* (L.) R. Br.                         Cluster Spiderhead     **Plate 35**

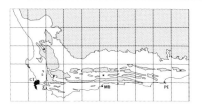

An erect shrub 0.2-0.4 m tall, 0.5 m across. Main stem 15 mm in diameter. Leaves curved upwards, 25-70 mm long, 30-60 mm wide, hairless, dissected, with 20-25 tips with sharp, fine points; stalk 20-25 mm long. Flowerhead globose, 25-50 mm long, 35-45 mm across, lax, up to 3 per branch, *each comprising 4-8 headlets of 20-40 flowers each*, with a sweet scent; *flowerhead stalk 6-10 mm long. Involucral bracts few, closely overlapping.* Perianth cream, with adpressed, white, silky hairs. Style curved, 8-10 mm long. Pollen presenter 2 mm long, club-shaped, knee-bent at base.

DISTRIBUTION: Cape Flats and Cape Peninsula. HABITAT: Sandstone slopes and flats, 0-330 m. STATUS: Locally common, occurring in fairly dense isolated stands. FLOWERS: August to October. FRUITS: Released within 2 months of flowering.

***Serruria roxburghii*** R. Br.                           Short-leaf Spiderhead     **Plate 35**

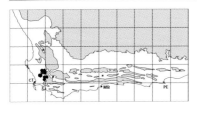

An erect shrub 0.4-1 m tall, 0.5 m across. Main stem 10 mm in diameter. *Leaves curved upwards, 10-25 mm long, 5-10 mm wide, hairless when mature, dissected, with 13-17 tips with sharp, fine points; stalk 8-10 mm long.* Flowerhead globose, 8-25 mm across, 3-7 per branch, each comprising 10-14 flowers, with a sweet scent; flowerhead stalk very short. *Involucral bracts ovate.* Perianth pink, with short, semi-adpressed, silver-white hairs. Style slightly curved inwards, 5-10 mm long. Pollen presenter 2 mm long, club-shaped.

DISTRIBUTION: Paarl Mountain, Paardeberg (Malmesbury) and Riebeek-Kasteel. HABITAT: Sandy patches, 120-160 m. STATUS: *Red Data Book* status: Endangered, as a result of loss of habitat to agriculture, invasion by alien plants and too-frequent fires. Known from only 3 localities which in 1987 totalled about 3000 plants. Several recently discovered populations are threatened by agriculture. FLOWERS: September to November. FRUITS: Released within 2 months of flowering.

***Serruria nervosa*** Meisn.                               Fluted Spiderhead     **Plate 35**

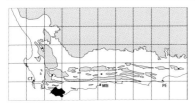

A low, erect shrub 0.5 m tall, 0.3 m across. Main stem 7 mm in diameter. *Leaves curved upwards, 20-45 mm long, 10-20 mm wide, hairless, dissected, with 11-19 tips with sharp, fine points; stalk 10 mm long.* Flowerhead flat-topped, 5-15 mm long, 22-28 mm across, dense, *comprising 1-3 headlets totalling 20-22 flowers*, with a sweet scent; *flower-head stalk 2-6 mm long, hairless.* Involucral bracts absent. *Floral bracts 10 mm long, ribbed.* Perianth pink, with erect white hairs. Style curved, 6-7 mm long. Pollen presenter 1 mm long, club-shaped.

DISTRIBUTION: Klein River Mountains to Elim Flats and seawards. HABITAT: Calcareous and acid sands, 20-100 m. STATUS: Locally abundant, usually as scattered plants. FLOWERS: July to November. FRUITS: Released within 2 months of flowering.

NOTE: Due to confusion with *S. bolusii*, these species may be more restricted to the higher hills than shown on the maps.

***Serruria bolusii*** E. Phillips & Hutch.                 Agulhas Spiderhead     **Plate 35**

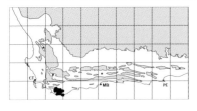

A low, erect shrub 0.3 m tall, 0.3 m across. Main stem 7 mm in diameter. Leaves curved upwards, 18-45 mm long, 10-20 mm wide, hairless, dissected, with 8-20 fine, sharp points. Flowerhead globose, 20-40 mm across, *comprising 4-12 headlets of 5-20 flowers each*; flowerhead stalk 20 mm long, hairless. Involucral bracts lanceolate, acute. Floral bracts 10 mm long, ribbed. *Perianth pink with adpressed white hairs.* Style curved, 6-7 mm long. Pollen presenter 1 mm long, club-shaped.

DISTRIBUTION: Agulhas Flats around Elim and southwards. HABITAT: Calcareous and acid sands, 20-100 m. STATUS: Locally abundant, often in dense stands. FLOWERS: July to November. FRUITS: Released within 2 months of flowering.

NOTE: *Serruria bolusii* and *S. nervosa* are very similar in appearance. A close inspection of the flowerhead structure is required to distinguish these species, although the spreading hairs of the perianth parts of *S. nervosa* give it a fluffy appearance.

## *Serruria* The Tulbagh Spiderhead

The Tulbagh Spiderhead is a robust plant bearing a *dense, untidy, flat-topped flowerhead on a very short common stalk.* Its long, stout leaves are comparable only to those of the Stalked Spiderheads, to which the Tulbagh Spiderhead is closely related.

*Serruria triternata* (Thunb.) R. Br.    Tulbagh Spiderhead    **Plate 36**

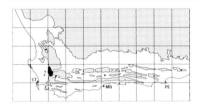

An erect shrub up to 1.5 m tall, 0.5 m across. Main stem 20 mm in diameter. *Leaves stout, curved upwards, 65-140 mm long, 30-35 mm wide, hairless when mature, dissected, with 12-16 tips with pointed calluses; stalk 20-45 mm long.* Flowerhead flat-topped, 30-45 mm long, 65-120 mm across, dense, comprising 3-25 headlets of 20-35 flowers each; *flowerhead stalk short, hairy.* Involucral bracts ovate. Perianth silvery cream, with adpressed, white, silky hairs. Style straight, 3-7 mm long. Pollen presenter 0.5 mm long, conical.
DISTRIBUTION: Elandskloof Mountains. HABITAT: Sandstone soils, 400-950 m.
STATUS: *Red Data Book* status: Rare. This species was previously listed as Endangered owing to pine and hakea infestation, but several additional populations, each of a few hundred plants, have been discovered. FLOWERS: August to October. FRUITS: Released within 2 months of flowering.

## *Serruria* The Stalked Spiderheads

The Stalked Spiderheads are easily distinguished by the length of their *flowerhead stalks (more than 80 mm long).* The exception is *S. confragosa,* as its stalk is shorter (up to 50 mm) and also leafy, unlike the leafless stalks of other Stalked Spiderheads. The flower-head is either lax with many clusters of headlets or it comprises many simple headlets. The leaves of the Stalked Spiderheads are among the stoutest and most robust in the genus and are often clustered in tufts at the base of the flowerhead.

*Serruria confragosa* Rourke    Wavy Spiderhead    **Plate 36**

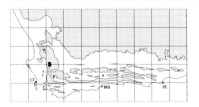

*An erect, sparsely branched shrub, with erect, wavy stems,* 0.6-1 m tall, up to 1 m across. Main stem 15 mm in diameter. Leaves erect, 30-60 mm long, 20-27 mm wide, hairless, dissected, with 6-9 tips, whorled at intervals along the stem. Flowerhead flat-topped, 30-35 mm long, 30-60 mm across, lax, comprising 6-15 headlets of 14-20 flowers each; *flowerhead*

*stalk 20-50 mm long.* Involucral bracts absent. Perianth pink, with adpressed, white, silky hairs. Style straight, 10-12 mm long. Pollen presenter 3 mm long, club-shaped.

DISTRIBUTION: Koue Bokkeveld and Groot Winterhoek Mountains. HABITAT: Dry, sandstone soil, 1000-1250 m. STATUS: Known from 3 localities totalling 500 scattered plants. *Red Data Book* status: Rare. FLOWERS: September to November. FRUITS: Released within 2 months of flowering.

**Serruria meisneriana** Schltr.　　　　　　　　　　　　Dainty Spiderhead　　**Plate 36**

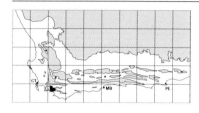

A slender, erect shrub 0.3-0.5 m tall, up to 0.5 m across. Main stem 10 mm in diameter. Leaves erect, 35-90 mm long, 25-30 mm wide, hairless, dissected, with 12-17 tips with fine points; stalk 5-50 mm long. Flowerhead 45-55 mm long, 25-35 mm across, lax, 1-3 per branch, comprising 6-12 headlets of 2-7 flowers each; *flowerhead stalk 80-140 mm long. Involucral and floral bracts strongly keeled, ovate, pink, 8-10 mm long. Perianth pink with dark, rounded tips, hairless.* Style straight, 9 mm long. *Pollen presenter 1.5 mm long, conical.*

DISTRIBUTION: Between the Babylonstoring and Groenland Mountains. HABITAT: Fynbos on shale soils, 450-650 m. STATUS: Only about 5000 plants of this species exist at 2 known localities. *Red Data Book* status: Rare. FLOWERS: July to October. FRUITS: Released within 2 months of flowering.

NOTE: Although placed with the Stalked Spiderheads, this species is clearly related to the Whip-leaf Spiderheads (page 104), from which it differs in that it is an erect plant.

**Serruria leipoldtii** E. Phillips & Hutch.　　　　　Louis Leipoldt's Spiderhead　　**Plate 36**

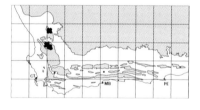

*A multi-stemmed, erect shrub 0.3-1 m tall, 0.3 m across, with a rootstock. Leaves erect, 65-105 mm long, 20-25 mm wide, hairless, dissected, with 25-35 tips with sharp, fine points; stalk 25-50 mm long.* Flowerhead umbrella-shaped, 15-30 mm long, 20-35 mm across, lax, comprising 4-10 headlets of 10-18 flowers each; *flowerhead stalk 40-100 mm long.* Involucral bracts absent. *Floral bracts hairy.* Perianth pink, with adpressed, silver-white, silky hairs. Style straight, 8-9 mm long. Pollen presenter 1.55 mm long, club-shaped, knee-bent at base.

DISTRIBUTION: Northern Cederberg, with dubious records from the Bokkeveld escarpment near Nieuwoudtville. HABITAT: Dry sandstone soils, 900-1100 m. STATUS: Usually encountered as isolated plants. *Red Data Book* status: Rare. FLOWERS: September to December. FRUITS: Released within 2 months of flowering.

**Serruria elongata** (P.J. Bergius) R. Br.　　　　　　Long-stalk Spiderhead　　**Plate 37**

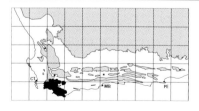

An erect shrub 0.7-1.5 m tall, 0.8 m across. Main stem 15 mm in diameter. *Leaves whorled below flowerhead stalk, curved upwards, 50-150 mm long, 50-70 mm wide, hairless, dissected, with 60-70 rounded tips with fine points; stalk 20-50 mm long.* Flowerhead rounded to flat-topped, 200-380 mm long, 60-120 mm across, lax, comprising 5-25 headlets of 15-25 flowers each, with a sweet scent; *flowerhead stalk 150-310 mm long.* Involucral bracts absent. *Floral bracts hairless.* Perianth pink, with short, adpressed, silver, silky hairs. Style straight, 7-11 mm long. Pollen presenter club-shaped, 1 mm long.

DISTRIBUTION: Du Toit's Kloof and Riviersonderend to Bredasdorp Mountains, and Elim Flats. HABITAT: Sandstone sands on flats and slopes, 150-800 m. STATUS: Locally abundant in patches of a few hundred plants. FLOWERS: July to October. FRUITS: Released within 2 months of flowering.

*Serruria williamsii* Rourke                     King Spiderhead     **Plate 37**

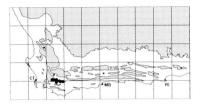

A sparsely branched, erect shrub 1-2 m tall, 1.5 m across. Main stem 30 mm in diameter. *Leaves whorled below flowerhead stalk, curved upwards, 150-220 mm long, 30-40 mm wide, stout, fleshy, hairless, dissected, with 19-25 tips; stalk 100-125 mm long.* Flowerhead ovoid, 300-550 mm long, 100-150 mm across, comprising 5-20 headlets of 10-100 flowers each; *flowerhead stalk 100-300 mm long.* Involucral bracts absent.
Perianth pink, with short, adpressed, silver, silky hairs. Style straight, 10 mm long. Pollen presenter 2 mm long, club-shaped.
DISTRIBUTION: Riviersonderend Mountains. HABITAT: Sandstone soils, 900-1100 m.
STATUS: Known only from a small number of isolated, dense populations of a few hundred plants.
*Red Data Book* status: Rare. FLOWERS: February to December, mainly August to November.
FRUITS: Released within 2 months of flowering.

*Serruria altiscapa* Rourke                     Stately Spiderhead     **Plate 37**

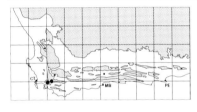

A sparsely branched, compact, rounded shrub, 0.2-0.3 m tall, with flowerheads extending up to 1-2 m, 0.3 m across. Main stem 10-15 mm in diameter. *Leaves whorled near ground level below flowerhead stalk, erect, 120-230 mm long, 65-140 mm wide, dissected, with 20-30 tips; stalk 60-75 mm long.* Flowerhead cylindrical, 700-1250 mm long, 80-120 mm across, comprising 9-20 headlets of 20-40 flowers each; *flowerhead stalk 200-900 mm long.* Perianth silvery carmine, with silky hairs, bulbous at base. *Involucral bracts ovate, with prominent wings.* Style straight, 12-14 mm long. Pollen presenter 1-2 mm long, club-shaped.
DISTRIBUTION: Bokkop Mountain above Villiersdorp and west of Viljoen's Pass.
HABITAT: Sandstone soils, southern slopes, 700-1250 m. STATUS: A few scattered, dense populations, each of a few hundred plants, are threatened by invading pines and hakeas. *Red Data Book* status: Rare. FLOWERS: August to October. FRUITS: Released within 2 months of flowering.

*Serruria lacunosa* Rourke                     Matsikamma Spiderhead     **Plate 37**

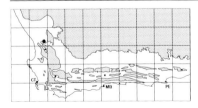

A sparsely branched, erect shrub 0.5-1 m tall, 0.7 m across. Main stem 20 mm in diameter. Leaves 60-80 mm long, 40-60 mm wide, stout, hairless when mature, dissected, with 7-12 tips; stalk 20-25 mm long. Flowerhead globose, 100-170 mm long, 25-30 mm across, *comprising a solitary headlet of 28-35 flowers; flowerhead stalk 85-140 mm long,* several flowerheads borne from the axils of uppermost leaves. Perianth with silky hairs. Involucral bracts lanceolate, hairless. Style straight, 10-12 mm long, *bending backwards to face the flowerhead stalk during flowering, hairy on lower two-thirds.* Pollen presenter 1.5 mm long, club-shaped.
DISTRIBUTION: Summit of Matsikamma Mountain. HABITAT: Sandstone sands in moist areas, 700-800 m. STATUS: Known from 4 very small, localized populations. *Red Data Book* status: Endangered. FLOWERS: September to April, mainly September to December. FRUITS: Released within 2 months of flowering.

## *Serruria* The Paw Spiderheads

The Paw Spiderheads have *slightly to strongly curved flowers borne in a simple flowerhead with a conspicuous stalk.* All 6 *Serruria* species which have hairs on the lower style fall within this group. Paw Spiderheads also retain part of the style on the fruit. They tend to be montane species.

Paw Spiderhead species can be distinguished by their habit – single-stemmed or multi-stemmed, erect or creeping – the nature of the hairs on the leaf, whether hairs on the buds are spreading or adpressed, and whether there are hairs on the lower style.

*Serruria aitonii* R. Br.                                          Marshmallow Spiderhead     **Plate 38**

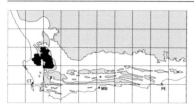

A rounded shrub 0.5-1 m tall, 0.5 m across. Main stem 20 mm in diameter. *Leaves silver, with crispy hairs, curved upwards, 19-45 mm long, 15-20 mm wide, dissected, with 35-50 rounded tips; stalk 8-15 mm long.* Flowerhead globose, 20-25 mm across, comprising usually a solitary headlet or up to 8 per branch, each with 15-20 flowers, with a sweet scent; *flowerhead stalk 5-65 mm long, with long hairs; flowers sometimes straight.* Involucral bracts ovate. Perianth silvery carmine, with spreading, silver hairs. *Style hairless,* straight to curving inward, 7-10 mm long. Pollen presenter 1 mm long, club-shaped. DISTRIBUTION: Cederberg and Sandveld to Groot Winterhoek Mountains and Piketberg. HABITAT: Montane, rocky, sandstone soils, 900-1600 m. STATUS: Dense stands of hundreds of plants in isolated populations. FLOWERS: July to November. FRUITS: Released within 2 months of flowering.

*Serruria reflexa* Rourke                                                Milky Spiderhead     **Plate 38**

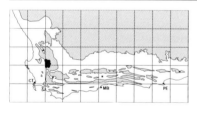

An erect, sparsely branched shrub 0.8-2 m tall, 0.3 m across. Main stem 10-15 mm in diameter. *Leaves erect, 10-25 mm long, 20-25 mm wide, with silver, silky hairs, dissected, with 15-25 tips; stalk 2-8 mm long.* Flowerhead globose, 25-35 mm across, 1-3 per branch, comprising a solitary headlet of 15-25 flowers; *flowerhead stalk 50-70 mm long, hairy, held almost horizontally to stem.* Involucral bracts ovate. Perianth 18-20 mm long, white, with spreading, white, silky hairs. Style slightly curved, 16-18 mm long, *bending out towards ovary* in open flowers. Pollen presenter 1 mm long, club-shaped. DISTRIBUTION: Koue Bokkeveld to Olifants River Mountains between The Baths and Visgat. HABITAT: Sandstone soils, 400-760 m. STATUS: Isolated stands of a few hundred scattered plants. FLOWERS: September to November. FRUITS: Released within 2 months of flowering.

*Serruria fucifolia* Salisb. ex Knight                                    Northern Spiderhead     **Plate 38**

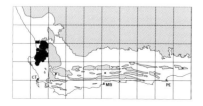

An erect shrub 0.8-1.5 m tall, 1 m across. Main stem 30 mm in diameter. *Leaves curved upwards, 35-60 mm long, 15-20 mm wide, with dull grey, crispy hairs, dissected, with 12-15 rounded tips with fine points; stalk 15-25 mm long.* Flowerhead globose, 15-20 mm across, 1-3 per branch, comprising a solitary headlet of 20-30 flowers, with a sweet scent; *flowerhead*

*stalk 20-60 mm long, hairy.* Involucral bracts lanceolate. Perianth silver-grey to purple, with adpressed, silver, silky hairs. *Style hairless,* curving inward, 9 mm long. Pollen presenter 1 mm long, linear to thread-like, knee-bent at base.
DISTRIBUTION: Sandveld to Hopefield Flats, Gifberg to Olifants River Mountains and Piketberg. HABITAT: Sandstone and sandy soils, 150-920 m. STATUS: Common as scattered plants in extensive populations. FLOWERS: July to October. FRUITS: Released within 2 months of flowering.

***Serruria dodii*** E. Phillips & Hutch.　　　　　　　　　　Hex River Spiderhead　　**Plate 38**

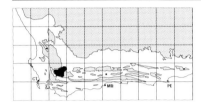

*An erect shrub 0.6-1 m tall*, 0.5 m across. Main stem 10 mm in diameter. *Leaves curved upwards, 30-50 mm long, 15-20 mm wide, with silver, silky hairs, dissected, with 25-30 rounded tips; stalk 5-10 mm long.* Flowerhead globose, 20-25 mm across, comprising a solitary headlet of 12-25 flowers, with a sweet scent; flowerhead stalk 6-40 mm long, densely covered with hairs. Involucral bracts ovate-acute. Perianth silver, with adpressed, silver, silky hairs. *Style hairy in lower third*, curving inward, 12-13 mm long. Pollen presenter 2 mm long, club-shaped, knee-bent at base.
DISTRIBUTION: Hex River Mountains and Keeromsberg. HABITAT: Sandstone soils, montane, 900-1400 m. STATUS: Usually in dense, isolated populations. FLOWERS: August to November. FRUITS: Released within 2 months of flowering.
NOTES: Historically there is some confusion between *S. dodii* and *S. pedunculata.* A possible new species resembling *S. dodii* occurs in the Riviersonderend Mountains.

***Serruria pedunculata*** (Lam.) R. Br.　　　　　　　　　　Fan-leaf Spiderhead　　**Plate 39**

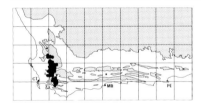

An erect to spreading shrub 0.6-1 m tall, 0.5 m across. Main stem 15 mm in diameter. *Leaves erect, 20-50 mm long, 15-25 mm wide, fan-shaped, with grey hairs, dissected, with 45-60 tips rounded and calloused or with fine points; stalk 8-15 mm long.* Flowerhead globose, 25-35 mm across, 1-5 per branch, comprising a solitary headlet of 15-30 flowers, with a sweet scent; flowerhead stalk 30-70 mm long, hairy. Involucral bracts ovate. *Perianth carmine, with long, spreading, white hairs. Style hairy in lower third*, curving inward, 8-12 mm long. Pollen presenter 2 mm long, club-shaped, knee-bent at base.
DISTRIBUTION: Cederberg and Olifants River Mountains to Du Toit's Kloof and Riviersonderend Mountains; with an outlying population on Piketberg. HABITAT: Sandstone soils, 150-1600 m. STATUS: Dense, isolated populations. FLOWERS: August to December. FRUITS: Released within 2 months of flowering.
NOTE: *Serruria pedunculata* grades into a form characterized by a more rounded habit and adpressed hairs. Atlassers are recording this as *S. dodii* (which it otherwise resembles) until it is formally recognized. However, in many areas it is impossible to distinguish between the two forms. In the northern areas and on the eastern side of the Limietberg, the plants have a more spindly habit, longer flowerhead stalks and spreading hairs on the perianth tips. On western slopes and to the south, plants are typically more bushy, have shorter flowerhead stalks and flat hairs on the perianth tips.

***Serruria flava*** Meisn.                                    Wuppertal Spiderhead    **Plate 39**

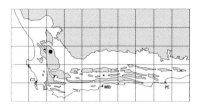

An erect shrub 0.4-0.8 m tall, 0.5 m across. Main stem 15 mm in diameter. *Leaves curved upwards, 12-35 mm long, 10-25 mm wide, with silver, silky hairs, dissected, with 25-50 tips with red, rounded calluses; stalk 5-10 mm long.* Flowerhead globose, 25-30 mm across, comprising a solitary headlet of 12-25 flowers; flowerhead stalk 20-45 mm long. Involucral bracts ovate. *Perianth yellow, with short, adpressed, silver hairs. Style hairy in lower third,* curving slightly inwards, 14-15 mm long. Pollen presenter 2 mm long, linear, knee-bent at base.
DISTRIBUTION: Ezelbank near Wuppertal. HABITAT: Sandstone and quartzite soils, 1050-1250 m. STATUS: Known from a single population of 3000 plants in scattered clumps. *Red Data Book* status: Rare. FLOWERS: August to December. FRUITS: Released within 2 months of flowering.

***Serruria balanocephala*** Rourke                            Acorn Spiderhead    **Plate 39**

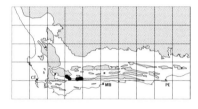

An erect shrub 0.5-1 m tall, 1.5 m across. Main stem 20 mm in diameter. *Leaves ascending, 40-60 mm long, 15-30 mm wide, with grey hairs, dissected, with 15-30 tips; stalk 10-20 mm long.* Flowerhead globose, 25-30 mm across, up to 5 per branch, comprising a solitary headlet of 20-30 flowers; flowerhead stalk 20-50 mm long, with crispy hairs. Involucral bracts ovate. *Perianth carmine, with long, spreading, white hairs. Style hairy in lower third,* curving strongly inwards, 12-14 mm long, red. Pollen presenter 1 mm long, acorn-shaped, with a narrow neck.
DISTRIBUTION: Western Langeberg. HABITAT: Sandstone soils, 600-650 m. STATUS: Scattered populations of several hundred plants. *Red Data Book* status: Rare. FLOWERS: August to November. FRUITS: Released within 2 months of flowering.

***Serruria acrocarpa*** R. Br.                      Common Rootstock Spiderhead    **Plate 39**

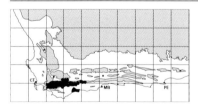

*A multi-stemmed, erect shrub with a rootstock, 0.3-0.5 m tall, 0.3 m across. Leaves erect, 20-50 mm long, 15-25 mm wide, hairless when mature, dissected, with 15-45 rounded tips with fine points; stalk 20-25 mm long.* Flowerhead globose, 15-20 mm across, 1-7 per branch, comprising a solitary headlet of 10-25 flowers, with a sweet scent; flowerhead stalk 10-32 mm long, densely covered with hairs. Involucral bracts ovate.
*Perianth yellow or pink, with adpressed, short, yellow or white hairs. Style hairy in lower third,* curving inward, 6-8 mm long. *Pollen presenter 0.5 mm long, club-shaped.* Fruits with the beak-like base of the style retained.
DISTRIBUTION: Hottentots-Holland to Riviersonderend Mountains and central Langeberg; an outlying population on Potberg. HABITAT: Sandstone soils, 50-480 m. STATUS: Common over extensive areas as scattered plants. FLOWERS: July to February. FRUITS: Released within 2 months of flowering.
NOTE: This is a resprouter related to *S. balanocephala*; some intermediate populations have been discovered in the Langeberg.

*Serruria gremialis* Rourke                                     Riviersonderend Spiderhead     **Plate 40**

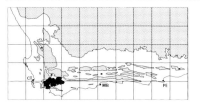

*A sprawling shrub with creeping stems and a root-stock*, 0.5 m tall, up to 1 m across. *Leaves pointing vertically from a horizontal stem,* 10-30 mm long, 10-25 mm wide, with crispy hairs when young, dissected, with 30-45 tips with pointed calluses; stalk 2-12 mm long. Flowerhead globose, 25-30 mm across, hairless, 1-4 per branch, comprising a solitary headlet of 15-25 flowers; flowerhead stalk 25-30 mm long. Involucral bracts ovate, sharply pointed, densely covered with velvety hairs. Perianth with adpressed, long, silver, silky hairs. *Style hairy in lower third*, curving inward, 12-15 mm long. *Pollen presenter cylindrical with a swollen base.*
DISTRIBUTION: Riviersonderend and Stettyns Mountains. HABITAT: Northern sandstone slopes, 270-760 m. STATUS: Scattered plants in large, extensive populations. FLOWERS: July to February. FRUITS: Released within 2 months of flowering.

*Serruria incrassata* Meisn.                                        Silver-paw Spiderhead     **Plate 40**

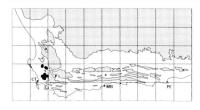

*A prostrate shrub with creeping stems and a root-stock*, 0.1 m tall, up to 1 m across. *Leaves pointing vertically from a horizontal stem,* 25-50 mm long, 10-15 mm wide, with crispy hairs, dissected, with 20-30 tips with round calluses; stalk 10-15 mm long. Flowerhead globose, 10-20 mm across, 1-5 per branch, comprising a solitary headlet of 20-30 flowers, with a strong sweet scent; *flowerhead stalk curving upward, 25-75 mm long*, hairless. Involucral bracts ovate, margin hairy, overlapping. Perianth pink, with long, adpressed, silver, silky hairs. *Style hairless*, curving inward, 9-12 mm long. Pollen presenter 1 mm long, club-shaped, slightly knee-bent at base.
DISTRIBUTION: Klipheuwel near Paarl, and hills east of Moorreesburg. HABITAT: Granite and heavy shale soils, 150-330 m. STATUS: *Red Data Book* status: Vulnerable, owing to agriculture. Ten populations totalling 1 500 plants are known. FLOWERS: July to October.
FRUITS: Released within 2 months of flowering.

*Serruria cygnea* R. Br.                                               Swan Spiderhead     **Plate 40**

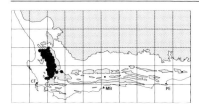

*A prostrate shrub with a rootstock*, 0.1 m tall, up to 1 m across. *Branches hairless. Leaves pointing vertically from a horizontal stem,* 25-70 mm long, 17-23 mm wide, hairless when mature, stout, dissect-ed, with 27-34 rounded tips with fine points; stalk 20-25 mm long. Flowerhead globose, 15-25 mm across, 1-50 per branch, lying on ground, comprising a solitary headlet of 12-18 flowers, with a sweet scent; flowerhead stalk 20-50 mm long, hairless. Involucral bracts ovate, scattered. Perianth pink to brown, with short, adpressed, silky hairs. *Style hairless*, curving inward, 9-12 mm long. Pollen presenter 0.5 mm long, club-shaped.
DISTRIBUTION: Sandveld, Cederberg to Slanghoek and Hex River Mountains.
HABITAT: Sandstone and Cederberg shale soils, 350-950 m. STATUS: Occurs abundantly in dense populations or isolated patches of scattered plants. FLOWERS: September to November.
FRUITS: Released within 2 months of flowering.

*Serruria effusa* Rourke                              Candelabra Spiderhead     **Plate 40**

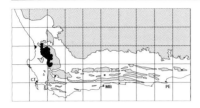

*A prostrate or creeping shrub* in mats up to 2 m across, up to 1 m tall, with a single main stem. *Branches laxly drooping, hairy. Leaves pointing vertically from a horizontal stem, 40-90 mm long, 10-45 mm wide, with shaggy grey hairs or hairless, stout, dissected, with 10-18 rounded tips with fine points; stalk 20-40 mm long.* Flowerhead globose, 20-30 mm across, *3-18 per branch*, comprising a solitary headlet of 12-18 flowers; flowerhead stalk 15-90 mm long, often curving upwards from the downcurved branches. Involucral bracts ovate, dense, margin occasionally hairy. Perianth pink to brown, with short, adpressed, silky hairs. *Style hairless*, curving inward, 12-14 mm long. Pollen presenter 1 mm long, club-shaped. DISTRIBUTION: Sandveld and Cederberg to Olifants River Mountains. HABITAT: Sand and shale soils, often where these soil types meet, 100-750 m. STATUS: Occurs abundantly in isolated patches of a few hundred plants. FLOWERS: July to October, mainly August and September. FRUITS: Released within 2 months of flowering.

### *Serruria* The Stalkless Spiderheads

The Stalkless Spiderheads are distinguished by their *straight flowers* and hairless styles. They have a *single flowerhead per branch*. The *stalk of the flowerhead may be absent* or, when present, *is effectively hidden by leaves clasping the base of the flowerhead.* The perianth has white hairs at the tip. Two of these species – *S. brownii* and *S. millefolia* – with their erect stems and short, dissected leaves on a short leafstalk, have a distinctly bottlebrush-like appearance.

*Serruria hirsuta* R. Br.                              Swartkops Spiderhead     **Plate 41**

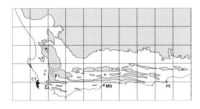

An erect shrub 0.3-0.5 m tall, 0.5 m across. Main stem 20 mm in diameter. *Leaves erect, 30-35 mm long, 15-20 mm wide, with silky hairs, dissected, with 9-15 tips with fine points; stalk 15-20 mm long.* Flowerhead globose, 20-45 mm long, 25-30 mm across, comprising a solitary headlet of 35-40 flowers, with a strong sweet scent; *flowerhead stalk 0-10 mm long. Involucral bracts covering stalk base,* linear, margin hairy. Perianth pink, with long, spreading, white hairs. Style straight, 10 mm long, hairless. Pollen presenter 1 mm long, club-shaped. DISTRIBUTION: Southern Cape Peninsula above Simon's Town. HABITAT: Sandstone soils, 360-470 m. STATUS: Known from a single population containing about 1500 plants. *Red Data Book* status: Rare. FLOWERS: July to October. FRUITS: Released within 2 months of flowering.

*Serruria villosa* (Lam.) R. Br.                    Golden Spiderhead    **Plate 41**

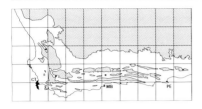

An erect shrub 0.3-0.5 m tall, 0.3 m across. Main stem 10 mm in diameter. Leaves curved upwards, 20-40 mm long, 10-15 mm wide, with silky hairs, dissected, with 16-18 tips; stalk 8-20 mm long. Flowerhead globose, 20-25 mm across, comprising a solitary headlet of 18-22 flowers, with a sweet scent; stalkless. Involucral bracts lanceolate. *Perianth yellow, base hairless, tip with spreading, white, shaggy hairs.* Style straight, 10-11 mm long, hairless. Pollen presenter 1 mm long, club-shaped.
DISTRIBUTION: Cape Peninsula south of Constantia. HABITAT: Sandstone flats and slopes, 0-350 m. STATUS: Common, a social species. Dense colonies can still be found south of Constantiaberg. FLOWERS: April to July. FRUITS: Released 2 months after flowering.

*Serruria rostellaris* Salisb. ex Knight                    Remote Spiderhead    **Plate 41**

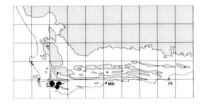

An erect shrub 0.3-0.5 m tall, 0.3 m across. Main stem 10 mm in diameter. *Leaves erect, 15-25 mm long, 12-18 mm wide, hairless, dissected, with 12-17 tips with fine points; stalk 6-10 mm long.* Flowerhead globose, 10-20 mm across, comprising a solitary head-let of 15 flowers; *stalkless. Involucral bracts encircling flowerhead base purplish,* lanceolate. Perianth white to pink, with long, spreading, white hairs. Style straight, 10 mm long, hairless. Pollen presenter 2 mm long, club-shaped.
DISTRIBUTION: Groenland, Babylonstoring, Klein River Mountains and Caledon Swartberg. HABITAT: Sandstone soils, moist slopes, 450-800 m. STATUS: Uncommon and seldom encountered; extremely localized in dense clumps. FLOWERS: September to November. FRUITS: Released within 2 months of flowering.

*Serruria deluvialis* Rourke                    Grass Spiderhead    **Plate 42**

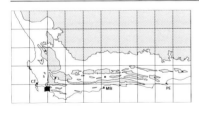

A creeping to almost erect, laxly branched shrub, 0.1-0.3 m tall, 0.4 m across. Main stem 15 mm in diameter. *Leaves erect, 45-80 mm long, 10-20 mm wide, hairless, dissected, with 1-5 tips; stalk 15-60 mm long. Flowerhead globose, 15-18 mm across, comprising a solitary headlet of 10-14 flowers*; stalkless. Involucral bracts linear. Perianth silvery cream, densely covered with woolly hairs. *Style 7-8 mm long,* straight. Pollen presenter 2-3 mm long, linear, knee-bent at base.
DISTRIBUTION: Kogelberg in Palmiet River Valley from Arieskraal to Louws River. HABITAT: Seasonally waterlogged sandstone soils, 100-300 m. STATUS: Extremely cryptic and therefore hard to find; occurring in dense, isolated populations at 4 known sites totalling 1000 plants. This species would become extinct if dams were to be built on the lower Palmiet River. *Red Data Book* status: Vulnerable. FLOWERS: September to November, mainly October. FRUITS: Released within 2 months of flowering.

***Serruria rebeloi*** Rourke                    Clandestine Spiderhead    **Plate 42**

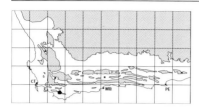

A creeping, laxly branched shrub to 0.2 m tall, 1 m across. Main stem 15 mm in diameter. Leaves pointing vertically from a horizontal stem, 30-50 mm long, 10-20 mm wide, hairless, dissected, with 1-4 tips but usually only 1. Flowerhead globose, 10-12 mm across, comprising a solitary headlet (rarely 4 headlets) of 4-9 flowers, stalkless. Involucral bracts lanceolate, deep carmine. Perianth silvery cream, densely covered in woolly hairs. Style 7-8 mm long, straight, connected at base by a fleshy red swelling and falling off after flowering. Pollen presenter 1 mm long, club-shaped. DISTRIBUTION: Perdeberg west of Napier. HABITAT: Seepages on gentle slopes, sandstone soils, 480-600 m. STATUS: Extremely cryptic, creeping under other plants and therefore hard to find. Known from a single locality with several populations over a 5-km area, probably numbering only a few hundred individuals. FLOWERS: October/November. FRUITS: Released within 2 months of flowering.

***Serruria brownii*** Meisn.                    Bottlebrush Spiderhead    **Plate 42**

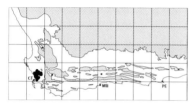

An erect shrub 0.3-0.5 m tall, 0.3 m across. Main stem 10 mm in diameter. *Leaves crowded, curved upwards, 15-25 mm long, 12-18 mm wide, with grey hairs, dissected, with 7-11 blunt tips with fine points; stalk 5 mm long.* Flowerhead cylindrical, 20-25 mm long, 15-20 mm across, comprising a solitary headlet of 15-20 flowers, with a sweet scent; flowerhead stalk 5-15 mm long. Involucral bracts lanceolate. Perianth carmine or brown, with short, addressed, silver hairs. Style curved inwards, 10 mm long. Pollen presenter 1 mm long, club-shaped. DISTRIBUTION: Flats from Hopefield to Cape Town. HABITAT: Granite soils, shales and heavy sands, 50-250 m. STATUS: *Red Data Book* status: Endangered, due to agriculture, alien acacias and grazing. Known from 2 major localities with isolated populations of several hundred scattered plants. Almost extinct near Durbanville. FLOWERS: June to October. FRUITS: Released within 2 months of flowering.

***Serruria millefolia*** Salisb. ex Knight                    Millileaf Spiderhead    **Plate 42**

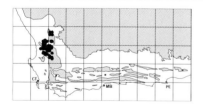

An erect shrub 0.3-0.5 m tall, 0.5 m across. Main stem 5 mm in diameter. *Leaves crowded, erect, 5-14 mm long, 5-10 mm wide, with grey, crispy hairs, dissected, with 8-10 blunt tips with fine points; stalk 3-5 mm long.* Flowerhead globose, 10-25 mm across, comprising a solitary headlet of 22-28 flowers; flowerhead stalk short. Involucral bracts ovate. Perianth cream to green, with long, spreading, white, silky hairs. Style straight, 6-7 mm long. Pollen presenter 1 mm long, club-shaped. DISTRIBUTION: Bokkeveld escarpment and Sandveld to Olifants River Mountains. HABITAT: Sands, 350-800 m. STATUS: *Red Data Book* status: Vulnerable, due to agriculture. Scattered to dense colonies tend to be isolated. FLOWERS: August to December. FRUITS: Released within 2 months of flowering.

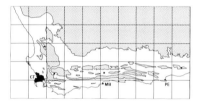

### *Serruria* The Skirted Spiderheads

The Skirted Spiderheads have *solitary flowerheads with a distinct stalk and flowers which are straight (or very slightly kinked) in bud.* They can be divided into 2 groups: the Sprawling Skirted Spiderheads (*S. aemula, S. cyanoides, S. furcellata, S. trilopha, S. linearis* and *S. gracilis*) and the Mountain Skirted Spiderheads (*S. stellata, S. heterophylla, S. phylicoides, S. rosea* and *S. florida*). The Mountain Skirted species tend to be erect plants with a conspicuous involucre comprising a series of bracts below the flowers. By contrast, the Sprawling Skirted Spiderheads, which occur in lowland areas, tend to be sprawling or straggly and although most possess a distinct involucre of bracts, these are not conspicuous once the flowers have begun to open. The lowland forms are seriously threatened by urbanization and agriculture.

---

***Serruria aemula*** Salisb. ex Knight        Strawberry Spiderhead    **Plate 43**

A straggly, much-branched shrub 0.2-0.5 m tall, 0.5 m across. Main stem 15 mm in diameter. Leaves erect, 12-20 mm long, 4-8 mm wide, hairless when mature, dissected, with 1-7 tips with fine points; stalk 8-12 mm long. Flowerhead globose, 7-13 mm long, 12-18 mm across, solitary or up to 12 per branch, *each comprising a solitary headlet of 12-20 flowers, with a sweet scent; flowerhead stalk 0-14 mm long. Involucral bracts linear, with long hairs.* Perianth pink, with long, silver hairs. Style straight, 5-8 mm long, hairless. Pollen presenter 1 mm long, club-shaped.

DISTRIBUTION: Cape Flats from Cape Town to Firgrove. HABITAT: Sands, 0-70 m.

STATUS: *Red Data Book* status: Endangered, owing to urbanization. A few populations totalling between 600 and 1000 plants still exist, mainly along road verges and under powerlines. Historically this species occurred in huge stands just outside Cape Town from Milnerton to Rondebosch, and was probably the most commonly collected spiderhead in European herbaria. FLOWERS: July to October. FRUITS: Released within 2 months of flowering.

□ VARIATIONS: In the Firgrove area a more densely leaved and flowered variety *congesta* occurs. *Serruria foeniculacea* R. Br. from Rondevlei is considered here to be another form of this species.

---

***Serruria cyanoides*** (L.) R. Br.        Wynberg Spiderhead    **Plate 43**

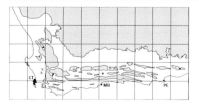

*A multi-stemmed, erect shrub with a rootstock,* 0.3-0.5 m tall, up to 1 m across. *Stems short and erect. Leaves hairless when mature,* curved upwards, 25-65 mm long, 10-30 mm wide, dissected, with 7-11 tips with fine points; stalk 15-20 mm long. Flowerhead globose, 15-25 mm across, comprising a solitary headlet of 15-20 flowers, with a sweet scent; *flowerhead stalk 15-30 mm long, with long hairs.* Involucral bracts ovate, with long hairs. Perianth pink, with spreading to adpressed, long, silver hairs. Style straight, 6-10 mm long, hairless. Pollen presenter 2 mm long, club-shaped.

DISTRIBUTION: Cape Peninsula and Cape Flats, with a dubious record from Slanghoek Mountains. HABITAT: Sands, 0-150 m. STATUS: *Red Data Book* status: Vulnerable, owing to invasion by alien plants. Once widespread, it now survives at the upper limits of its altitude range in isolated populations of a few hundred plants. FLOWERS: July to October. FRUITS: Released within 2 months of flowering.

***Serruria furcellata*** R. Br.                    Kraaifontein Spiderhead    **Plate 43**

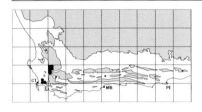

A multi-stemmed, erect shrub with a rootstock, 0.3-0.5 m tall, up to 1 m across. *Leaves hairless*, bright green, erect, 20-45 mm long, 8-15 mm wide, dissected, with 6-9 tips with fine points; stalk 15-25 mm long. Flowerhead globose, 15-25 mm across, comprising a solitary headlet of 18-24 flowers, with a sweet scent; *flowerhead stalk 15-30 mm long.* Involucral bracts ovate, with long hairs. *Perianth pink, swollen at base*, with long, spreading, silver hairs. Style straight, 8-11 mm long, hairless. Pollen presenter 2 mm long, club-shaped.

DISTRIBUTION: Cape Flats mainly from Brackenfell and Kraaifontein, with a curious population in the Elandskloof Mountains. HABITAT: Sands, 90-310 m. STATUS: *Red Data Book* status: Endangered. Once common, but its habitat has largely been replaced by suburbia. In 1987 fewer than 250 plants remained at Northpine on the Cape Flats, and the Elandskloof Mountains population is restricted to a few scattered plants. FLOWERS: August to October. FRUITS: Released within 2 months of flowering.

***Serruria trilopha*** Salisb. ex Knight                    Trident Spiderhead    **Plate 43**

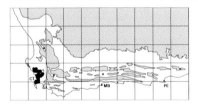

A sprawling, multi-stemmed shrub with a rootstock, 0.3-0.8 m tall, 0.8 m across. *Leaves erect, 5-25 mm long, 5-10 mm wide, hairless when mature, dissected, with 3-7 sharp tips; stalk 3-5 mm long.* Flowerhead globose, 15-25 mm across, comprising a solitary headlet of 10-18 flowers, with a faint coconut smell; *flowerhead stalk 6-20 mm long, with long hairs.* Involucral bracts lanceolate, margin hairy. *Perianth pink, hairless at base, tips with silky, silver-grey hairs.* Style straight, 6-9 mm long, hairless. Pollen presenter 2 mm long, club-shaped.

DISTRIBUTION: Cape Peninsula and Cape Flats to Malmesbury. HABITAT: Sands, 50-310 m. STATUS: *Red Data Book* status: Endangered, owing to urbanization and agriculture. In 1987 about 500 scattered plants were surviving in isolated populations, mainly to the north of Cape Town's suburbs. FLOWERS: August to October. FRUITS: Released within 2 months of flowering.

***Serruria linearis*** Salisb. ex Knight                    Needle-leaf Spiderhead    **Plate 44**

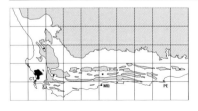

A multi-stemmed, erect shrub with a rootstock, 0.4-0.8 m tall, 0.5 m across. *Leaves erect, 25-60 mm long, 1-6 mm wide, hairless when mature, needle-like or dissected, with 1-3 tips; stalk 20-40 mm long.* Flowerhead globose, 20-30 mm long, 15-32 mm across, 1-4 per branch, comprising a solitary headlet of 15-20 flowers; flowerhead stalk 15-30 mm long. *Involucral bracts ovate, hairless.* Perianth pink, with long, spreading, silver, silky hairs. Style straight, 6-9 mm long, red, hairless. Pollen presenter 2 mm long, club-shaped, knee-bent at base.

DISTRIBUTION: Dassenberg Flats near Malmesbury. HABITAT: Sands, 120-190 m.
STATUS: *Red Data Book* status: Endangered, owing to agriculture and invasion by alien acacias.
Occurring as extensive populations of well-scattered plants. FLOWERS: August to November.
FRUITS: Released within 2 months of flowering.

***Serruria gracilis*** Salisb. ex Knight                    Fine Spiderhead    **Plate 44**

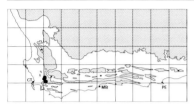

*A prostrate shrub with creeping stems and a root-stock*, 0.05-0.1 m tall, up to 1 m across. *Leaves pointing vertically from a horizontal stem, 15-30 mm long, 10-15 mm wide, hairless when mature, dissected, with 7-10 tips with fine points; stalk 5-15 mm long.* Flowerhead globose, 15-25 mm across, 1 or 2 per branch, comprising a solitary headlet of 25-40 flowers, with a strong sweet scent; flowerhead stalk 10-25 mm long, with long hairs. Involucral bracts lanceolate, hairless, purple-pink. *Perianth slender*, pink to red, with short, appressed, silver hairs. Style straight, 11 mm long, hairless. Pollen presenter 1 mm long, club-shaped.
DISTRIBUTION: Cape Flats at Durbanville to Hottentots-Holland and Du Toit's Kloof Mountains, with dubious records from Hopefield and the Elandskloof Mountains.
HABITAT: Sands and granite slopes, 150-310 m. STATUS: The lowland form has a *Red Data Book* status of Vulnerable. Usually encountered as isolated populations of scattered plants.
FLOWERS: July to October. FRUITS: Released within 2 months of flowering.
□ VARIATION: Leaves and flowerheads are larger in lowland forms – still recognized as a separate species, *S. pinnata* R. Br. (Graceful Spiderhead) – than in forms on the mountains.

***Serruria stellata*** Rourke                    Star Spiderhead    **Plate 44**

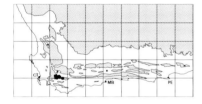

*A prostrate shrub with creeping stems*, 0.05-0.2 m tall, up to 1 m across. Main stem 20 mm in diameter. *Leaves pointing vertically from a horizontal stem, 50-80 mm long, 10-30 mm wide, hairless, dissected, with 6-15 tips with fine points; stalk 20-50 mm long.* Flowerhead globose, 30-35 mm across, 1-9 per branch, comprising a solitary headlet of 25-50 flowers, with a sweet scent; flowerhead stalk 20-45 mm long, hairless. Involucral bracts ovate, tips pointed, hairless, purple-pink. *Perianth slender*, carmine, densely covered with long, shaggy hairs. Style straight, 12-14 mm long, hairless. Pollen presenter 4 mm long, club-shaped.
DISTRIBUTION: Western Riviersonderend Mountains from Wolfieskop to Galgeberg above Greyton; Stettyns Mountains. HABITAT: Sandstone sands, 900-1200 m. STATUS: Locally abundant. FLOWERS: September to November. FRUITS: Released within 2 months of flowering.
□ VARIATION: Eastern forms have diffuse trailing branches, whereas western ones form dense mats.

***Serruria heterophylla*** Meisn.                                    Spindly Spiderhead     **Plate 44**

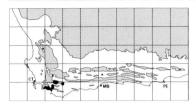

A spindly, erect shrub 0.4-1 m tall, 0.2 m across, usually with an underground roostock. Main stem 8 mm in diameter. *Leaves erect, 25-35 mm long, 1-25 mm wide, hairless, linear or dissected, with 1-8 tips (1-3 tips below flowerheads) with fine points; stalk 5-10 mm long.* Flowerhead globose, 15-20 mm long, 20-25 mm across, 1-3 per branch, comprising a solitary headlet of 12-16 flowers, with a sweet scent; flowerhead stalk 15-30 mm long. *Involucral bracts prominent, 8-14 mm long, 6-8 mm wide, ovate, yellow or cream, hairless.* Perianth pink, with spreading, white, silky hairs. Style straight, 8 mm long, hairless. Pollen presenter 2 mm long, club-shaped.

DISTRIBUTION: Kleinmond and Klein River Mountains, with possible records from Caledon Swartberg and Riviersonderend Mountains. HABITAT: Sandstone soils, 90-310 m.

STATUS: A highly social species known from 2 major locations. FLOWERS: July to October. FRUITS: Released within 2 months of flowering.

***Serruria phylicoides*** (P.J. Bergius) R. Br.                    Bearded Spiderhead     **Plate 45**

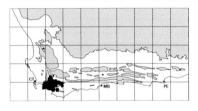

An erect shrub 0.4-1 m tall, 0.3 m across. Main stem 10 mm in diameter. Leaves erect, 25-60 mm long, 10-30 mm wide, hairless, dissected, with 20-30 sharp to rounded tips; stalk 15-20 mm long. Flowerhead globose, 15-20 mm across, 1-4 per branch, comprising a solitary headlet of 15-30 flowers; flowerhead stalk 15-25 mm long. *Involucral bracts numerous, prominent, 6-8 mm long, linear to lanceolate, cream to orange; inner series with sparse, short hairs.* Perianth carmine, with long, spreading, white, silky hairs. Style straight, 10 mm long. Pollen presenter 1 mm long, club-shaped.

DISTRIBUTION: Du Toit's Kloof to Hottentots-Holland to Riviersonderend and Klein River Mountains. HABITAT: Sandstone sands, slopes and flats, 330-1800 m. STATUS: Most frequently encountered as dense isolated patches. FLOWERS: August to November. FRUITS: Released within 2 months of flowering.

□ VARIATIONS: Striking differences in the flowerheads occur at different altitudes, resulting from variations in the width and colour of the involucral bracts. They may cause confusion with *S. rosea* and *S. heterophylla.* Forms from lower altitudes tend to have wider, paler involucral bracts.

***Serruria rosea*** E. Phillips                    Rose Spiderhead    **Plate 45**

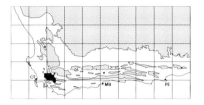

An erect shrub 0.8-1.5 m tall, 0.5 m across. Main stem 15 mm in diameter. Leaves curved upwards, 30-60 mm long, 20-25 mm wide, hairless, dissected, with 25-60 tips with fine points; stalk 15-25 mm long. Flowerhead globose, 20-30 mm across, 2-7 per branch, comprising a solitary headlet of 15-20 flowers; flowerhead stalk 15-30 mm long, hairy to hairless. *Involucral bracts prominent, 8-25 mm long, 4-14 mm wide, ovate, pink, margin hairy.* Perianth pink, densely covered with long, spreading, silky hairs. Style straight, 6-11 mm long, hairless. Pollen presenter 2 mm long, club-shaped. DISTRIBUTION: Slanghoek and Du Toit's Kloof to Hottentots-Holland and Riviersonderend Mountains. HABITAT: Sandstone sands, 300-620 m. STATUS: Dense, isolated stands containing several hundred plants occur sporadically. FLOWERS: August to October. FRUITS: Released within 2 months of flowering.

□ VARIATIONS: Striking differences in the flowerheads occur with altitude – paralleling the pattern seen in *S. phylicoides* – with narrower, paler involucral bracts at higher altitudes.

***Serruria florida*** (Thunb.) Salisb. ex Knight            Blushing Bride    **Plate 45**

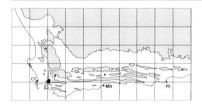

An erect shrub 0.8-2 m tall, 0.5 m across. Main stem 20 mm in diameter. Leaves erect, 45-100 mm long, 30-40 mm wide, hairless, dissected, with 10-20 tips with sharp points; stalk 15-50 mm long. Flowerhead globose, 45-55 mm across, 1-8 per branch, comprising a solitary headlet of 45-60 flowers; flowerhead stalk 25-45 mm long, hairless. *Involucral bracts prominent, larger than flowerheads, 20-40 mm long, 8-15 mm wide, ovate, ivory to pink, hairless.* Perianth white tipped with pink, with long, silky hairs. Style straight, 8-12 mm long, hairless. Pollen presenter 2 mm long, linear to thread-like. DISTRIBUTION: Assegaaiboskloof near Franschhoek. HABITAT: Granite slopes, 600-620 m. STATUS: *Red Data Book* status: Vulnerable, due to invasion of its habitat by pines and hakeas. Known from 1 population of perhaps 1000 plants which occur in 6-8 isolated stands of a few hundred plants. FLOWERS: July to October. FRUITS: Released within 2 months of flowering. NOTE: This species is one of those responsible for our knowledge that fire is essential in fynbos ecology and that, between fires, many species disappear underground as seed banks.

## *Serruria* The Whip-leaf Spiderheads

The Whip-leaf Spiderheads are *prostrate plants bearing small flowerheads with 4-10 flowers. The floral bracts are relatively large* and showy compared to the flowers. *The leaves have 1-4 (usually 3) tips, and point vertically* from the red, creeping stems. The Whip-leaf Spiderheads are closely related to *S. meisneriana* in the Stalked Spiderheads (see page 90) which also has showy floral bracts.

*Serruria decumbens* (Thunb.) R. Br.      Peninsula Spiderhead    **Plate 46**

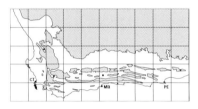

*A prostrate shrub 0.1 m tall, 0.5 m across, with red, creeping stems. Leaves pointing vertically from a horizontal stem, 50-120 mm long, 10-15 mm wide, hairless, dissected, with 3 or 4 tips*; stalk 15-30 mm long. Flowerhead 20-25 mm long, 25-35 mm across, flat-topped, 1-16 per branch, comprising 3-6 headlets of 4-10 flowers each, with a sweet scent; *flowerhead stalk 10-50 mm long, hairless. Involucral bracts absent. Perianth dark carmine, with short, adpressed, silver hairs.* Style straight, 12-14 mm long. Pollen presenter 3 mm long, linear, tip pointed, knee-bent at base.

DISTRIBUTION: Southern Cape Peninsula from Kommetjie to Olifantsbos. HABITAT: Sandstone soils, rocky areas, 70-310 m. STATUS: Localized patches of dense or scattered plants. *Red Data Book* status: Rare. FLOWERS: July to October. FRUITS: Released within 2 months of flowering.

*Serruria flagellifolia* Salisb. ex Knight      Houwhoek Spiderhead    **Plate 46**

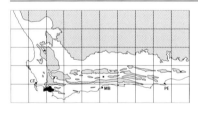

*A prostrate shrub 0.1 m tall, 1 m across, with red, creeping stems and leaves spaced 25-35 mm apart. Leaves pointing vertically from a horizontal stem, 25-100 mm long, 10 mm wide, hairless, dissected, with 1-4 tips*; stalk 20-40 mm long. Flowerhead globose, 12-17 mm across, 1-12 per branch, comprising a solitary headlet of 6-12 flowers, with a sweet scent; flowerhead stalk 20-35 mm long, hairless. *Involucral bracts ovate, cream. Perianth pink, hairless.* Style straight, 5-8 mm long. Pollen presenter 0.5 mm long, club-shaped.

DISTRIBUTION: Kogelberg, Groenland and Babylonstoring Mountains. HABITAT: Sandstone soils, middle slopes, 150-400 m. STATUS: Extremely cryptic and likely to be misidentified as *Cassytha* species. Occurs in dense, isolated colonies. *Red Data Book* status: Rare. FLOWERS: June to November. FRUITS: Released within 2 months of flowering.

## *PARANOMUS* Salisb. **The Sceptres**

The genus *Paranomus* is best distinguished by its leaves, which may be either entire or dissected. *Dissected leaves have a grooved upper surface ending in a fine point*, and are always slightly curled upwards. Entire leaves are not found in all species, but where they do occur, they are borne on younger branches, especially those with flowerheads. They do not have a network of veins as do the leaves of other proteas, but have a simple parallel venation. The *flowerheads are spike-like and comprise many headlets, each of which has an involucral bract and a set of 4 flowers. Each flower is subtended by a leathery floral bract. The bracts become woody with age*, forming tiny round shells. The flowers have 4 free perianth segments, which are usually hairy on the outer surface. The ovary is surrounded by stiff, white hairs, and the style may be hairy or hairless. The fruit is a smooth nut surrounded by a ring of hairs at the base and has a persistent style.

To identify the 18 *Paranomus* species a 10x magnification hand lens is required, but groups within the genus are easily recognized. Distinguishing features are the position, length and density of hairs on the style; the size and shape of the flowerheads; and the size and shape of the leaves.

## A QUICK KEY TO THE SCEPTRES

### ALL LEAVES DIVIDED

**The Fine-leaf Sceptre**
(Page 110, Plate 50)
Leaves 10-20 mm long, all divided
Flowerhead globose, dense and hairy
Style hairy

**The Cornflower Sceptres**
(Page 106, Plate 47)
Almost all leaves divided,
uppermost leaves lobed
Flowerhead globose, with few flowers
Style hairless

**The Common Sceptres**
(Page 107, Plate 47)
All leaves divided
Leaves longer than 20 mm
Flowerhead elongate
Style hairy

### LOWER LEAVES DIVIDED, UPPER LEAVES ENTIRE

**The Woolly Sceptre**
(Page 111, Plate 50)
Flowerhead densely covered
with woolly hairs
Involucral bracts linear, brown

**The Elongate Sceptres**
(Page 112, Plate 50)
Leaves below flowerhead
spatulate
Perianth with fine hairs

### *Paranomus* The Cornflower Sceptres

The Cornflower Sceptres are the only sceptres with almost *all leaves dissected and with hairless styles.* The dissected leaves vary greatly in shape and *a few of the uppermost leaves are entire.* Generally, the small, usually dense *flowerheads are globose and have few flowers* (12-66) per flowerhead. Most other sceptres have more than 70 flowers per flowerhead (exceptions being *P. abrotanifolius* and *P. capitatus*).

---

***Paranomus dregei*** (H. Buek ex Meisn.) Kuntze                Scented Sceptre        **Plate 47**

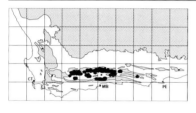

A branched shrub 0.6-1.7 m tall. Leaves up to 50 mm long, hairless, variable in shape, entire and flat below flowerhead, dissected elsewhere, tips rounded and reddish. Flowerhead 25-50 mm long, 20-25 mm across, dense or somewhat lax, with a sweet scent; stalk 0-20 mm long, clasped by upper leaves. *Perianth 14 mm long*, cream, covered with long, shaggy hairs, all segments similar. *Style hairless. Pollen presenter 2 mm long*, slightly broader than style, with 8 longitudinal ridges.
DISTRIBUTION: Witteberg to Anysberg and Swartberg, Touwsberg, Warmwaterberg and Rooiberg; Outeniqua Mountains, with a dubious record from Kouga Mountains.
HABITAT: Sandstone soils, 900-1400 m. STATUS: Widespread as scattered plants in extensive populations. FLOWERS: May to October. FRUITS: Released a few months after flowering.
☐ VARIATIONS: Older plants have fewer dissected leaves. Swartberg plants generally have fewer dissected leaves and larger, more compact flowerheads.

---

***Paranomus esterhuyseniae*** Levyns                Kouga Sceptre        **Plate 47**

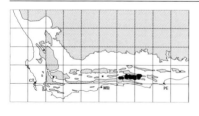

A small, branched shrub up to 0.7 m tall. Leaves 20-50 mm long, mostly dissected with slender segments but may be entire below flowerhead, hairless, pale, with rounded tips. *Flowerhead 15-30 mm across, globose, velvety*; stalk 0-20 mm long, hairy, surrounded by leaves. *Perianth 8 mm long*, cream, covered with shaggy hairs, all segments similar. *Style hairless*, slender. Pollen presenter 1.2 mm long, yellow, slightly knee-bent at base.
DISTRIBUTION: Kouga and Baviaanskloof Mountains. HABITAT: Sandstone soils, 900-1400 m. STATUS: In isolated clumps of a few hundred plants. *Red Data Book* status: Rare. FLOWERS: August to November. FRUITS: Released a few months after flowering.

*Paranomus centaureoides* Levyns                    Ladismith Sceptre    **Plate 47**

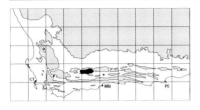

A branched shrub 1-1.5 m tall. *Leaves leathery, clasping stem*, 10-60 mm long, hairless, lower leaves dissected, upper leaves scantily dissected to entire and linear, tips colourless, rounded. *Flowerhead globose, 20-25 mm across, with 8-20 flowers projecting in a tuft from the dark brown involucral bracts*; stalk absent. Perianth 17-18 mm long, slender, pink to maroon, hairy, all segments similar. *Style hairless*, rarely with a few hairs immediately above ovary. Pollen presenter 2.5-2.8 mm long, linear, not wider than style.

DISTRIBUTION: Klein Swartberg between Ladismith and Seweweekspoort. HABITAT: Sandstone sands, 1000-2000 m. STATUS: Isolated patches of 2 or 3 plants, with an estimated total population of 2000 plants. *Red Data Book* status: Rare. FLOWERS: June to November. FRUITS: Released a few months after flowering.

### *Paranomus* The Common Sceptres

The Common Sceptres are the largest group of sceptres and have *only 1 form of leaf*, i.e. dissected leaves. All, with the exception of *Paranomus* sp. nova, have *hairy styles*, a feature they share with *P. capitatus*, from which they differ by having *leaves longer than 20 mm* and a flowerhead longer than 25 mm.

Perianth length is a useful feature to measure when trying to identify members of this group.

*Paranomus* sp. nova                    Palmiet Sceptre    **Plate 47**

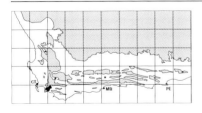

A branched shrub 0.4-1 m tall. *Leaves all similar, dissected*, 40-60 mm long, tips rounded. *Flowerhead a congested spike, elongate, 30-40 mm long*, 20 mm across; stalk 0-10 mm long, densely covered with hairs. Perianth 7-9 mm long, pink, with short hairs at base and long, woolly hairs at tip, all segments similar. *Style hairless*, red. *Pollen presenter 1 mm long*, slightly wider than style, ovate to club-shaped.

DISTRIBUTION: Palmiet River Valley in southwestern Elgin basin. HABITAT: Shales, 200-300 m. STATUS: Known from 3 dense, isolated populations of which only 1, containing about 1000 plants, has not subsequently been destroyed by agriculture. *Red Data Book* status: Vulner-able. FLOWERS: August to November. FRUITS: Released a few months after flowering.

***Paranomus candicans*** (Thunb.) Kuntze                    Powder Sceptre    **Plate 48**

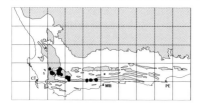

A much-branched shrub up to 2 m tall. *Leaves covered with silvery hairs*, 40-70 mm long, much dissected, with long segments, occasionally hairless when mature, *tips slender, pointed and hairless.* Flowerhead 20-60 mm long, 10-30 mm across, lax; stalk up to 40 mm long. *Perianth 10-13 mm long, 1 segment less hairy than others*, yellow, with silver-grey hairs and long hairs at tip. Style hairy only on lower middle part. Pollen presenter 1 mm long, not much wider than style.
DISTRIBUTION: Hex River Mountains to Langeberg. HABITAT: Sandstone sands, 600-2000 m. STATUS: Scattered plants in extensive stands. FLOWERS: June to November. FRUITS: Released a few months after flowering.
☐ VARIATIONS: In northern forms leaves become hairless with age, and hairs on the perianth and floral bracts tend to be more bristly.

***Paranomus tomentosus*** (E. Phillips & Hutch.) N.E. Br.        Hairy-leaf Sceptre    **Plate 48**

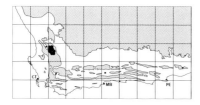

A branched shrub up to 3 m tall. *Stems covered with a white wool. Leaves 25-40 mm long, covered with silvery white hairs, tips rounded, curling upwards and hidden by hairs*, much dissected into short segments; stalk 10-20 mm long. Flowerhead 30-60 mm long, 30-35 mm across; stalk 0-20 mm long, densely covered with soft hairs. Perianth 17 mm long, with silver, curly hairs at base and long hairs at tip, 1 segment less hairy than others. Style with short hairs on lower three-quarters. Pollen presenter 2 mm long, dark red, slightly wider than style, slightly knee-bent at base.
DISTRIBUTION: Cederberg. HABITAT: Sandstone sands, 1200-1600 m. STATUS: In isolated populations on rocky outcrops. FLOWERS: August to October. FRUITS: Released a few months after flowering.

***Paranomus spicatus*** (P.J. Bergius) Kuntze                Kogelberg Sceptre    **Plate 48**

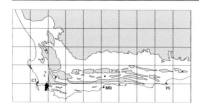

A much-branched shrub up to 1 m tall. *Leaves up to 70 mm long, all alike*, much dissected, with blunt, pale tips. *Flowerhead 40-80 mm long,* 25-40 mm across, with a faint sweet scent; stalk 20-80 mm long, densely covered with hairs. Perianth about 14 mm long, pink, covered with silvery white hairs. *Style densely covered with woolly hairs over two-thirds of its length*, pink, hairless at tip and base. *Pollen presenter 1.5 mm long, wider than style, green.*
DISTRIBUTION: Hottentots-Holland Mountains from Sir Lowry's Pass to Pringle Bay. HABITAT: Sandstone sands, 0-300 m. STATUS: Scattered plants in about 3 populations, thought to total about 800 plants. *Red Data Book* status: Rare. FLOWERS: September to November. FRUITS: Released a few months after flowering.

*Paranomus bolusii* (Gand.) Levyns                    Overberg Sceptre    **Plate 48**

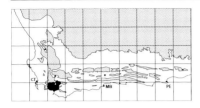

A much-branched shrub up to 1 m tall. *Leaves up to 50 mm long*, much dissected, somewhat flatter below flowerheads, tips pointed. *Flowerhead 20-70 mm long*, 15-30 mm across, with a faint sweet scent; stalk 20-50 mm long, densely covered with hairs. Perianth 10-12 mm long, all segments equally covered with silvery white hairs. *Style red-pink, with sparse hairs on middle third. Pollen presenter 1 mm long, not much wider than style*, knee-bent at base.

DISTRIBUTION: Groenland, Riviersonderend, Babylonstoring and Klein River Mountains and Caledon Swartberg. HABITAT: Sandstone and Cederberg shales, 150-700 m. STATUS: Scattered plants occur in isolated, extensive populations. FLOWERS: June to November. FRUITS: Released a few months after flowering.

*Paranomus bracteolaris* Salisb. ex Knight                Smooth-leaf Tree Sceptre    **Plate 49**

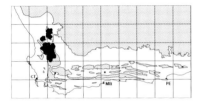

*A much-branched shrub 0.6-2 m tall*, with a single, short, *stout trunk*. Leaves 30-60 mm long, much dissected (but tending to be less dissected, and flattened in older bushes), with shaggy hairs, hairless when mature, tips pale. *Flowerhead very lax, 40-90 mm long*, 25-30 mm across, with a faint sweet scent; *stalk 20-50 mm long*, woolly. *Perianth 13-15 mm long (more than 4 times as long as its floral bract), with silver hairs at base and long hairs at tip, 1 segment less hairy than others*, slender, purple-pink. Style sparsely covered with short hairs on basal half. Pollen presenter 1 mm long, slightly wider than style, cylindrical.

DISTRIBUTION: Bokkeveld escarpment to Koue Bokkeveld and Olifants River Mountains. HABITAT: Sandstone sands, 250-1300 m. STATUS: Occurring in dense isolated stands and as scattered individuals over large areas. FLOWERS: August to October. FRUITS: Released a few months after flowering.

*Paranomus lagopus* (Thunb.) Salisb.                    Rabbit-paw Sceptre    **Plate 49**

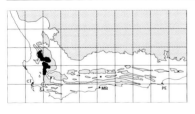

A much-branched shrub 0.6-1.3 m tall, with *lower branches tending to grow downwards or creep along the ground. Leaves much dissected, segments slender and curling upwards*, 10-50 mm long, hairless when mature, tips small, pointed. Flowerhead 30-90 mm (usually 30-60 mm) long, 20-25 mm across, with a faint sweet scent; *stalk 0-30 mm long*, with dense, shaggy hairs. *Perianth 9 mm long, with short hairs at base and long bristly hairs at the tip, 1 segment less hairy than others*, pink. Style sparsely covered with short hairs on basal half. *Pollen presenter 0.5-0.7 mm long*, slightly wider than style, ovate.

DISTRIBUTION: Olifants River, Koue Bokkeveld, Groot Winterhoek and Elandskloof Mountains. HABITAT: Sandstone sands, 200-1100 m. STATUS: Occurring in dense isolated stands and, less frequently, as scattered individuals over large areas. FLOWERS: September to November. FRUITS: Released a few months after flowering.
NOTE: In the Elandskloof Pass area of the Koue Bokkeveld it is difficult to distinguish between this species and *P. bracteolaris*.

**Paranomus abrotanifolius** Salisb. ex Knight                    Bredasdorp Sceptre    **Plate 49**

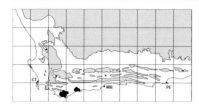

A much-branched shrub up to 0.9 m tall. *Leaves much dissected, hairless when mature*, 15-25 mm long, all similar, tips pointed. *Flowerhead globose*, 20-30 mm long, 20-25 mm across, with about 50 flowers in densely clustered headlets; stalk 0-20 mm long, densely covered with hairs. Perianth 7-9 mm long, purple-pink, densely covered with short hairs at base and sparsely covered with stiff hairs at tip, all segments similar. *Style with sparse hairs on basal half. Pollen presenter dark red, wider than style*, 0.8 mm long.
DISTRIBUTION: Elim Flats and Potberg. HABITAT: Sandstone sands, 140-1200 m. STATUS: *Red Data Book* status: Vulnerable, with only about 10 populations currently known. FLOWERS: May to December. FRUITS: Released a few months after flowering.

**Paranomus dispersus** Levyns                    Long-head Sceptre    **Plate 49**

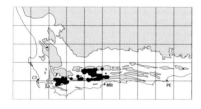

A branched shrub 0.6-1.5 m tall. *Leaves all similar, dissected, with some leaves nearer the branch tip sparsely dissected and flattened*, 40-80 mm long, tips rounded. *Flowerhead lax, elongate, 25-90 mm long*, 20-30 mm across; stalk 20-50 mm long, densely covered with hairs. Perianth 14-18 mm long, pink, with short hairs at base and long hairs at tip, all segments similar. *Style with scant hairs in middle*, red. *Pollen presenter 0.6-1 mm long*, slightly wider than style, ovate to club-shaped.
DISTRIBUTION: Riviersonderend to Outeniqua Mountains and Klein Swartberg and Rooiberg. HABITAT: Sandstone sands, 300-1200 m. STATUS: Variable, sometimes occurring in dense stands that dominate the veld, but also as isolated plants. FLOWERS: All year round, mainly August to November. FRUITS: Released a few months after flowering.

### *Paranomus* The Fine-leaf Sceptre

The Fine-leaf Sceptre is best recognized by its *small, globose, dense, hairy flowerheads* which give a fluffy-ball appearance to the flowerhead. In addition, the leaves are very small (the smallest in the genus) and much dissected, with slender segments. Other features of diagnostic importance are the *hairy style* and the *pollen presenter which is not much wider than the style.*

This is the only *Paranomus* species which (if the grooved leaves are ignored) could easily be mistaken for a *Serruria*, as the diagnostic headlets of 4 flowers are not easy to discern, except in bud.

*Paranomus capitatus* (R. Br.) Kuntze        Fine-leaf Sceptre   **Plate 50**

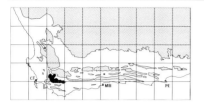

A branched shrub up to 1 m tall. *Leaves 10-20 mm long*, much dissected, segments slender, hairless when mature, tips pale; stalk shorter than 5 mm. *Flowerhead 15-25 mm across, globose, bearing about 30 flowers*; stalk 0-10 mm long, hairy. Perianth 9 mm long, dull purplish pink, covered with long, fine hairs which are very long at the tip, 1 segment with fewer hairs. *Style with sparse hairs only in lower middle, 7.5 mm long. Pollen presenter not much wider than style*, 0.6 mm long.
DISTRIBUTION: Du Toit's Kloof and Riviersonderend Mountains. HABITAT: Sandstone sands, 600-1200 m. STATUS: Known from only a few isolated populations comprising many scattered clusters of 3-10 plants. *Red Data Book* status: Rare. FLOWERS: October to December. FRUITS: Released a few months after flowering.
☐ VARIATIONS: In the west plants are smaller and have smaller, green leaves and more congested flowerheads. Eastern plants tend to be taller and lankier, and their leaves are more markedly silvery-haired.

### *Paranomus* The Woolly Sceptre

> The Woolly Sceptre has both dissected and entire leaves, and spatulate leaves subtending the flowerhead. It is distinguished from other sceptres with both leaf forms by its *densely woolly flowerhead and untidy, brown, linear involucral bracts.*

*Paranomus longicaulis* Salisb. ex Knight       Exploding Baked Apple   **Plate 50**

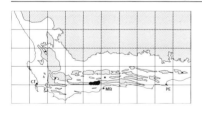

A sparsely branched shrub up to 2.5 m tall. Leaves 20-75 mm long, hairless, much dissected to entire and spatulate, tips rounded. Flowerhead 30-70 mm long, 30-40 mm across, elongate-globose, *surrounded by brown, linear involucral bracts at base.* Perianth 18 mm long, pink at base, black at the tip, covered with long, silver-white, shaggy hairs, all segments similar, *with brown, linear floral bracts more than half the length of the perianth.* Style probably hairless. Pollen presenter 2 mm long.
DISTRIBUTION: Eastern Langeberg from Garcia's Pass to Attaquaskloof. HABITAT: Sandstone sands, 400-600 m. STATUS: Poorly known from 4 populations. Probably more common than thought. *Red Data Book* status: Vulnerable. FLOWERS: All year round, mainly September to December. FRUITS: Released a few months after flowering.

## *Paranomus* The Elongate Sceptres

The Elongate Sceptres are undoubtedly the most beautiful of the sceptres. Like the Woolly Sceptre, they have both dissected and entire leaves, with *spatulate leaves subtending the flowerhead.* However, they lack the Woolly Sceptre's woolly flowerhead and untidy involucral bracts.

The Elongate Sceptres can be divided into two groups:
□ Silvery pink perianths and short (less than 11-mm) styles............................................
............................................................... *P. spathulatus, P. roodebergensis, P. adiantifolius*
□ Bright yellow perianths and long (more than 14-mm) styles .....................................
.................................................................................. *P. reflexus, P. sceptrum-gustavianus*

### *Paranomus spathulatus* (Thunb.) Kuntze  Langeberg Sceptre  **Plate 50**

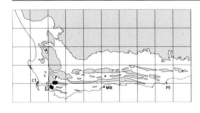

A branched shrub 0.5-2.5 m tall, variously single- or multi-stemmed. *Leaves of 2 forms*, 10-80 mm long, 5-70 mm wide, hairless, grey; entire leaves at ends of branches, spatulate to ovate; dissected leaves at base of plant or absent, with tips rounded, orange. Flowerhead 25-85 mm long, 23-33 mm across, dense; stalk 0-15 mm long, hairy. *Floral bracts hairy, pointed. Perianth pink,* 10-12 mm long, densely woolly in western populations, hairs adpressed in east, all segments similar. Style hairless. *Pollen presenter 2 mm long, linear, slightly knee-bent at base.*
DISTRIBUTION: Langeberg from Montagu Pass to Cloete's Pass. HABITAT: Sandstone sands, 300-600 m. STATUS: Abundant in sparse, isolated populations of a few dozen plants. FLOWERS: May to December. FRUITS: Released a few months after flowering.
□ VARIATIONS: In arid areas dissected leaves sometimes absent in older plants. Forms in the west are multi-stemmed and resprout after a fire, whereas those in the east are single-stemmed and killed by fire. A peculiar form from the Gamkaberg has a low, rounded habit, divided leaves and tall, emergent stems covered with narrow entire leaves; it is probably a new species.

### *Paranomus adiantifolius* Salisb. ex Knight  Hairy-style Sceptre  **Plate 51**

An erect, sparsely branched shrub 1-1.7 m tall. *Leaves of 2 forms:* entire leaves at ends of branches, 12-35 mm long, spatulate to triangular, hairless, margin cartilaginous, stalk clasping stem; dissected leaves up to 90 mm long, hairless, sparsely lobed in basal third, tip rounded. Flowerhead 50-70 mm long, 15-25 mm across, hairy; stalk 0-15 mm long. Perianth 13 mm long, pink within, densely covered with shiny white hairs, all segments similar. *Style hairless at tip, with long hairs at base,* 11 mm long. *Pollen presenter heart-shaped, wider than style, with hairs from base,* 1 mm long, with 8 ridges at the tip.
DISTRIBUTION: Wolfieskop in Riviersonderend Mountains and Groenland Mountains at Houhoek. HABITAT: Sandstone sands, 500-1000 m. STATUS: Known from only 4 populations at 2 locations. Estimates of total numbers vary from a few dozen to 5000 plants, but this species has not been recorded at Houhoek since 1982. *Red Data Book* status: Rare. FLOWERS: September to November. FRUITS: Released a few months after flowering.

***Paranomus roodebergensis*** (Compton) Levyns                    Honey-scented Sceptre    **Plate 51**

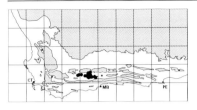

A much-branched shrub 1-2.5 m tall. *Leaves of 2 forms*, hairless; *entire leaves ovate to heart-shaped*, 8-25 mm long, overlapping, margin cartilaginous; dissected leaves 20-45 mm long, divided in the upper half. Flowerhead 30-40 mm long, 20-30 mm across, dense, with a strong honey scent; stalk absent. Involucral bracts yellow, tipped with red. *Floral bracts rounded, hairless at tip.* Perianth 12 mm long, pink, with silvery white hairs, all segments similar. Style hairless. Pollen presenter 2 mm long, cylindrical. DISTRIBUTION: Rooiberg, Huis River Pass and Touwsberg. HABITAT: Sandstone sands, 600-1300 m. STATUS: In small, isolated clumps of a few dozen scattered plants, but locally abundant on Rooiberg. *Red Data Book* status: Rare. FLOWERS: August to October. FRUITS: Released a few months after flowering.

***Paranomus sceptrum-gustavianus*** (Sparrm.) Hyl.                 King Gustav's Sceptre    **Plate 51**

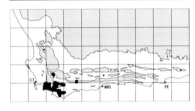

*A stout, branched shrub 1-1.8 m tall. Leaves of 2 forms*, occasionally only entire on older plants, hairless; entire leaves at tips of branches, 10-80 mm long, with wedge-shaped base, spatulate to rhomboidal, tip rounded, leathery, stalk stout; dissected leaves 65-120 mm long, divided in upper half, with a rounded tip. Flowerhead 45-70 mm long, 40-60 mm across, dense, *with an overpowering sweet scent*; stalk 0-10 mm long, with brown woolly hairs. *Floral bracts pointed at tip. Perianth pale cream*, 16-22 mm long, slender, covered with stiff, clasping, silvery hairs, 1 segment less hairy. Style 14-15 mm long, hairless. *Pollen presenter 2 mm long, dark, linear, knee-bent at base.* DISTRIBUTION: Hottentots-Holland to Bredasdorp and Riviersonderend Mountains, with occasional records from Hex River Mountains and Langeberg. HABITAT: Sandstone slopes, 150-500 m. STATUS: Typically only solitary plants or isolated clumps of up to half a dozen plants, although in some areas it occurs in dense patches of several dozen plants. FLOWERS: July to March. FRUITS: Released a few months after flowering.

***Paranomus reflexus*** (E. Phillips & Hutch.) Fourc.              Van Staden's Sceptre    **Plate 51**

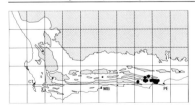

A branched shrub up to 1.5 m tall. *Leaves of 2 forms*: entire leaves 35 mm long, clasping stem, ovate to spatulate, hairless, stalk 15 mm long; dissected leaves 40-80 mm long, hairless, divided in upper half, segments slender, with red, pointed tips. *Flowerhead 80-140 mm long*, 50-70 mm across, elongate; stalk 10-40 mm long, 6 mm in diameter, with short hairs, clasped by upper leaves. *Perianth 30-35 mm long, green-yellow*, with short, pale hairs, all segments similar. *Flowers bending down (reflexing) as buds open.* Style hairless, pointing downwards once released. Pollen presenter 5 mm long, green, spindle-shaped, knee-bent at base. DISTRIBUTION: Elandsberg. HABITAT: Sandstone sands, 1000-2000 m. STATUS: Estimates give a total population size of 1000 plants in 6 populations, typically in small clumps of a few dozen plants along drainage lines. However, the species is poorly known and probably more common than the estimates suggest. *Red Data Book* status: Vulnerable, due to afforestation. FLOWERS: June to August. FRUITS: Released a few months after flowering.

## SOROCEPHALUS R. Br.  The Clusterheads

The clusterheads are poorly documented and many of the species are known from only a few localities or from a small number of herbarium specimens. An alternative common name for this genus is powderpuffs.

> The genus *Sorocephalus* is easily recognized by its *globose flowerhead which consists of numerous smaller headlets, each comprising 4-9 flowers* subtended by inconspicuous bracts. The *perianth is symmetrical* and fused in the basal half, straight in bud, short (8-25 mm), and the *styles are straight and thread-like. Leaves are entire*, small, either needle-like or with a groove on the upper surface. *The fruit is a hairless nut* with a lobed base.

The 3 main groups into which the genus is divided are based largely on the morphology of the fruit (which is difficult to find in the field) and the shape of the leaf. Other features which distinguish one species from another are the number of flowers in the headlets; the presence of hairs on the perianth limbs and claws, the shape of the pollen presenter; and the shape of the floral bracts.

## A QUICK KEY TO THE CLUSTERHEADS

**The Flat-leaf Clusterheads**
(Page 119, Plate 54)
Leaves flattened
Flowerhead contains more than 10 headlets
Fruit hairless, narrowly lobed at base

**The Needle-leaf Clusterheads**
(Page115, Plate 52)
Leaves needle-like, with prominent channel on upper surface
Fruit hairless, broadly lobed at base

**The Diminutive Clusterhead**
(Page118, Plate 53)
Leaves linear
Flowerhead small, with 4 or 5 headlets
Involucral bracts lanceolate
Fruit hairy

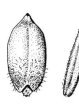

## *Sorocephalus* The Needle-leaf Clusterheads

The Needle-leaf Clusterheads (section *Mischocaryon*) all have *long, needle-like leaves, with a prominent channel on the upper leaf surface.* The flowerheads consist of more than 30 flowers. The 6 species are confined to an area south of Bain's Kloof and the Breede River.

Important features distinguishing the species in this group include leaf length, the number of flowers per headlet, and the shape of the flowerhead.

### *Sorocephalus pinifolius* (Salisb. ex Knight) Rourke Long-leaf Clusterhead **Plate 52**

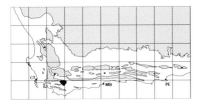

An erect, sparsely branched shrub with a single stout main stem, reaching a height of 1 m. *Leaves 40-60 mm long, needle-shaped, long and slender, channelled on upper surface*, tip with a fine point. Flowerhead 25 mm across, globose to ovoid, terminal; stalkless. Involucral bracts 8-9 mm long, lanceolate, tip tapering to a narrow point, densely covered with short hairs. Headlet usually with 8 flowers (occasionally 7 or 9). *Perianth limbs hairless*, 12 mm long, claws with shaggy hairs, tube 3 mm long, cream with black tips. Floral nectaries linear. Style 10 mm long, thread-like. *Pollen presenter ovoid.*
DISTRIBUTION: Riviersonderend Mountains near Tygerhoek. HABITAT: Cool, southern mountain slopes, 450-800 m. STATUS: *Red Data Book* status: Endangered. Known from 1 population of 500 plants. FLOWERS: June to October. FRUITS: Released after flowering.

### *Sorocephalus alopecurus* Rourke Woolly-stalk Clusterhead **Plate 52**

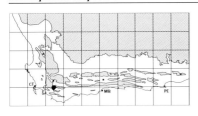

An erect, sparsely branched shrub up to 1 m tall. *Leaves 30-50 mm long*, needle-shaped, upper surface channelled, tip with a fine point, hairless. *Flowerhead cylindrical, 50-60 mm long, 20 mm across*, terminal, solitary or clustered, with a sweet scent; stalk often long, woolly. Involucral bracts 5-6 mm long, linear, tapering. Headlet with 8 or 9 flowers. *Perianth limbs and claws hairy*, 11 mm long, tube 3 mm long, cream. Floral nectaries linear. Style 10 mm long, thread-like. Pollen presenter ovoid.
DISTRIBUTION: Riviersonderend Mountains near Greyton. HABITAT: Southern mountain slopes, 450-800 m. STATUS: *Red Data Book* status: Endangered. Known from 1 population of 400 plants. FLOWERS: July to September. FRUITS: Released after flowering.

*Sorocephalus clavigerus* (Salisb. ex Knight) Hutch.          Erect Clusterhead          **Plate 52**

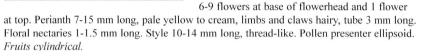

*An erect, sparsely branched shrub up to 1 m tall,* very variable. *Stems stout. Leaves 7-25 mm long, needle-shaped,* upper surface channelled, overlapping, tip with a fine point, hairless when mature. Flowerhead 20-40 mm across, globose to broadly cylindrical, terminal, solitary. Involucral bracts 7-12 mm long, lanceolate, tip pointed. Headlets with 6-9 flowers at base of flowerhead and 1 flower at top. Perianth 7-15 mm long, pale yellow to cream, limbs and claws hairy, tube 3 mm long. Floral nectaries 1-1.5 mm long. Style 10-14 mm long, thread-like. Pollen presenter ellipsoid. *Fruits cylindrical.*

DISTRIBUTION: Hottentots-Holland to Klein River Mountains. HABITAT: Well-drained, sandy or stony soils, 450-1200 m. STATUS: Occurring in discrete clumps of a few plants. FLOWERS: July to December. FRUITS: Released after flowering.

□ VARIATIONS: The leaves, bracts and flowers are longest in southern forms. Bracts may be hairless or hairy on the basal half, or they may be short-haired. The last-mentioned form predominates in the south.

*Sorocephalus palustris* Rourke          Mat Clusterhead          **Plate 52**

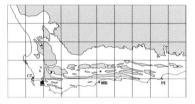

*A low, sprawling shrublet forming mats 1 m across,* rarely up to 0.2 m tall. Leaves 15-20 mm long, needle-like, upper surface channelled, hairless when mature, tip with a fine point. Flowerhead 20 mm across, globose, terminal. Involucral bracts lanceolate, tip tapering to a narrow point. Headlets with 4-7 flowers at base of flowerhead, becoming 1-flowered at top. Perianth 10 mm long, limbs woolly, claws hairy, tube 1.5 mm long, white. *Floral nectaries 0.5 mm long.* Style 10 mm long, thread-like. Pollen presenter cylindrical-ellipsoid, scarcely distinct from style. *Fruits ellipsoid-ovate, with short hairs at base.*

DISTRIBUTION: Kogelberg. HABITAT: Peaty soils in southern gullies, 1050-1200 m. STATUS: *Red Data Book* status: Endangered. Known from 2 populations totalling 20 plants. FLOWERS: September to December. FRUITS: Released after flowering.

*Sorocephalus crassifolius* Hutch.                    Flowerless Clusterhead    **Plate 53**

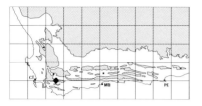

A low, rounded, much-branched shrublet 0.3-0.5 m tall, with *short stems arising from a woody rootstock. Leaves stout, needle-like, upper surface channelled, 20-25 mm long, 2 mm wide*, hairless, tip with a fine point. *Flowerhead small, 15 mm across*, almost globose; stalkless. Involucral bracts lanceolate, tip tapering to a narrow point, hairless at the tip. *Headlet with 4 flowers*; stalked. Perianth 9 mm long, *limbs and claws virtually hairless*, tube 1 mm long, cream. Floral nectaries 1 mm long. Style thread-like. Pollen presenter ellipsoid to cylindrical, dark brown.
DISTRIBUTION: Kanonkop to Galgeberg in the Riviersonderend Mountains near Greyton. HABITAT: Peaty ledges and steep southern slopes, 1400-1500 m. STATUS: *Red Data Book* status: Vulnerable. Known from 3 populations, each an isolated clump totalling fewer than several dozen plants. FLOWERS: December to February. FRUITS: Released after flowering. NOTE: Beware: the similarity in the leaf shapes of this species and *Spatalla salsoloides* (page 122) may lead to confusion. However, the clusterhead bears flowers in fours, not singly, and seldom has a reddish tint.

*Sorocephalus teretifolius* (Meisn.) E. Phillips                Pinhead Clusterhead    **Plate 53**

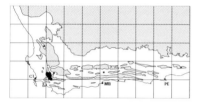

A low, erect shrublet up to 0.7 m tall, with a single stem. *Leaves 10-14 mm long, needle-shaped*, upper surface channelled, tip with a fine point, hairless when mature. *Flowerhead with flowers (each with its floral bract) arising from a globose base*, 15-20 mm across, solitary. Involucral bracts 2-3 mm long, massed around base of receptacle, hairless, margin fringed. Perianth 6-7 mm long, carmine, limbs woolly, claws hairless, tube 1 mm long. Floral nectaries 1 mm long. Style 10-12 mm long, thread-like. Pollen presenter cylindrical to ellipsoid.
DISTRIBUTION: Du Toit's Kloof and Wemmershoek Mountains and Blokkop above Villiersdorp. HABITAT: Rocky, dry, high slopes, 1500-1850 m. STATUS: *Red Data Book* status: Rare. Known from 3 populations totalling 1500 plants which occur in dense, isolated clumps of fewer than a dozen plants. FLOWERS: November and December. FRUITS: Released after flowering.
□ VARIATION: Plants at high altitudes may be half the size of those at lower altitudes.
NOTE: This species does not have distinct headlets. It could therefore be mistaken for members of other genera, especially *Vexatorella*, but its needle-like leaves prevent confusion with species of *Leucospermum* or *Serruria.*

## *Sorocephalus* The Diminutive Clusterhead

The Diminutive Clusterhead (section *Dasycaryon*) is intermediate between the genera *Sorocephalus* and *Spatalla* in that it has *hairy fruit*, a feature not found in other clusterheads. Its flowerhead is also the smallest among those of the clusterheads, containing only *16-20 flowers.*

*Sorocephalus tenuifolius* R. Br.      Diminutive Clusterhead **Plate 53**

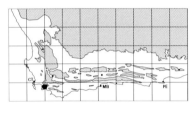

An erect, well-branched shrublet 0.5-1 m tall. Leaves linear, 10 mm long, round-tipped, hairless when mature. *Flowerhead globose, 15 mm long, 15 mm across, containing 4 or 5 headlets*, terminal. *Involucral bracts lanceolate, tapering to the base,* 10 mm long, with shaggy hairs. *Headlet 4-flowered.* Perianth 12 mm long, claws densely woolly, tube 2 mm long, cream to yellow. Floral nectaries 0.5 mm long. Style thread-like, 10 mm long. Pollen presenter narrowly ellipsoid. *Fruits hairy, with a small stalk.*

DISTRIBUTION: Palmiet River Valley south of Elgin at Arieskraal. Two extremely dubious localities (from herbarium records) exist: 'alpine moist places near the Breede River' (1805), and 'in stony ground near Elim' (1838). HABITAT: Moist, sandy slopes on flats, 400 m. STATUS: Until recently, believed to be extinct. When the only known colony of 500 plants was ploughed up in 1985 for an apple orchard, some plants were rescued and taken to Kirstenbosch National Botanical Garden; unfortunately, they did not survive. Another population was discovered in November 1995.

FLOWERS: January and February. FRUITS: Released after flowering.

NOTE: This species is superficially very similar to *Spatalla prolifera* (page 122).

## *Sorocephalus* The Flat-leaf Clusterheads

The Flat-leaf Clusterheads (section *Sorocephalus*) are easy to discern from other clusterheads by their *flat leaves*. The *flower-heads contain more than 10 4-flowered headlets*. These species only occur north of a line from Wellington to Worcester.

*Sorocephalus imbricatus* (Thunb.) R. Br.                     Tile-leaf Clusterhead     **Plate 54**

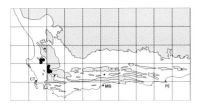

A slender, sparsely branched shrub 0.7-1.5 m tall, with a single main stem. *Leaves flattened, lanceolate, 5 mm wide*, 15 mm long, tip with a fine point or hooked, hairless when mature, scabrous. Flowerhead 40 mm across, globose, terminal, usually solitary, with a sweet scent. Involucral bracts 14 mm long, lanceolate, tip tapering to a narrow point, scabrous, margin fringed, pink. Headlet 4-flowered, stalked. Perianth 10 mm long, limbs densely covered with long, straight, silky hairs, *claws with club-shaped, glandular hairs*, tube 3 mm long, cream. *Floral nectaries absent.* Style 9 mm long, thread-like. Pollen presenter narrowly ovoid to ellipsoid.

DISTRIBUTION: Piketberg, Groot Winterhoek and Elandskloof Mountains. HABITAT: Sandstone and Cederberg shale, 450-620 m. STATUS: *Red Data Book* status: Endangered. Of the 3 localities, only the population in the Elandskloof Mountains is extant. Known from 3 plants in 1972 and 2 plants in 1987, although several more are known now. Isolated clumps of 2 to 20 plants.
FLOWERS: September to December. FRUITS: Released after flowering.

*Sorocephalus scabridus* Meisn.                     Tulbagh Clusterhead     **Plate 54**

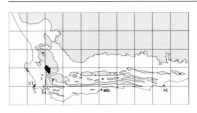

An erect, sparsely branched shrub up to 0.8 m tall. *Leaves linear, needle-shaped with a flattened upper surface*, 20-30 mm long, curved inwards and hooked at tip, hairless when mature, scabrous. Flowerhead 20-25 mm across, globose, stalkless. Involucral bracts 7-8 mm long, lanceolate, hairless, margin fringed. *Headlet with 7-9 flowers. Perianth limbs hairless*, 8 mm long, claws with long, silky hairs, tube 3 mm long, pink with black tips. *Floral nectaries absent. Style merging imperceptibly with the ovary*, 10 mm long, thread-like. *Pollen presenter ovoid.*

DISTRIBUTION: Groot Winterhoek to Olifants River Mountains. HABITAT: Montane flats between rocks on sandstone sands, 900-1850 m. STATUS: *Red Data Book* status: Vulnerable. Known from a single population of 200 plants in the Olifants River Valley; other historical localities to the south have not been relocated or the species has become extinct there.
FLOWERS: October to January. FRUITS: Released after flowering.

*Sorocephalus lanatus* (Thunb.) R. Br.                    Common Clusterhead    **Plate 54**

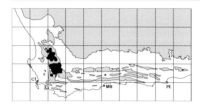

A low, much-branched, erect to sprawling shrub up to 0.8 m tall, *variable in many features. Leaves needle-shaped with a flattened or concave upper surface,* 5-18 mm long, overlapping, clasping the stem, hairless or densely covered with hairs, scabrous. Flowerhead 10-30 mm across, globose, terminal. Involucral and floral bracts variable, lanceolate to ovate. Headlet usually with 4 flowers (or 8 or 9, rarely 5, 6 or 7). *Perianth limbs densely covered with long hairs,* 8-12 mm long, pink, claws hairy, tube 2-3 mm long. Floral nectaries 1 mm long. Style 8-10 mm long, thread-like. *Pollen presenter ellipsoid to cylindrical.* Fruits cylindrical, narrow at base.

DISTRIBUTION: The most widespread clusterhead, occurring from Cederberg to Groot Winterhoek and Hex River Mountains. HABITAT: Varied at high altitudes, 1500-1850 m. STATUS: Small colonies of a few dozen plants occur on most higher peaks. FLOWERS: September to April, peaking in December. FRUITS: Released after flowering.

□ VARIATIONS: Branching varies from sparse in the north to dense in the south. In dry habitats the plant sometimes forms a prostrate, stunted shrub. Multi-stemmed forms occur in the Koue Bokkeveld. Leaves are longest in wetter areas to the southwest. Bracts vary considerably in length, width and hair cover. There are usually 4 or 8 flowers per headlet, but the number may vary between 4 and 9.

*Sorocephalus capitatus* Rourke                    Woolly Clusterhead    **Plate 54**

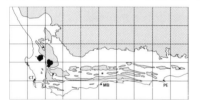

An erect, well-branched shrub 0.7-1 m tall, with a stout main stem branching at 0.3 m. *Leaves narrowly lanceolate,* 6-12 mm long, slightly 3-ridged or flat on upper surface, hairless when mature, scabrous. Flowerhead 20-30 mm across, globose, terminal, solitary or in clusters of 3. Involucral bracts 9 mm long, 1-5 mm wide, lanceolate to ovate. Headlets with 8 or 9 flowers, in dense clusters. Perianth 12 mm long, *limbs and claws woolly on outermost flowers, limbs hairless on inner flowers,* tube 5 mm long, pink or cream. *Floral nectaries 3 mm long, curved inwards.* Style 9 mm long, thread-like. *Pollen presenter pinhead-shaped.*

DISTRIBUTION: Piketberg and Onderboskloof in the Koue Bokkeveld. STATUS: *Red Data Book* status downgraded from Endangered to Rare. It is known from only 2 populations totalling 3000 plants, which occur in small, discrete clumps. HABITAT: Sandy patches between sandstone outcrops, 910-1200 m. FLOWERS: September to February. FRUITS: Released after flowering.

□ VARIATIONS: Piketberg forms have lanceolate involucral bracts whereas Onderboskloof forms have broadly ovate bracts.

## *SPATALLA* Salisb. **The Spoons**

> The genus *Spatalla* is most easily recognized by the undivided leaves, *headlets with either 3 flowers or 1 flower, the perianth which is always curved away from the centre of the headlet,* 1 perianth part which may be much larger than the other 3 free perianth parts, and by the prominent, spoon-like pollen presenter. *Fruits are hairy, cylindrical nuts with a truncate and stalked base.*
>
> The spoons are clearly related to the clusterheads in that they have retained 4 floral bracts below the headlet, even though there may be only either 3 flowers or 1 flower per headlet. In the Unispoons, which have 1 flower per headlet, there may be fewer than 4 bracts, but the 1:1 ratio of bracts to flowers that is characteristic of the clusterheads is never achieved in the spoons.

Features used to distinguish one *Spatalla* species from another include the shape of the flowerhead and the shape, size and hairiness of the floral bracts; the presence of hairs on the style; the shape of the pollen presenter; and the size and hairiness of the leaves.

## A QUICK KEY TO THE SPOONS

**The Unispoons**
(Plate 55)
1 flower per headlet
4 floral bracts per flower

**The Triplespoons**
(Page 127, Plate 58)
3 flowers per headlet
1 floral bract per flower,
and 1 spare

### *Spatalla* **The Unispoons**

> The Unispoons (section *Spatalla*) are easily identified by their *flowerheads which consist of many 1-flowered headlets.* That these are headlets and not single flowers can be detected by the presence of 3 or 4 floral bracts below each one. Unispoons occur only south of the Breede River in the west and, with the exception of *S. barbigera* on the Swartberg, south of the Little Karoo in the east.

The Unispoons can be divided into 5 distinct groups (see key, next page). In addition, they show a progression from the primitive state of having 4 floral bracts as in the clusterheads (*Spatalla prolifera*); to the gradual fusion of the base of 3 of the floral bracts (*S. salsoloides, S. setacea, S. nubicola, S. parilis*); to the fusion of the upper two-thirds of the 3 floral bracts (*S. barbigera, S. colorata, S. longifolia, S. curvifolia, S. racemosa*); to all 4 floral bracts fused, with 1 of them smaller than the others (*S. ericoides* and *S. squamata*); to finally, in *S. mollis*, only 3 fused floral bracts remaining.

## Key to groupings within the Unispoons

1  Perianth lobes equal. Pollen presenter cylindrical or ovoid to pinhead-shaped ...................
................................................................................ *S. setacea, S. nubicola, S. salsoloides*
1a Perianth lobes unequal, upper perianth segment boat-shaped. Pollen presenter an
   asymmetrically obovoid, helmet-shaped disc ........................................................ go to 2
2  Flowerhead with stalk 10-70 mm long. Leaves needle-shaped, with a slight groove
   (10x lens!) on the upper surface .......................... *S. longifolia, S. curvifolia, S. racemosa*
2a Flowerhead stalkless. Leaves needle-shaped, without a groove on the upper surface ....
   ...................................................................................................................... go to 3
3  Style hairy, headlet with 3 floral bracts (2 fused) ..................................................... *S. mollis*
3a Style hairless, headlet with 4 floral bracts ................................................................ go to 4
4  Headlet stalkless ..................................................... *S. prolifera, S. squamata, S. ericoides*
4a Headlet with a stalk 1-3 mm long ................................. *S. colorata, S. barbigera, S. parilis*

---

***Spatalla prolifera*** (Thunb.) Salisb. ex Knight                    Palmiet Spoon    **Plate 55**

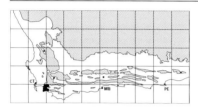

An erect, slender, sparsely branched shrublet up to
1 m tall, with a single main stem. Leaves 10-30 mm
long, linear to needle-shaped, thread-like, tip with
a fine point, hairless when mature. Flowerhead
10-20 mm across, globose to almost globose, a congested but few-flowered raceme, solitary, terminal;
*stalkless. Headlet 1-flowered; stalkless. Floral bracts
free, linear-lanceolate*, 3-5 mm long, 0.5-1 mm
wide, equal-sized, red. Perianth 8 mm long, with segments unequal, 1 limb helmet-shaped and
others curved forward, outer surface densely covered with shaggy hairs, *tips hairless on inner
surface*, tube 1-2 mm long, pink. Style straight, curved forward at tip, 7 mm long. Pollen presenter
an asymmetrically conical to obovoid, ear-like disc.
DISTRIBUTION: Hottentots-Holland Mountains to Kleinmond adjacent to the Palmiet and
Steenbras Rivers. HABITAT: Swamps, marshes and riverbanks, 50-460 m. STATUS: *Red Data
Book* status: Endangered, owing to dam building and Defence Ministry activities. Currently known
from only 3 patches in 2 extant populations consisting of discrete, dense clumps of a few hundred
plants. FLOWERS: September to December. FRUITS: Released after flowering.

---

***Spatalla salsoloides*** (R. Br.) Rourke                    Kink-style Spoon    **Plate 55**

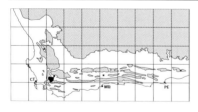

A semi-erect, much-branched shrub *with spreading,
prostrate stems bearing upward-curving branches*,
forming mats up to 1 m across and 1 m tall. *Leaves
curved inwards*, 15-30 mm long, needle-shaped, tip
with a fine point, hairless when mature. Flowerhead
20 mm long, 10 mm across, globose to ovoid, a
densely congested raceme, terminal, solitary; stalkless.
*Headlet 1-flowered*; stalkless. Floral bracts 5-6 mm
long, 1-2 mm wide, lanceolate, tip pointed, 3 fused in lower third and 1 free, margin fringed.
Perianth 8-9 mm long, curved forward in limb region in bud, silvery carmine, segments equal,
limbs and claws with shaggy hairs, tube 2 mm long. Style curved forward at tip, 9 mm long. *Pollen
presenter cylindrical-ellipsoid, knee-bent at base.*
DISTRIBUTION: Du Toit's Peak and Goudini Sneeukop above Du Toit's Kloof. HABITAT: Rocky
southern slopes, 1500-1850 m. STATUS: Known from 2 populations totalling about 1500 plants.
*Red Data Book* status: Rare. FLOWERS: October to December. FRUITS: Released after flowering.

***Spatalla setacea*** (R. Br.) Rourke                              Needle-leaf Spoon     **Plate 55**

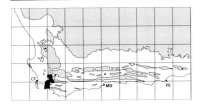

An erect, well-branched, rounded shrub with a single, stout main stem, becoming 1 m tall. *Leaves 20-30 mm long*, needle-shaped, tip with a long, fine point, hairless when mature, loosely overlapping. *Flowerhead globose to ovoid, a dense, congested raceme*, 10-25 mm across, terminal; stalkless. *Headlet 1-flowered*; stalk 1 mm long. Floral bracts 4-5 mm long, lanceolate, tip pointed, 3 fused at base and 1 free, margin fringed. *Perianth inflated at base*, 10-12 mm long, curved forward in bud, silvery pink, limbs and claws densely covered with shaggy hairs, tube 1 mm long. Style curved forward at tip, 9 mm long, slender. *Pollen presenter cylindrical-ellipsoid.*
DISTRIBUTION: Slanghoek to Hottentots-Holland Mountains. HABITAT: Peaty soils on southern slopes, 900-1250 m. STATUS: Occurring in scattered clumps of a few to a few dozen individuals. FLOWERS: October to December. FRUITS: Released after flowering.
□ VARIATION: The floral bracts of northern forms are hairy, whereas those of southern forms tend to be hairless.

***Spatalla nubicola*** Rourke                              Medusa Spoon     **Plate 55**

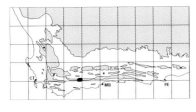

An erect to rounded shrub 1-1.5 m tall, with main stem stout, branching from 0.2 m above ground. *Leaves straight*, 10-15 mm long, needle-shaped, tip with a fine point, hairless when mature. *Flowerhead a dense raceme*, 30-40 mm long, 10-15 mm across, cylindrical, terminal; stalkless. *Headlet 1-flowered; stalkless.* Floral bracts 5 mm long, lanceolate, tip pointed, 3 fused in basal third and 1 free, margin fringed. Perianth 11 mm long, curved forward in limb region, segments equal, carmine, limbs and claws with long silvery hairs, tube 5 mm long. Style 9 mm long, thread-like. *Pollen presenter asymmetrically ovoid to pinhead-shaped.*
DISTRIBUTION: Central Langeberg at Lemoenshoek and Naaukrans Peaks. HABITAT: Upper steep, southern slopes, in peaty soils, 1600 m. STATUS: Known from only 2 highly localized populations (estimated at 5000 plants) comprising scattered individuals. *Red Data Book* status: Rare. FLOWERS: September to December. FRUITS: Released after flowering.

***Spatalla parilis*** Salisb. ex Knight                              Spike Spoon     **Plate 56**

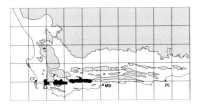

An erect, well-branched shrub with a single, stout main stem, up to 1.5 m tall. Leaves 15-20 mm long, needle-shaped, tip with a fine point, hairless when mature. Flowerhead 30-60 mm long, 10-15 mm across, cylindrical, a long narrow spike, terminal or in clusters of up to 6 per flowering branch; *stalkless. Headlet 1-flowered; stalk 2-3 mm long. Floral bracts narrowly lanceolate, tip tapering to a narrow point, 4-6 mm long, 3 fused at base and 1 free.* Perianth 9-10 mm long, strongly curved forward in bud, segments unequal, 1 helmet-shaped, limbs and claws with long hairs, tube 2-3 mm long. Style straight, 6-7 mm long, erect. Pollen presenter an asymmetrically obovoid, ear-like disc.
DISTRIBUTION: Hottentots-Holland to Riviersonderend Mountains to Langeberg at Gouritz River. HABITAT: Cool, southern slopes in peaty soils, 300-1550 m. STATUS: Rare in the west, small scattered colonies are more common in the east. FLOWERS: All year round. FRUITS: Released after flowering.

**Spatalla barbigera** Salisb. ex Knight                 Fine-leaf Spoon   **Plate 56**

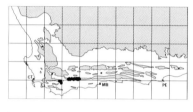

An erect, rounded shrub up to 0.8 m tall with a single, stout stem, branching at 0.2 m. *Leaves with permanent, downy hairs*, 14-16 mm long, needle-shaped, tip with a fine point, curved inwards. Flowerhead 20-40 mm long, 10-20 mm across, narrowly cylindrical, terminal or in clusters of up to 5 per branch; stalkless. *Headlet 1-flowered; stalk 0-1 mm long. Floral bracts lanceolate, tip pointed, with downy hairs*, 5 mm long,
3 fused in basal third and 1 free. *Perianth creamy yellow*, 7-9 mm long, strongly curved in bud, segments unequal, 1 helmet-shaped, with long hairs, tube 1.5 mm long. Style curved at top, 6 mm long. Pollen presenter an asymmetrically obovoid, ear-like disc.
DISTRIBUTION: A unique pattern, from eastern Langeberg to Outeniqua Mountains and Klein and Groot Swartberg. HABITAT: Varied, 400-620 m. STATUS: Scattered clumps containing a few plants. *Red Data Book* status: Rare. FLOWERS: May to November. FRUITS: Released after flowering.

**Spatalla colorata** Meisn.                 Shiny Spoon   **Plate 56**

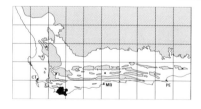

An erect, sparsely branched shrublet up to 0.8 m tall, with a single main stem. *Leaves hairless when mature*, 7-15 mm long, needle-shaped, tip with a fine point. *Flowerhead up to 15 mm long, 10 mm across*, rounded to cylindrical, terminal, solitary; stalkless. *Headlet 1-flowered, hairless, red to carmine, shiny*; stalk shorter than 1 mm. *Floral bracts 3-4 mm long, lanceolate, tip pointed, hairless*, margin fringed with
long hairs, 3 fused in basal third and 1 free. Perianth 8-9 mm long, strongly curved in bud, carmine, segments unequal, 1 helmet-shaped and more densely woolly than others, tube 1 mm long. Style curved forward at tip, 7 mm long, thread-like, arising from back of ovary. Pollen presenter an asymmetrically obovoid, ear-like disc.
DISTRIBUTION: Riviersonderend Mountains to central Langeberg at Lemoenshoek. HABITAT: Cool, southern slopes, 900-1400 m. STATUS: Never common in any area, it is found as scattered individuals in low numbers. *Red Data Book* status: Rare. FLOWERS: July to November. FRUITS: Released after flowering.

**Spatalla squamata** Meisn.                 Silky Spoon   **Plate 56**

A small, much-branched, rounded shrub up to 0.5 m tall, with a single, stout main stem. Leaves 5-12 mm long, linear, needle-shaped, tip with a fine point, hairless, slightly curved inwards. Flowerhead 20-30 mm long, 10 mm across, cylindrical to globose, solitary; *stalkless. Headlet 1-flowered, hairless; stalkless. Floral bracts hairless, fused to form a distinct upper and lower lip around the headlet*, 5-7 mm long, 4 mm wide,
ovate, tip pointed; *after flowering floral bracts enlarge considerably and turn carmine, persisting through summer.* Perianth 8 mm long, densely covered with long hairs, limbs curved at right angles to claws, *inner surface of claws densely covered with crispy hairs*, carmine, segments unequal, 1 helmet-shaped, tube 1-1.5 mm long. Style curved forward at tip, 7-8 mm long. Pollen presenter an asymmetrically obovoid, ear-like disc.
DISTRIBUTION: Agulhas Plain. HABITAT: Sandstone sands and hills, 30-460 m. STATUS: Occurring as scattered individuals. FLOWERS: August to October. FRUITS: Released after flowering.

***Spatalla ericoides*** E. Phillips                                          Erica-leaf Spoon          **Plate 56**

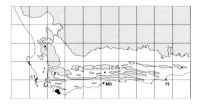

An erect, rounded, laxly branched shrub up to 0.8 m tall, with a single, slender main stem. Leaves 7-12 mm long, needle-shaped with a flattened upper surface, round-tipped, hairless when mature, slightly curved inwards. Flowerhead up to 30 mm long, 15 mm across, cylindrical, a dense raceme, solitary, terminal; *stalkless. Headlet 1-flowered; stalkless. Floral bracts densely covered with silky hairs, red to carmine, not enlarging after flowering, 3 fused in basal two-thirds and 1 free, forming a distinct upper and lower lip,* 6 mm long, ovate, tip pointed. Perianth 10 mm long, silvery pink, curved in bud, segments unequal, 1 helmet-shaped, *sparsely covered with crispy hairs,* tube 1 mm long. Style curved forward at tip, 7 mm long. Pollen presenter an asymmetrically obovoid, ear-like disc, pink.
DISTRIBUTION: Agulhas Plain at Hagelkraal and Klein Hagelkraal. HABITAT: Limestone sands, 10-250 m. STATUS: *Red Data Book* status recently downgraded from Endangered to Vulnerable. Known from 2 localities of 500 plants. FLOWERS: August to October. FRUITS: Released after flowering.

***Spatalla longifolia*** Salisb. ex Knight                                   Pink-stalked Spoon        **Plate 57**

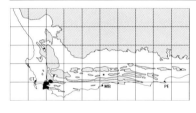

An erect, rounded, rigid shrub up to 1 m tall, with a single, stout main stem, branching at 0.2 m. *Leaves 25-45 mm long, needle-shaped with a channelled upper surface, turning black a few days after collection,* narrowing to a slender stalk, tip with a fine point, hairless when mature. Flowerhead 30-100 mm long, 15 mm across, a cylindrical raceme, terminal, solitary; *stalk 20-30 mm long.* Headlet 1-flowered, with silky, straight hairs; stalk 4-5 mm long. *Involucral bract needle-shaped, 8-15 mm long. Floral bracts lanceolate, 3 mm long, 3 fused in lower third* and 1 free, margin fringed. Perianth 8-9 mm long, greyish pink, segments unequal, 1 helmet-shaped and spreading forward, limbs and claws densely covered with shaggy hairs, *claws carmine and swollen on inner surface,* tube 1 mm long. Style curved forward at tip, 6 mm long. Pollen presenter an asymmetrically obovoid, ear-like disc. DISTRIBUTION: Hottentots-Holland Mountains from Franschhoek and Villiersdorp to Kleinmond Mountains. HABITAT: Rocky slopes with sandstone sands, 300-915 m. STATUS: Almost always found as solitary plants in loose associations that seldom number more than a dozen plants. FLOWERS: August to November. FRUITS: Released after flowering.

***Spatalla curvifolia*** Salisb. ex Knight                                   White-stalked Spoon       **Plate 57**

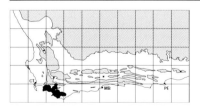

A low, rounded, much-branched shrublet up to 0.8 m tall. *Leaves 25-50 mm long, needle-shaped with a channelled upper surface, narrowing to a slender stalk,* tip with a fine, blunt point, strongly to weakly curved inward. Flowerhead 30-70 mm long, 10-15 mm across, a dense, many-flowered raceme, terminal or axillary; *stalk 10-70 mm long.* Headlet 1-flowered; stalked. *Involucral bract needle-like, 2-11 mm long.* Floral bracts 3-4 mm long, ovate, tip pointed, with silky, straight hairs, *3 fused entirely and 1 fused only at base,* forming an upper and lower lip, tightly clasping the perianth. Perianth 7-9 mm long, curved forward, creamy white or pale yellow, segments unequal, 1 helmet-shaped, others with *fleshy, red swellings at base of claws,* limbs and claws with shaggy hairs, claws red, tube

1-1.5 mm long. Style straight, slightly flattened, 7 mm long, slender. Pollen presenter an asymmetrically obovoid, ear-like disc, deep purple. Fruits develop within enlarged floral bracts. DISTRIBUTION: Kogelberg to Babylonstoring and Bredasdorp Mountains and flats seaward of these, with isolated populations on the Riviersonderend Mountains at Genadendal and Caledon Swartberg. HABITAT: Sandstone soils, sandy or rocky slopes, 0-350 m. STATUS: The most frequently encountered member of the genus. A social plant occurring abundantly in small clumps of a few dozen plants. FLOWERS: All year round, with new flowerheads continuously developing below older ones, as in *S. parilis.* FRUITS: Released after flowering.

☐ VARIATIONS: Flowerhead stalks are very much shorter in the east (5-35 mm long) than in the west (30-75 mm long). Leaves sometimes vary from strongly curved inwards to straight within a single population.

**Spatalla racemosa** (L.) Druce                    Lax-stalked Spoon    **Plate 57**

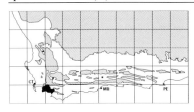

A small, slender, laxly branched shrublet up to 0.5 m tall, with a single main stem. Leaves 15-35 mm long, needle-shaped with a channelled upper surface, tip with a fine point, narrowing to a slender stalk. *Flowerhead small, 10-30 mm long, a lax cylindrical raceme*; stalk 10 mm long. Headlet 1-flowered, with silky, straight hairs; stalk 4-5 mm long. *Involucral bract awl-shaped, 1-2 mm long. Floral bracts 3 fused in basal two-thirds* and 1 free, 2-3 mm long, ovate, tip pointed, with silky, straight hairs. Perianth 7 mm long, strongly curved forward in bud, segments unequal, 1 helmet-shaped, limbs and claws with long hairs, tube 2 mm long, greyish pink. Style straight, 5 mm long, laterally compressed and slightly channelled above. Pollen presenter an asymmetrically obovoid, ear-like disc. *Fruits 7 mm long, narrowly cylindrical, visibly protruding beyond floral bracts that are not swollen.* DISTRIBUTION: Kogelberg to Groenland to Babylonstoring and to Klein River Mountains, with a record from near Villiersdorp. HABITAT: Sandstone soils, stony, sandy flats, 150-620 m. STATUS: Very common locally, occurring in scattered populations of a few hundred plants. FLOWERS: September to March. FRUITS: Released after flowering.

**Spatalla mollis** R. Br.                    Woolly Spoon    **Plate 57**

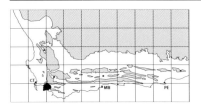

An erect, rounded, much-branched shrub up to 0.8 m tall, branching from a single stem near the base. Leaves 15-20 mm long, needle-shaped, tip with a fine, blunt point, hairless when mature. Flowerhead 30-40 mm long, 10 mm across, cylindrical, terminal; stalkless to almost stalkless. Headlet 1-flowered; stalk 1-2 mm long. Floral bracts 2 mm long, 3 in number, *2 fused in basal half to form a lip*, with silky, straight hairs. Perianth 7-9 mm long, strongly curved forward in bud, segments unequal, 1 helmet-shaped, densely covered with woolly hairs, white or mauve. *Style hairy on basal third*, straight, 5 mm long. Pollen presenter an asymmetrically obovoid, ear-like disc.
DISTRIBUTION: Hottentots-Holland and Groenland to Kleinmond Mountains.
HABITAT: Montane on riverine peaty soils, 450-920 m. STATUS: Almost always encountered as scattered colonies of a few dozen plants. FLOWERS: July to December. FRUITS: Released after flowering.

## *Spatalla* The Triplespoons

The Triplespoons (section *Cyrtostigma*) bear *3 flowers per headlet* and are thus more closely related to the clusterheads than the Unispoons are. They occur north of the Riviersonderend River in the west and on the Swartberg and Kammanassie Mountains in the east.

Two groups can be distinguished by using a hand lens:
□ Pollen presenter helmet-shaped and perianth segments unequal .........................................
............................................................................................... *S. argentea, S. propinqua*
□ Pollen presenter ovoid, with style bent at right angles near the tip .........................................
.......................................... *S. tulbaghensis, S. caudata, S. confusa, S. thyrsiflora, S. incurva*

Of the latter group, only *S. incurva* has unequal perianth segments. Leaf hairiness, the presence of a short shoot or lump below the extra floral bract, and the shape of the flowerheads can be used to distinguish between the other species.

**Spatalla tulbaghensis** (E. Phillips) Rourke                    Shaggy-hair Spoon    **Plate 58**

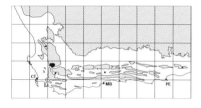

*A low, much-branched, rounded shrub* with a single main stem, up to 0.5 m tall. *Leaves needle-shaped with a flattened or slightly concave upper surface, margin with long hairs,* 8-15 mm long, linear. *Flowerhead 10-20 mm across, globose,* terminal, solitary or in a cluster of up to 6 per branch; stalkless to almost stalkless. *Headlet 3-flowered;* stalk 1 mm long. Floral bracts 5 mm long, 1.5 mm wide, lanceolate, margin fringed. Perianth 10 mm long, curved in bud, segments equal, limbs hairy, claws with long thick hairs, tube 5 mm long. Style curved forwards at tip, 7-8 mm long. Pollen presenter conical-oblong.
DISTRIBUTION: Witsenbergvlakte and Skurweberg Pass. HABITAT: Moist, coarsely sandy soils on flats, 910 m. STATUS: *Red Data Book* status: Endangered, owing to agriculture. Currently known from 2 populations of less than 100 plants, which form small, dense, isolated stands.
FLOWERS: September to December. FRUITS: Released after flowering.

**Spatalla caudata** (Thunb.) R. Br.                    Woolly-hair Spoon    **Plate 58**

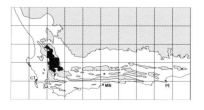

*An erect shrub with long, erect, straight stems,* up to 1 m tall, arising from a single stout main trunk. *Leaves with sparse hairs on upper surface,* 8-18 mm long, linear, needle-like with a concave upper surface. *Flowerhead 50-60 mm long (occasionally 70 mm), a cylindrical raceme,* stalkless, terminal, often with 2 or 3 extra flowerheads arising immediately below; stalkless. Headlet 3-flowered; stalk 1 mm long. Floral bracts 5 mm long, upper 3 lanceolate with a pointed tip, lower 1 lanceolate-linear, with shaggy hairs. *Perianth densely covered with woolly to shaggy hairs,* 10 mm long, carmine, curved in bud, segments equal, limbs curved at right angles to claws, *tube 4-5 mm long.* Style thread-like, curved forward at tip, 8 mm long. Pollen presenter asymmetrically ovoid with a conical tip.

DISTRIBUTION: Cederberg to Groot Winterhoek to Hex River Mountains. HABITAT: Sandstone sands along streams or seeps, 910-1250 m. STATUS: Frequently encountered as dense, isolated stands. FLOWERS: August to October. FRUITS: Released after flowering.

*Spatalla confusa* (E. Phillips) Rourke                    Long-tube Spoon     **Plate 58**

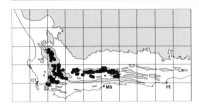

*A low, spreading, creeping to almost erect shrub* 0.5-1 m tall, forming mats 1-1.5 m across. *Leaves hairless when mature,* 6-14 mm long, linear, needle-like with a flattened or grooved upper surface, tip with a fine, blunt point, bright green with a red or orange tint. *Flowerhead 10-25 mm long,* 10 mm across, a lax raceme, terminal; stalkless to almost stalkless. Headlet 3-flowered; stalk 1 mm long. *Floral bracts hairless,* 4-7 mm long, lanceolate, tip with a short point or tapering to a narrow point, clasping perianth at base. *Perianth with thin hairs on claws,* 8 mm long, curved forward in bud, segments equal, silvery hairs on limbs, pink, *tube 4-5 mm long.* Style curved forward at tip, 6-7 mm long, arising from back of ovary. Pollen presenter asymmetrically ovoid with a conical tip.

DISTRIBUTION: The most widespread *Spatalla* species, occurring from the Cederberg to Hottentots-Holland Mountains and to the Swartberg and Kammanassie Mountains, Touwsberg and Rooiberg. Absent from the Langeberg and Outeniqua Mountains. HABITAT: Rock crevices on summits, 1350-2300 m. STATUS: Isolated stands. FLOWERS: August to March, mainly November and December. FRUITS: Released after flowering.

□ VARIATIONS: A more erect form occurs in the west. The foliage of forms on northern slopes is always tinted carmine.

*Spatalla thyrsiflora* Salisb. ex Knight                    Swan-neck Spoon     **Plate 58**

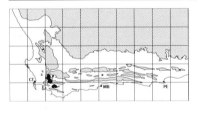

*A sprawling shrub with a rootstock and stems trailing to form mats* 1.5 m across. Leaves 15-30 mm long, needle-shaped, tip with a fine point, hairless, slightly curved inwards. Flowerhead 20-40 mm long, 15 mm across, ovoid-cylindrical, terminal, lax; stalked to stalkless. *Headlet 3-flowered; stalk 2 mm long,* with shaggy hairs. *Flowerless floral bract subtending a branching shoot,* 5-6 mm long, 1.5 mm wide, lanceolate, green tipped with carmine, median floral bract flattened. Perianth 12-14 mm long, curved forward in bud, segments equal, limbs woolly and at right angles to claws, claws with shaggy hairs, tube 1.5 mm long. *Style arched like a swan's neck,* 10-11 mm long. *Pollen presenter ovoid with a conical tip, black.*

DISTRIBUTION: Du Toit's Kloof and Stettyns Mountains, and Caledon Swartberg. HABITAT: Sandstone and granite soils, montane, 900-1550 m. STATUS: Occurring in dense, isolated populations. The Caledon Swartberg population has not been relocated since the early 1800s. FLOWERS: August to December. FRUITS: Released after flowering.

*Spatalla incurva* (Thunb.) R. Br.                    Swan-head Spoon     **Plate 59**

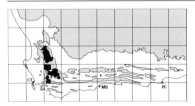

An erect to spreading, well-branched shrub, with a single, stout main stem, becoming 1 m tall. *Branches densely covered with crispy hairs. Leaves needle-shaped, tip with a fine point,* 7-18 mm long, slightly curved inwards, hairless or with sparse, downy hairs. Flowerhead 40 mm long, 15 mm across, terminal; stalk 0-10 mm long. *Headlet 3-flowered; stalk 1-4 mm*

*long.* Floral bracts 3 mm long, 2 mm wide, ovate, tip pointed or tapering to a narrow point; flowerless floral bract subtending a reduced shoot. Perianth 7-8 mm long, curved forward in bud, pale pink to carmine, limbs hairy and unequal, claws with shaggy hairs, tube 2 mm long. *Style straight at base, curved at right angles near tip*, 6 mm long. *Pollen presenter asymmetrically obovoid. Fruits hairy.*
DISTRIBUTION: Cederberg to Du Toit's Kloof Mountains and Keeromsberg. HABITAT: Dry, rocky slopes, sandstone sands, 1200-2500 m. STATUS: Common and frequently encountered. FLOWERS: September to March. FRUITS: Released after flowering.

### *Spatalla argentea* Rourke         Silver-leaf Spoon    **Plate 59**

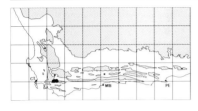

An erect, well-branched shrub up to 0.8 m tall, with a single main stem branching at 0.2 m. *Leaves silvery, densely covered with downy hairs*, 10-15 mm long, needle-shaped, tip with a fine point, slightly incurving. Flowerhead 20-30 mm long, 15 mm across, terminal, solitary or in clusters of up to 4 per shoot; stalkless. Headlet 3-flowered; stalk 2-3 mm long. Floral bracts 4 mm long, 2 mm wide, broadly ovate, tip pointed, densely covered with silky, straight hairs, margin fringed; flowerless floral bract subtending a reduced shoot. *Perianth with 1 segment large and helmet-shaped*, 8 mm long, strongly curved in bud, limbs and claws densely covered with shaggy hairs, silvery pink, tube 1.5 mm long. Style straight, 6 mm long. *Pollen presenter an asymmetrically obovoid, ear-like disc, black.*
DISTRIBUTION: Wolfieskop to Jonaskop in the Riviersonderend Mountains. HABITAT: Sandy patches among boulders on dry, northern slopes, 475-1350 m. STATUS: Scattered isolated individuals occur in several populations estimated at 1000 plants, usually in association with *Leucadendron nervosum. Red Data Book* status: Rare. FLOWERS: October to January. FRUITS: Released after flowering.

### *Spatalla propinqua* R. Br.         Lax Spoon    **Plate 59**

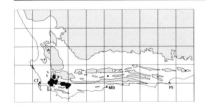

An erect shrub up to 1 m tall, with a single, stout main stem. *Leaves hairless when mature*, 15-25 mm long, needle-shaped, occasionally with upper surface channelled, with a fine point 1 mm long at tip. *Flowerhead narrowly cylindrical to conical, long and slender, 10-30 mm long, 10 mm across*, lax, terminal or in clusters of up to 5 flowerheads arising around a stalk 10-30 mm long. *Headlet 3-flowered*; stalk with shaggy hairs. Floral bracts 3-5 mm long, ovate, tip tapering to a narrow point, with shaggy hairs, margin densely fringed; flowerless floral bract smaller, subtending an abortive shoot. Perianth 8 mm long, pink, *1 segment larger and helmet-shaped*, limbs and claws densely covered with shaggy hairs, *tube with shaggy hairs*, 1 mm long. Style straight at base, strongly curved at tip, 6-7 mm long. *Pollen presenter an asymmetrically obovoid, ear-like disc, dark. Fruits hairless or with minute hairs at base.*
DISTRIBUTION: Slanghoek to Hottentots-Holland and Riviersonderend Mountains.
HABITAT: Swampy, cool, southern slopes, 200-620 m. STATUS: Known from about 10 populations estimated to contain 2000 plants, and encountered as isolated patches of less than a few dozen plants. *Red Data Book* status: Rare. FLOWERS: June to March. FRUITS: Released after flowering.

## *LEUCOSPERMUM* R. Br.  **The Pincushions**

The genus *Leucospermum* is most easily identified by the long styles that protrude from the flowerhead, creating the impression of a pincushion. *The flowerheads are axillary, never terminal, and the involucral bracts are small and inconspicuous.* The 3 outer perianth segments are partly fused to form a tube at the bottom of the flower, while the fourth segment is mostly free and often elongated. *The leaves sometimes have many glandular teeth at their tip.* The exact function of these is unknown, although they may be nectaries. Virtually all Proteaceae with more than 3 glandular teeth on the leaves belong to the genus *Leucospermum*. The hairs on the leaves are of 2 types: long, thin hairs (trichomes) which occur in all other local Proteaceae genera, and short, curly hairs which are confined to pincushions. These curly hairs give the leaves the appearance of being covered by a thin layer of white or grey wool and can be rubbed off.

Care is needed to distinguish species of *Leucospermum* from those of *Diastella* and *Vexatorella*, but the axillary flowerheads, inconspicuous involucral bracts and the partly fused 3 outer perianth segments are unique to the pincushions. All *Leucospermum* species, with the exception of those in the Flat, Louse and Sandveld groupings, have large flowerheads which cannot be confused with those of either *Diastella* or *Vexatorella* species.

The *Leucospermum* sections fall into 4 major groupings which are easily recognized:

☐ Large, bird-pollinated flowerheads, with all 4 perianth lobes fused at the tips below the anthers ........................ Cylindrical, Tree, Wide-tubed, Showy and Fireworks Pincushions

☐ Medium-sized, yellow, insect- or mammal-pollinated flowerheads, with 3 perianth lobes fused below the anthers and 1 free ............................... Sandveld and Hook Pincushions

☐ Small, insect-pollinated flowerheads. The 4 perianth lobes are usually free at the tips and curl back to resemble 4 small lice ......................................................... Louse Pincushions

☐ Flat-topped flowerheads, pollinated by both insects and birds. The perianth does not curl back after opening .......................................................................... Flat Pincushions

The pollen presenters, the leaf shape and number of glandular teeth at the leaf tips, the involucral bracts and the plant's growth form are most often used to distinguish between the different species. With experience, most pincushions can be identified by their leaves alone.

## A QUICK KEY TO THE PINCUSHIONS

### STYLE LONGER THAN 35 MM

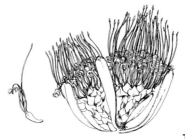

**The Cylindrical Pincushions** (Page 132, Plate 60)
Plant multi-stemmed, with a rootstock
Involucral receptacle cylindrical, with rounded tip
Includes all non-Cape species

**The Wide-tubed Pincushions**
(Page 136, Plate 62)
Involucral receptacle conical or conical-flattened
Perianth tube narrow at base and widening towards the tip

**The Fireworks Pincushions**
(Page 142, Plate 66)
Style longer than 50 mm
Stigma curved or bending downwards on opening
Involucral receptacle narrowly conical, with a pointed tip

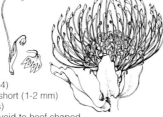

**The Showy Pincushions**
(Page 139, Plate 64)
Anthers borne on short (1-2 mm) filaments (10x lens)
Pollen presenter ovoid to hoof-shaped

**The Tree Pincushions**
(Page 134, Plate 61)
Tree-like habit, with a thick basal trunk
Leaves with about 10 glandular teeth
Pollen presenter conical with a sharp tip

### STYLE SHORTER THAN 35 MM

**The Hook Pincushions**
(Page 152, Plate 72)
Flowerhead very small, with 4 to 12 flowers
Style recurved, with knob at tip

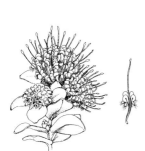

**The Flat Pincushions**
(Page 153, Plate 73)
Involucral receptacle flat
Flowerhead turban-shaped
Style thread-like

**The Louse Pincushions**
(Page 148, Plate 70)
Leaves usually with a single glandular tooth at tip
Flowerheads small and globose, often in clusters of 2 to 6
Perianth segments separate at tip and curl back to form 4 small 'lice' around each style

**The Sandveld Pincushions**
(Page 145, Plate 68)
Leaves densely covered with a greyish layer of fine hairs
Flowers straight in bud, bright yellow
Perianth with 3 segments fused and 1 free

## *Leucospermum* The Cylindrical Pincushions

The Cylindrical Pincushions (section *Crassicaudex*) are characterized by the *cylindrical shape of the involucral receptacle*. They include all the summer-rainfall and tropical species, as well as the widespread *L. cuneiforme* from the Cape. All species are erect, multi-stemmed shrubs with a woody underground rootstock and with variable, wedge-shaped leaves.

***Leucospermum saxosum*** S. Moore     Escarpment Pincushion     **Plate 60**

A multi-stemmed shrub up to 2 m tall, with a rootstock. *Leaves oblanceolate or wedge-shaped to elliptic, base narrow to stalked, with 3-6 glandular teeth*, 55-115 mm long, 6-25 mm wide. Flowerhead usually solitary, 40-60 mm across; stalk 10-15 mm long. Perianth 30-35 mm long, yellow-orange but red when mature, *tube funnel-shaped and 6 mm long.* Style 45-55 mm long, orange but red when mature. *Pollen presenter narrowly conical, tip pointed, scarcely distinct from style.*
DISTRIBUTION: Chimanimani Mountains and Drakensberg escarpment from Tzaneen to Pilgrim's Rest in Northern Province and Mpumalanga. HABITAT: Quartzite soils on rocky slopes, 1300-2350 m. STATUS: Poorly known, but well collected on Chimanimani Mountains; known from only 2 locations in Northern Province/ Mpumalanga. *Red Data Book* status: Rare in Northern Province/Mpumalanga. FLOWERS: All year round, mainly September to December. FRUITS: Released 1-2 months after flowering.

***Leucospermum cuneiforme*** (Burm. f.) Rourke     Wart-stemmed Pincushion     **Plate 60**

Uniquely distinguished by the *warts and pustules present on the bases of the stems arising from the underground rootstock.* Occasional specimens reach a height of 3 m. *Leaves generally wedge-shaped* but variable, 45-110 mm long, 6-30 mm wide, with 3-10 glandular teeth. Flowerhead ovoid, 50-90 mm across; stalk 15 mm long. Perianth 25-40 mm long. Style 38-55 mm long, yellow but orange when mature. Pollen presenter conical with a pointed tip to broadly conical.
DISTRIBUTION: Riviersonderend Mountains, Langeberg, Outeniqua Mountains, to Qolora in the Eastern Cape; isolated populations occur on the Potberg and central Swartberg. HABITAT: Varied, 0-1200 m. STATUS: Usually encountered as a few scattered plants. FLOWERS: All year round, with a peak from August to February. FRUITS: Released 1-2 months after flowering.
☐ VARIATIONS: A very variable species (an amalgamation of what were previously 5 separate species). Growth form varies from a prostrate dwarf shrub to a tall shrub. The leaf and flowerhead also vary considerably in size. Local forms may occur, but as these grade into each other from east to west they have not been formally recognized. For example, leaf width increases from east (6-22 mm) to west (12-30 mm), with more glandular teeth on the wider leaves.

*Leucospermum innovans* Rourke                    Pondoland Pincushion    **Plate 60**

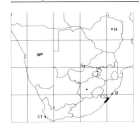

An erect, multi-stemmed shrub up to 1 m tall, with *slender (5 mm in diameter) stems. Leaves very broadly wedge-shaped to obovate, with a distinct stalk,* 70-100 mm long, 30-50 mm wide, with 5-10 glandular teeth. Flowerhead globose, 80-90 mm across; stalk 15 mm long. *Perianth tube swollen at base but narrow at the top,* 10-12 mm long, yellow. Style 50 mm long, very slender, yellow. Pollen presenter narrowly conical, tip pointed.
DISTRIBUTION: Subtropical coastal belt of Eastern Cape and KwaZulu-Natal between Lusikisiki and Port Shepstone.
HABITAT: Pondoland sourveld, rocky sandstone soils, 0-250 m. STATUS: Occurs in isolated patches of a few plants. *Red Data Book* status: Vulnerable. FLOWERS: July to December, mainly September and October. FRUITS: Released 1-2 months after flowering.

*Leucospermum gerrardii* Stapf                    Soapstone Pincushion    **Plate 60**

*A dwarf shrub with underground stems in addition to a woody rootstock, and with erect stems seldom taller than 0.4 m, giving a cushion-like appearance. Leaves linear to oblanceolate, with raised veins,* 50-90 mm long, 8-20 mm wide, with 1-4 glandular teeth. Flowerhead ovoid, 40-70 mm across; stalk 10-20 mm long. Perianth 30-35 mm long, yellow but orange to scarlet when mature. Style 50 mm long, yellow. Pollen presenter narrowly conical, tip pointed.
DISTRIBUTION: Barberton and Carolina in Mpumalanga, Swaziland escarpment and central KwaZulu-Natal lowlands at Mapumulo, Ndwedwe and New Hanover. HABITAT: Grassland, 1300-2000 m. STATUS: Northern populations may be quite extensive, but southern populations are typically isolated and scattered. FLOWERS: All year, mainly September to November. FRUITS: Released 1-2 months after flowering.
□ VARIATION: The leaves of lowland forms are broader (15-20 mm) than those of escarpment forms (8-16 mm).

## *Leucospermum* The Tree Pincushions

The Tree Pincushions (section *Conocarpodendron*) are characterized by their *tree-like habit*, reaching heights of 4 m, with *a single, thick, basal trunk.* The involucral receptacle is conical to narrowly conical with a pointed tip and bears stout, rigid styles 50-60 mm long, with a *conical pollen presenter ending in a sharp tip.* The involucral bracts have a long, narrow point that is sometimes recurved.

*Leucospermum conocarpodendron* (L.) H. Buek subsp. *conocarpodendron*

Grey Tree Pincushion     **Plate 61**

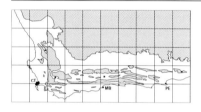

*A large, rounded shrub or tree, 3-5 m tall,* 3-6 m across. Trunk single, stout, 150-400 mm in diameter, bark 30-50 mm thick. Mature stems densely covered with thick hairs. *Leaves with a dense layer of minute woolly hairs, grey-silver,* sparsely interspersed with long, straight hairs, variable in shape, 60-115 mm long, 25-50 mm wide, rounded to pointed with 3-10 glandular teeth; stalkless. Flowerhead globose to ovoid, 70-90 mm across, usually borne in groups of up to 3; stalk 15 mm long. *Involucral bracts ovate, tip tapering to a narrow point.* Perianth 35-50 mm long, yellow. Style 45-55 mm long, stout. *Pollen presenter broadly conical, tip pointed.*
DISTRIBUTION: Northern Cape Peninsula from Devil's Peak to Llandudno. HABITAT: Granite and sandstone soils, dry slopes facing north and west, 0-160 m. STATUS: Locally abundant, dominating plant communities. FLOWERS: August to December. FRUITS: Released 1-2 months after flowering.

*Leucospermum conocarpodendron* subsp. *viridum* Rourke     Green Tree Pincushion     **Plate 61**

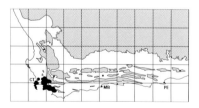

*A large, rounded shrub or tree, 3-5 m tall,* 3-6 m across. Trunk single, stout, 150-400 mm in diameter, bark 30-50 mm thick. Mature stems densely covered with thick hairs. *Leaves deep green when mature, without minute, woolly hairs (occasionally with edges hairy),* variable in shape, 60-115 mm long, 25-50 mm wide, rounded to pointed, with 3-10 glandular teeth; stalkless. Flowerhead globose to ovoid, 70-90 mm across, usually borne in groups of up to 3; stalk 15 mm long. *Involucral bracts ovate, tip tapering to a narrow point.* Perianth 35-50 mm long, yellow. Style 45-55 mm long, stout. *Pollen presenter broadly conical, tip pointed.*
DISTRIBUTION: Cape Peninsula, Cape Flats (Kanonberg), Hottentots-Holland to Franschhoek Mountains, Kogelberg, Kleinmond, Babylonstoring and Klein River Mountains to Stanford. HABITAT: Varied, 0-350 m. STATUS: Usually encountered in stands of several dozen plants dominating the landscape, less frequently as isolated plants. FLOWERS: August to December. FRUITS: Released 1-2 months after flowering.
☐ VARIATIONS: The leaf size and number of glandular teeth vary widely within populations.

*Leucospermum glabrum* E. Phillips          Outeniqua Pincushion    **Plate 61**

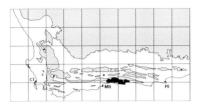

An erect, rounded shrub 2.5 m tall. Trunk single, 100 mm in diameter. *Mature stems hairless. Leaves hairless, obovate to broadly obovate, with 7-14 glandular teeth*, 80-120 mm long, 30-50 mm wide; *almost stalkless.* Flowerhead ovoid, 70-90 mm across; almost stalkless. *Involucral bracts with recurved tips tapering to a narrow point.* Perianth 35 mm long, bright orange to carmine. Style 50-60 mm long, stout. Pollen presenter conical, tip pointed.
DISTRIBUTION: Outeniqua and Tsitsikamma Mountains. HABITAT: Cool, southern slopes on peaty soils, 150-500 m. STATUS: Infrequently encountered as isolated populations.
FLOWERS: August to October. FRUITS: Released 1-2 months after flowering.

*Leucospermum pluridens* Rourke          Robinson Pincushion    **Plate 61**

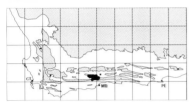

An erect, tree-like shrub up to 3 m tall. Trunk stout, woody, up to 200 mm in diameter. *Mature stems densely covered with crispy hairs. Leaves with 7-10 prominent glandular teeth, often deeply incised,* hairless or hairy, oblong to wedge-shaped, 55-100 mm long, 20-35 mm wide. Flowerhead ovoid, 80 mm long, 60 mm wide, usually borne singly; almost stalkless. *Involucral bracts tapering to very long (20 mm), recurved tips.* Perianth yellow but carmine when mature, tube 10 mm long and cylindrical. Style 55-60 mm long, stout. Pollen presenter conical, tip pointed, lower half orange, upper half yellow.
DISTRIBUTION: Outeniqua Mountains, Rooiberg and Gamkaberg. HABITAT: Northern foothills at the arid fynbos margin, 520-1200 m. STATUS: Restricted to a few localities where it is never abundant. *Red Data Book* status: Vulnerable, as its habitat is threatened by too-frequent burning and ploughing. FLOWERS: September to December. FRUITS: Released 1-2 months after flowering.

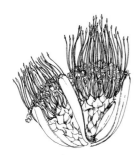

## *Leucospermum* The Wide-tubed Pincushions

The Wide-tubed Pincushions (section *Tumiditubus*) are characterized by their *conical or conical-flattened involucral receptacle, with a perianth tube that is narrow at the base and widens towards the upper end.* All species are erect or sprawling shrubs with a single main stem.

The leaf shape and number of glandular teeth, the shape of the pollen presenter and length of the style are used to distinguish between the species of Wide-tubed Pincushions. On the basis of habitat they can be divided into 2 subgroups:
☐ On Recent sands and limestones .............. *L. fulgens, L. muirii, L. praecox, L. truncatum*
☐ On sandstone mountains ..... *L. erubescens, L. profugum, L. spathulatum, L. utriculosum*

### *Leucospermum praecox* Rourke                    Mossel Bay Pincushion    **Plate 62**

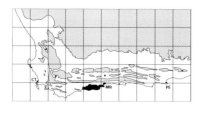

An erect, rounded shrub 2-3 m tall, up to 4 m across. Trunk up to 80 mm in diameter. *Leaves obovate to wedge-shaped, with 5-11 pointed, glandular teeth,* hairless, 35-70 mm long, 15-30 mm wide. Flowerhead 60 mm across, globose, in clusters of up to 4. *Perianth with short hairs,* 30 mm long, tube 6-8 mm long, yellow but orange when mature. *Style 38-48 mm long,* pale yellow but orange when mature, bending inwards. *Pollen presenter narrowly conical, tip pointed.*
DISTRIBUTION: Riversdale Flats from Puntjie to Mossel Bay. HABITAT: Tertiary and sandstone sands on flats, 0-250 m. STATUS: Locally abundant over large areas where it creates superb floral displays. *Red Data Book* status: Vulnerable, as its habitat is rapidly being ploughed up. FLOWERS: April to September. FRUITS: Released 1-2 months after flowering.

### *Leucospermum fulgens* Rourke                    Potberg Pincushion    **Plate 62**

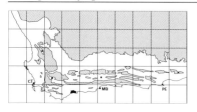

An erect, rounded shrub up to 3 m tall, up to 4 m across. Trunk up to 100 mm in diameter. *Leaves oblanceolate to oblong, with 2-4 rounded, glandular teeth, hairy, hairless when mature,* 60-90 mm long, 15-20 mm wide. Flowerhead globose to ovoid, 60-80 mm across, usually solitary but occasionally in twos; stalkless. *Perianth hairless at base, with long hairs at tip,* 35-40 mm long, pink to orange but crimson when mature, tube 8-10 mm long. *Style 46-53 mm long,* straight to slightly curved. Pollen presenter narrowly conical, tip pointed.
DISTRIBUTION: Potberg between Cupido's Kraal and Elandspad. HABITAT: White Tertiary sands on hillocks south of mountain slopes, 150-170 m. STATUS: Known from several populations comprising very dense, isolated stands. *Red Data Book* status: Vulnerable, despite its occurrence within De Hoop Nature Reserve. FLOWERS: August to January. FRUITS: Released 1-2 months after flowering.

***Leucospermum truncatum*** (H. Buek ex Meisn.) Rourke        Limestone Pincushion    **Plate 62**

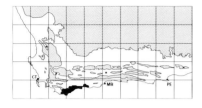

An erect, rounded shrub up to 2 m tall. *Leaves oblanceolate to narrowly wedge-shaped, 8-15 mm wide*, 45-90 mm long, ending abruptly with 3 glandular teeth, grey. Flowerhead globose, 30-40 mm across, in clusters of 2 or 3; stalk 20 mm long. *Perianth hairy*, 12-18 mm long, golden yellow but orange when mature, tube 5 mm long. *Style 18-35 mm long*, straight or slightly curved. *Pollen presenter club-shaped to cylindrical with a rounded tip.*
DISTRIBUTION: Soetanysberg near Elim to the Riversdale Flats at Vermaaklikheid.
HABITAT: Limestone soils, 0-270 m. STATUS: Usually encountered as dense isolated stands.
FLOWERS: August to December. FRUITS: Released 1-2 months after flowering.
□ VARIATIONS: A larger form with leaves up to 90 mm long, larger flowerheads and woolly-haired involucral bracts occurs in the west. Leaves in the east are more obovate and tend to resemble those of *L. praecox.*

***Leucospermum muirii*** E. Phillips        Albertinia Pincushion    **Plate 62**

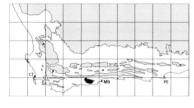

An erect, rounded shrub up to 1.5 m tall. *Leaves wedge-shaped to linear, 4-10 mm wide*, 40-60 mm long, with soft hairs, hairless when mature, with 3-7 glandular teeth. *Flowerhead 20-30 mm across, globose*, borne singly or in groups of up to 4; stalk 10-20 mm long. *Perianth with sparse, minute hairs at tip*, 12-15 mm long, pale yellow to yellow-green, tube 5 mm long. *Style 13-22 mm long*, straight.
Pollen presenter club-shaped to cylindrical, not distinct from style.
DISTRIBUTION: Albertinia Flats to Melkhoutfontein and Still Bay. HABITAT: White Tertiary sands, 90-260 m. STATUS: Small, dense stands are usually encountered. *Red Data Book* status: Rare, but deserves a higher ranking as the species is seriously threatened by agriculture.
FLOWERS: July to October. FRUITS: Released 1-2 months after flowering.

***Leucospermum erubescens*** Rourke        Oudtshoorn Pincushion    **Plate 63**

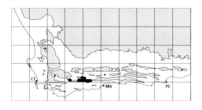

An erect shrub up to 2 m tall. Leaves oblanceolate-elliptic to oblong, 70-85 mm long, 10-20 mm wide, usually ending abruptly with 3 glandular teeth, occasionally rounded and with up to 7 glandular teeth, hairless. *Flowerhead slightly asymmetrical*, 50-65 mm across, in clusters of 4 to 8 at the tips of branches; *stalk 20-30 mm long, with a distinct junction at the head. Perianth with soft hairs at tip,*
30-35 mm long, yellow but crimson when mature, tube 10-12 mm long. Style slightly curved inwards, 40-55 mm long, yellow but crimson when mature. Pollen presenter club-shaped to cylindrical with a rounded tip.
DISTRIBUTION: Langeberg from Montagu to Brandrivier, Warmwaterberg at Warmbad.
HABITAT: Dry, rocky hills and gravel flats, 500-670 m. STATUS: Many scattered populations occur. FLOWERS: August to January. FRUITS: Released 1-2 months after flowering.

***Leucospermum utriculosum*** Rourke        Breede River Pincushion     **Plate 63**

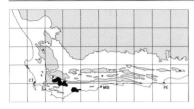

An erect to spreading, *lax shrub with horizontally spreading, interlocking branches*, 1-2 m tall, 2-3 m across. Leaves oblanceolate to wedge-shaped, 45-70 mm long, 10-20 mm wide, hairless, ending abruptly with 3-5 glandular teeth; tapering to a distinct stalk. Flowerhead 50-80 mm across, depressed-globose, usually solitary or in clusters of 3; stalk 10 mm long. *Perianth with long, silky hairs, pouched,* 27 mm long, silver, tube 7 mm long. Style curved inwards at the tip, 35-50 mm long, tapering, pale yellow. *Pollen presenter conical-ovoid.*

DISTRIBUTION: Breede River Valley from Villiersdorp to Stormsvlei; northern foothills of the Potberg. HABITAT: Dry, rocky northern slopes, 60-700 m. STATUS: Known from dense isolated stands in the north and many scattered plants in the south. FLOWERS: May to March, mainly September to November. FRUITS: Released 1-2 months after flowering.

□ VARIATIONS: Potberg forms have a yellow style and perianth and a green pollen presenter, whereas Robertson forms have an orange to copper-coloured style and perianth, a crimson pollen presenter and rusty brown hairs on the perianth tips.

***Leucospermum spathulatum*** R. Br.        Cederberg Pincushion     **Plate 63**

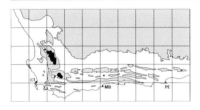

*A prostrate to sprawling shrub forming dense mats up to 3 m across,* seldom higher than 0.3 m, single-stemmed at base. *Leaves obovate to spatulate, pointing almost vertically from a horizontal stem, silvery, with soft hairs, 14-30 mm long, 7-17 mm wide, usually with a single (rarely 2 or 3) glandular teeth.* Flowerhead 50-70 mm across, depressed-globose, solitary or in twos; stalk 10 mm long.

Perianth 14 mm long, deep orange to crimson, tube 8 mm long. *Style 30-40 mm long, tip bent sharply inwards,* tapering, scarlet to crimson. Pollen presenter cylindrical, tip rounded.

DISTRIBUTION: Cederberg and Koue Bokkeveld Mountains, with an isolated population on the northwestern Langeberg. HABITAT: Dry, rocky, sandstone slopes, 1500-1850 m. STATUS: Encountered as isolated populations. FLOWERS: September to January, mainly October. FRUITS: Released 1-2 months after flowering.

***Leucospermum profugum*** Rourke        Piketberg Pincushion     **Plate 63**

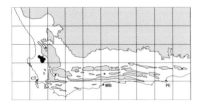

*A trailing shrub* 2-8 m across, with an *exposed woody rootstock. Leaves oblanceolate to obovate, 29-55 mm long, 6-18 mm wide, with soft hairs, hairless when mature, tip rounded to ending abruptly with 3 or 4 glandular teeth,* usually pointing vertically from a horizontal stem. Flowerhead solitary, 90-120 mm across, depressed-ovoid; stalk 30-35 mm long. Perianth 35-40 mm long, yellow-orange but reddish orange or salmon-pink when mature, *tube with a 15-mm pouch.* Style curved inwards, *45-62 mm long,* tapering. Pollen presenter narrowly ovoid to conical, tip pointed.

DISTRIBUTION: Piketberg from Versveld Pass to Aurora. HABITAT: Well-drained, sandstone soils, 400-850 m. STATUS: Known from 6 sparse populations totalling about 1000 plants. *Red Data Book* status: Rare. FLOWERS: September to December. FRUITS: Released 1-2 months after flowering.

## *Leucospermum* The Showy Pincushions

The Showy Pincushions (section *Brevifilamentum*) are characterized by *short filaments (1-2 mm long),* which attach the anthers to the perianth limbs. Leaves tend to be linear-oblong to elliptic, often with a heart-shaped base. *The pollen presenter is ovoid to hoof-shaped.* This group includes some of the more popular garden and display pincushions.

*Leucospermum tottum* (L.) R. Br. var. ***tottum***     Ribbon Pincushion     **Plate 64**

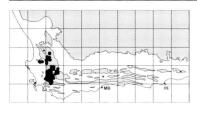

An erect, much-branched shrub, 1-2 m across, with a single main stem and horizontally spreading branches, up to 1.5 m tall. *Leaves lanceolate with a pointed tip to oblong-linear*, 25-60 mm long, 5-15 mm wide, hairless, with 1-3 glandular teeth; stalkless. Flowerhead usually solitary, 90-150 mm across, depressed-conical; stalk 20-30 mm long. *Involucral bracts membranous, hairless with a hairy margin*, loosely overlapping. Perianth 40-45 mm long, sparsely covered with hairs, tightly coiled when open, dull carmine to brown, tube 7 mm long. *Style curved slightly inwards, becoming horizontally spreading with age*, 50 mm long, pale pink. *Pollen presenter ovoid, tip pointed.*
DISTRIBUTION: Cederberg from Ezelbank to Koue Bokkeveld, Groot Winterhoek Mountains, Skurweweg, Hex River to Du Toit's Kloof Mountains above Villiersdorp; Piketberg.
HABITAT: Sandstone slopes, 300-2000 m. STATUS: Usually scattered individuals, but dense, isolated patches occur at the southern end of the distribution range. FLOWERS: September to January. FRUITS: Released 1-2 months after flowering.

*Leucospermum tottum* var. ***glabrum*** E. Phillips     Du Toit's Ribbon Pincushion     **Plate 64**

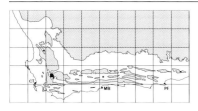

Similar to *L. tottum* var. *tottum*, but: *Branches hairless. Involucral bracts large, broad and hairless. Flowerhead turban-shaped with flowers erect.*
DISTRIBUTION: Jan du Toit's Kloof in the western Hex River Mountains. HABITAT: Sandstone slopes, 800-1200 m. STATUS: Known from scattered populations, each comprising a few hundred plants. FLOWERS: October to December.
FRUITS: Released 1-2 months after flowering.
NOTE: Discovered in 1921, this variety was relocated only in 1992. Although it is suspected of being a hybrid between *L. tottum* and *L. vestitum*, the large number of plants precludes this.

***Leucospermum vestitum*** (Lam.) Rourke                    Silky-hair Pincushion    **Plate 64**

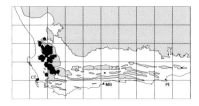

A stiffly erect to spreading shrub up to 2.5 m tall and 3 m across, with a single, stout main trunk. *Leaves oblong to elliptic to narrowly ovate, hairless,* 50-75 mm long, 10-30 mm wide, truncate or heart-shaped at base, with 2-4 glandular teeth. Flowerhead ovoid to globose, 70-90 mm across, usually solitary. *Involucral bracts membranous and hairless.* Perianth 35 mm long, with silky, straight hairs, orange but brilliant carmine when mature, tube 6 mm long. Style curved inwards, 50-60 mm long. *Pollen presenter almost hoof-shaped, tip pointed.*

DISTRIBUTION: Gifberg, Cederberg from Heerenlogementberg to Olifants River, Koue Bokkeveld, Hex River and Groot Winterhoek Mountains and to the Breede River Valley near Worcester; Piketberg; Paarl Mountain; Cape Peninsula. HABITAT: Varied on rocky sandstone slopes, 60-1350 m. STATUS: Extinct on Lion's Head and on Paarl Mountain. Still common as sparse, isolated populations elsewhere. FLOWERS: July to January, mainly October and November. FRUITS: Released 1-2 months after flowering.

□ VARIATION: Plants from the south tend to be more erect, whereas those of northern populations are more spreading.

***Leucospermum lineare*** R. Br.                    Needle-leaf Pincushion    **Plate 64**

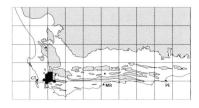

An erect to sprawling shrub up to 2 m tall, 3-4 m across when sprawling. *Leaves linear, hairless, flat or slightly channelled,* 40-100 mm long, 2-7 mm wide, with 1-3 glandular teeth. Flowerhead depressed-ovoid, 60-90 mm across, usually solitary or in groups of up to 3. Involucral bracts overlapping, hairy, cartilaginous. Perianth 30 mm long, with long hairs, pale yellow to orange, tube 7-8 mm long. Style strongly curved inwards, 50-55 mm long. Pollen presenter ovoid, with a pointed tip.

DISTRIBUTION: Slanghoek at Bain's Kloof to Du Toit's Kloof and Hottentots-Holland Mountains at Jonkershoek. HABITAT: Granite-derived clays, 300-1000 m. STATUS: Isolated, often dense populations. FLOWERS: July to January, mainly September and October. FRUITS: Released 1-2 months after flowering.

□ VARIATION: Two forms are known. The common form sprawls and has a yellow perianth and style. At Assegaaiboskloof a more erect form with a deep orange perianth and style and slightly larger features occurred. After having been lost for several decades, this form has been found at Middelberg west of Franschhoek and is being evaluated as a possible separate species.

***Leucospermum cordifolium*** (Salisb. ex Knight) Fourc.                    The Pincushion    **Plate 65**

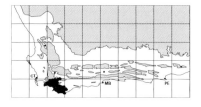

A rounded, spreading shrub up to 2 m across, 1.5 m tall, with *a single main stem and horizontally droop-ing branches.* Leaves 20-80 mm long, 20-45 mm wide, ovate to heart-shaped to oblong with a rounded tip, with up to 6 glandular teeth, covered with soft hairs, hairless when mature; *variable on same plant with a series of leaf forms along each stem progressing from basal leaves being ovate with 3 glandular teeth* at tip to leaves below flowerhead being smaller and rounder with 1 glandular tooth at tip. *Flowerhead borne at right angles to stem,* depressed-globose, 100-120 mm across, solitary or in clusters of 3; stalk 10-15 mm long. Involucral bracts overlapping, cartilaginous, sparsely covered

with hairs. Perianth 30-35 mm long, hairless, yellow or orange or crimson, tube 8-10 mm long. *Perianth margin fringed.* Style held horizontally, curved slightly inwards, 45-60 mm long. *Pollen presenter hoof-shaped.*
DISTRIBUTION: Kogelberg at Arieskraal and Kleinmond and Houhoek Pass to Bredasdorp Mountains and Elim Flats at Soetanysberg; Caledon Swartberg. HABITAT: Sandstone soils, 30-500 m. STATUS: Occurring as scattered plants or in dense clumps of several hundred plants. FLOWERS: August to January. FRUITS: Released 1-2 months after flowering.
NOTE: Several species were previously recognized by ignoring the progressive pattern of leaves along the stem, and the fact that older plants tend to produce only the leaf form with 3 glandular teeth at the tip. This species has become synonymous with the name 'pincushion' and features in many popular horticultural hybrids. It is widely planted and has become naturalized in many areas outside its natural range, mainly along roadsides and on rehabilitated land.

*Leucospermum patersonii* E. Phillips                    Silver-edge Pincushion    **Plate 65**

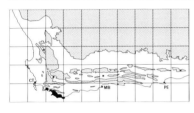

*A large, rounded shrub or tree* up to 4 m tall. Trunk stout, 100-200 mm in diameter. *Leaves oblong to broadly oblong, tip rounded with 3-8 glandular teeth,* 50-90 mm long, 30-50 mm wide, heart-shaped at base, hairless. Flowerhead erect, ovoid to globose, 80-90 mm across, usually solitary or in clusters of up to 3; stalk 10-20 mm long. Involucral bracts overlapping, tightly clasping the stalk, cartilaginous, hairy to hairless. Perianth 25-30 mm long, with long hairs, orange to crimson, tube 5 mm long. Style curved inwards at tip, *45-55 mm long. Pollen presenter hoof-shaped,* large.
DISTRIBUTION: Kleinmond at Heuningklipkloof, from Hermanus to Elim Flats at Cape Agulhas. HABITAT: Restricted to limestone soils, 50-300 m. STATUS: Extinct at Hermanus. It tends to occur in dense stands where it dominates the landscape, although in many places it is also found as scattered plants. FLOWERS: August to December. FRUITS: Released 1-2 months after flowering.

*Leucospermum cordatum* E. Phillips                    Heart-leaf Pincushion    **Plate 65**

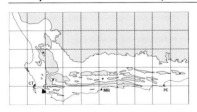

*A low, trailing shrub forming loose mats* 0.15-0.25 m high, 1-2 m across, with a single main stem. *Leaves ovate, with a single glandular tooth at the tip, heart-shaped at base,* 30-55 mm long, 10-25 mm wide, with soft hairs, hairless when mature. Flowerhead depressed-globose, 30-40 mm across; stalk 20-50 mm long. Involucral bracts cartilaginous, densely covered with long hairs. Perianth 15-18 mm long, cream to yellow, with long, thin hairs, tube 5 mm long. *Style strongly curved inwards near tip, 20-25 mm long,* white or pale pink but white when mature. *Pollen presenter narrowly conical, tip pointed, abruptly bent at junction with style.*
DISTRIBUTION: Kogelberg from Kogel Bay to Rooielsberg. HABITAT: Cederberg shales, often those high in manganese content, 15-85 m. STATUS: Known from a single population estimated at 2500 plants scattered over a few square kilometres. *Red Data Book* status: Rare. FLOWERS: July to December, mainly September to November. FRUITS: Released 1-2 months after flowering.

### *Leucospermum* The Fireworks Pincushions

The Fireworks Pincushions (section *Cardinistylus*) are characterized by their *long styles (55-80 mm long) which are hinged and move through 90° during flowering.* The pollen presenter is narrowly cylindrical with a pointed tip. *The involucral receptacle is narrowly conical with a pointed tip.* All 6 species are large shrubs, growing to 2-3 m tall, with a single main stem.

The 6 species in this section can be divided into 3 groups:
☐ Pollen presenters bent at right angles to the style and in a clockwise direction around the flowerhead ..................................................... *L. formosum, L. catherinae* (Wheel Pincushions)
☐ Pollen presenters bent at right angles to the style and pointing down towards the base of the flowerhead ................... *L. grandiflorum, L. gueinzii, L. praemorsum* (Fountain Pincushions)
☐ Entire style bending downwards during flowering ............... *L. reflexum* (Rocket Pincushion)

Further distinction between the species within the first 2 groups can be made by examining the involucral bracts, as well as the leaves which may appear either green (being hairless) or grey (being covered by fine, curly, woolly hairs).

### *Leucospermum formosum* (Andrews) Sweet     Silver-leaf Wheel Pincushion     **Plate 66**

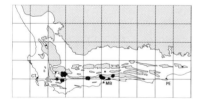

A large, erect shrub up to 3 m tall. *Leaves lanceolate-elliptic, covered with a dense mat of grey, fine, crispy hairs, 65-100 mm long,* 14-20 mm wide, with 3 glandular teeth; *stalkless or almost stalkless.* Flowerhead turban-shaped to depressed disc-shaped, 150 mm across, solitary or in groups of 2 or 3; stalk 10-20 mm long. *Involucral bracts ovate, tightly clasping the stalk,* thin and papery, hairy and with a fringe. Perianth 50 mm long, golden yellow, tube 10 mm long. Style progressively curving away from the centre after opening, 70-80 mm long, tapering and twisting clockwise near the tip, pale yellow but amber with a bronze flush when mature. Pollen presenter narrowly cylindrical, tip pointed, curved clockwise at right angles to style, white but pink when mature.
DISTRIBUTION: Riviersonderend Mountains; Langeberg and Outeniqua Mountains from Dassieshoek to Duiwelskop. HABITAT: Cool, southern slopes on peaty soil, 200-1000 m. STATUS: Known from only a few very isolated populations. *Red Data Book* status: Vulnerable, with some of these populations threatened by afforestation or agriculture. FLOWERS: September and October. FRUITS: Released 1-2 months after flowering.

### *Leucospermum catherinae* Compton     Catherine-wheel Pincushion     **Plate 66**

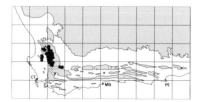

An erect shrub up to 3 m tall, spreading with age. *Leaves oblanceolate-elliptic, 90-135 mm long, 10-25 mm wide, narrowing to a stalked base, with 3 or 4 glandular teeth, hairless, green.* Flowerhead depressed-globose, but disc-shaped when mature, 150 mm across, usually solitary; stalk 10 mm long. *Involucral bracts ovate, tightly clasping the stalk,* overlapping, membranous, with a hairy margin.

Perianth 40-50 mm long, with long hairs at tip, pale orange, tube 6-7 mm long. Style 70-80 mm long, tapering and twisting clockwise near the tip, orange but coppery bronze when mature. Pollen presenter narrowly cylindrical, tip pointed, curved clockwise at right angles to style, magenta. DISTRIBUTION: Cederberg south of Middelberg to Koue Bokkeveld near Ceres; isolated populations on Piketberg and Bokkerivier Mountains. HABITAT: Sandstone soils along stream edges, 650-1350 m. STATUS: Apart from a few large stands, most plants are encountered in small, isolated patches of fewer than a dozen plants; isolated plants are not unusual. FLOWERS: September to December. FRUITS: Released 1-2 months after flowering.

*Leucospermum grandiflorum* (Salisb.) R. Br.          Grey-leaf Fountain Pincushion     **Plate 66**

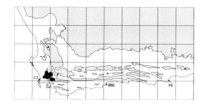

An erect shrub up to 2.5 m tall. *Leaves broadly elliptic to elliptic-oblong, 50-80 mm long, usually with 3 glandular teeth, rarely entire, with fine, crispy hairs*, grey, 20-30 mm wide. Flowerhead ovoid but depressed-ovoid when mature, 100-120 mm across; stalk up to 15 mm long. Involucral bracts ovate, margin densely covered with hairs, tip brown and membranous, base cartilaginous. *Perianth 45-50 mm long, pale greenish yellow*, with very few long hairs, tube 7 mm long. Style 70-75 mm long, tapering, slightly deflected in a clockwise direction, yellow but crimson when mature. Pollen presenter cylindrical, tip pointed, pink but carmine when mature. DISTRIBUTION: Paarl Mountain, Simonsberg and Paardeberg (Malmesbury), Durbanville Hills and Berg River Valley. HABITAT: Hot, dry slopes, usually granitic clays, 80-500 m. STATUS: *Red Data Book* status: Vulnerable. Only the populations on the 2 Swartland mountain islands have any future. Some 1500 plants are thought to remain in diffuse patches. FLOWERS: July to December. FRUITS: Released 1-2 months after flowering.

*Leucospermum gueinzii* Meisn.          Kloof Fountain Pincushion     **Plate 67**

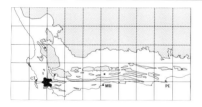

A stout, erect shrub, 2-3 m tall. *Leaves lanceolate, tip pointed, 75-100 mm long, usually with 1 but rarely up to 4 glandular teeth*, 20-30 mm wide, bright green, hairless, often covered with minute hairs when young. Flowerhead ovoid but depressed-ovoid when mature, 100-140 mm across, usually solitary but rarely in threes; stalk 10 mm long. Involucral bracts ovate, cartilaginous at base, tip membranous, margin hairy. *Perianth 55-60 mm long, tip orange*, sparsely covered with long hairs, green-yellow at base, tube 7 mm long. Style 70-75 mm long, tapering and curved away from centre, deep orange but bright crimson when mature. Pollen presenter cylindrical, tip pointed, directed away from centre. DISTRIBUTION: Hottentots-Holland Mountains from Jonkershoek to Verkykerskop, Groenland Mountains near Houhoek. HABITAT: Granite clays near streams in kloofs, 300-1000 m. STATUS: Occurs in isolated clumps in moist areas, usually kloofs. The Houhoek population has not been recorded since 1850. *Red Data Book* status: Rare. FLOWERS: August to December. FRUITS: Released 1-2 months after flowering.

***Leucospermum praemorsum*** (Meisn.) E. Phillips          Nardouw Fountain Pincushion     **Plate 67**

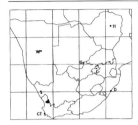

A large shrub or tree up to 5 m tall, 7 m across. Trunk single, stout, 300 mm in diameter, branching at height of 0.3 m. *Leaves oblong-oblanceolate*, 70-80 mm long, 15-20 mm wide, hairless, tip abrupt with 3-5 glandular teeth, hairy at base; *distinct stalk at base.* Flowerhead broadly obconical-depressed but narrowly obconical when mature, 70 mm across; stalk 7-10 mm long. *Involucral bracts loosely arranged, somewhat curved inwards, narrowly lanceolate-linear, with long, spreading, silky hairs.* Perianth 25-30 mm long, hairy, pale carmine, tube 8 mm long. Style almost straight, changing from curved in bud to almost flattened when open, 50-60 mm long, orange but deep crimson when mature. *Pollen presenter ellipsoid-cylindrical,* green.

DISTRIBUTION: Bokkeveld, Gifberg and Nardouw Mountains from Lokenberg to Wuppertal; sandy dunes northwest of Hondeklip Bay to Komaggas. HABITAT: Dry, sandy sandstone flats, 300-850 m. STATUS: A social species forming large populations of several thousand plants in dense stands. FLOWERS: All year round with a peak from July to December. FRUITS: Released 1-2 months after flowering.

***Leucospermum reflexum*** H. Buek ex Meisn.                    Rocket Pincushion     **Plate 67**

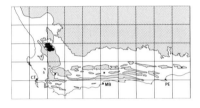

A large, rounded shrub up to 4 m tall. *Leaves elliptic to oblanceolate-oblong, 20-55 mm long, 5-13 mm wide, grey, covered with dense, crispy hairs*, with 2 or 3 glandular teeth. Flowerhead solitary, ovoid to globose, 80-100 mm across; stalk 30-60 mm long. Involucral bracts triangular, cartilaginous, margin hairy. *Perianth 40-50 mm long, curved at right angles at flowering*, tip hairy, deep orange to crimson, *tube 10 mm long. Style reflexing (changing in orientation from curved in bud to laid back along stem when open)*, 70-75 mm long, orange but deep crimson or yellow when mature. Pollen presenter cylindrical to awl-shaped, with a ring at the junction with the style.

DISTRIBUTION: Cederberg from Pakhuis to Wuppertal. HABITAT: Near streams on sandstone soils, 1000-2000 m. STATUS: Occurring in discrete, isolated stands of several hundred plants. FLOWERS: August to December. FRUITS: Released 1-2 months after flowering.

☐ VARIATION: A pale yellow form at Heuningvlei has been named *L. reflexum* var. *luteum* Rourke (from Latin, *luteus* = yellow).

## *Leucospermum* The Sandveld Pincushions

The Sandveld Pincushions (section *Leucospermum) vary* in form from erect to sprawling to creeping shrubs. Their *leaves have a dense, permanent, greyish layer of fine, crispy hairs* and vary in shape from oblanceolate to wedge-shaped to linear. The *perianth is usually straight in the bud, always bright yellow and very sweetly scented; 3 segments are fused at the tips and 1 is free.* The pollen presenter is club-shaped or cylindrical.

*Leucospermum hypophyllocarpodendron* (L.) Druce subsp. *hypophyllocarpodendron*
Green-snakestem Pincushion  **Plate 68**

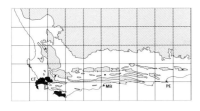

*A prostrate or rarely almost erect shrub* up to 0.2 m tall, with trailing stems forming mats 0.5-1.5 m across, arising from a stout underground rootstock. Stems hairless. *Leaves pointing vertically from a horizontal stem, variable in shape from narrowly oblanceolate to narrowly wedge-shaped, hairless and green,* 40-130 mm long, 2-15 mm wide, with 2-4 red glandular teeth. Flowerhead depressed-globose, 30-40 mm across, clustered in groups of up to 4; stalk 30-50 mm long. *Involucral bracts broadly ovate, tip pointed, 5-7 mm wide,* 4-6 mm long, closely clasping the stalk and overlapping, cartilaginous, hairless to covered with fine hairs. Perianth 20-22 mm long, separating into 3 fused segments and 1 free at flowering, hairy along margin, tube 10 mm long. Floral nectaries minute or absent. Style straight or slightly curved inwards, 20-26 mm long, slender, yellow. Pollen presenter club-shaped, tip rounded.
DISTRIBUTION: Cape Peninsula and across the Cape Flats to the Berg River Valley, Stellenbosch and Faure; Elim coastal flats from Franskraal to Brandfontein. HABITAT: Sandy flats, 0-300 m. STATUS: Extinct on the Cape Flats, it is now most common on the Peninsula and the Elim coast where it occurs as extensive patches of scattered plants. FLOWERS: August to January. FRUITS: Released 1-2 months after flowering.

*Leucospermum hypophyllocarpodendron* subsp. *canaliculatum* (H. Buek ex Meisn.) Rourke
Grey-snakestem Pincushion  **Plate 68**

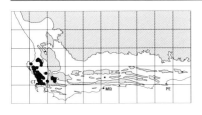

*A prostrate or rarely almost erect shrub* up to 0.2 m tall, with trailing stems forming mats 0.5-1.5 m across. *Stems with soft hairs,* arising from a stout underground rootstock. *Leaves pointing vertically from a horizontal stem, variable in shape from linear-channelled to narrowly oblanceolate or narrowly wedge-shaped, grey, usually with permanent, grey, crispy hairs, occasionally hairless when mature,* 40-130 mm long, 2-15 mm wide, with 2-4 red glandular teeth. Flowerhead depressed-globose, 30-40 mm across, clustered in groups of up to 4; stalk 30-50 mm long. *Involucral bracts broadly ovate, tip pointed, 5-7 mm wide,* 4-6 mm long, closely clasping the stalk, overlapping, cartilaginous, hairless or with fine hairs. Perianth 20-22 mm long, separating into 3 fused segments and 1 free at flowering, hairy along margin, tube 10 mm long. Floral nectaries 1 mm long. Style

straight or slightly curved inwards, 20-26 mm long, slender, yellow. Pollen presenter club-shaped, tip rounded.
DISTRIBUTION: Piketberg, Hopefield and Cape Flats to Milnerton and Kraaifontein; Riebeek Kasteel; Breede River Valley from Goudini to Brandvlei. HABITAT: Deep, white, Recent sands, 0-200 m. STATUS: Scattered plants occur in sparse populations in suitable habitat. Threatened by urbanization and alien plants, especially in the southern part of its range. FLOWERS: August to January. FRUITS: Released 1-2 months after flowering.

### *Leucospermum tomentosum* (Thunb.) R. Br.    Saldanha Pincushion    **Plate 68**

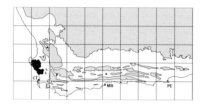

*An erect to semi-erect shrub, 0.4-1 m tall, 0.5-1 m across, arising from a persistent rootstock. Leaves linear to linear-spatulate, margin curled upwards causing leaves to be channelled*, 45-60 mm long, 3-5 mm wide, with up to 3 glandular teeth, densely covered with grey, crispy hairs. Flowerhead globose, 30-35 mm across, solitary or clustered in groups of up to 4; stalkless. *Involucral bracts lanceolate, tip pointed, cartilaginous*, 5 mm long, 3 mm wide, closely clasping the flowerhead, overlapping, outer surface with crispy hairs. Perianth 20 mm long, yellow, hairy, tube 4-5 mm long. Style straight, 17-20 mm long, slender, yellow. Pollen presenter cylindrical to narrowly elliptic.
DISTRIBUTION: Hopefield Flats from Hopefield and Vredenburg to Bokbaai.
HABITAT: Tertiary and Recent sand flats near sea, 0-80 m. STATUS: Scattered plants may form extensive stands, occasionally dominating the plant communities. *Red Data Book* status: Vulnerable, because ploughing and water extraction from its habitat are increasing as Cape Town expands. FLOWERS: June to November. FRUITS: Released 1-2 months after flowering.

### *Leucospermum rodolentum* (Salisb. ex Knight) Rourke    Sandveld Pincushion    **Plate 69**

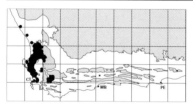

*An erect to spreading shrub up to 3 m tall, 4 m across, with a single main stem. Leaves elliptic to wedge-shaped, 40-65 mm long, 7-15 mm wide, densely covered with crispy hairs*, narrow at base, grey, tip abrupt or rounded, with 3-6 glandular teeth. Flowerhead globose, 30-35 mm across, in clusters of up to 4; stalk 0-5 mm long. Involucral bracts ovate, tip pointed, 5-7 mm long, 2-3 mm wide, cartilaginous, overlapping. Perianth 15-25 mm long, largely hairless, deep yellow, tube 5 mm long. Style straight, rarely bent, 15-25 mm long, tapering. Pollen presenter club-shaped to cylindrical with a rounded tip.
DISTRIBUTION: Sandveld, Hopefield and Cape Flats from Heerenlogementsberg to Kraaifontein and Salt River; Breede River Valley east of Brandvlei; Sandveld near Hondeklip Bay. HABITAT: Tertiary and Recent sand flats, 0-300 m. STATUS: Extinct south of Kalbaskraal. Often encountered as dense stands of several thousand plants. FLOWERS: August to November. FRUITS: Released 1-2 months after flowering.

***Leucospermum parile*** (Salisb. ex Knight) Sweet        Malmesbury Pincushion    **Plate 69**

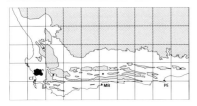

An erect to semi-erect, rounded shrub up to 1.5 m tall, with a single, stout main stem. *Leaves linear to oblong-linear*, 40-60 mm long, 6-8 mm wide, with short, crispy hairs, grey, with 1-3 glandular teeth, twisted. Flowerhead globose to depressed-globose, 30-35 mm across, in clusters of 2 to 6; stalkless. *Involucral bracts ovate, tip tapering to a narrow point, papery, hairless, red, margin hairy.* Perianth 15-20 mm long, with soft hairs, yellow, tube 4 mm long. Style straight, 15-20 mm long. Pollen presenter club-shaped to cylindrical with a rounded tip.

DISTRIBUTION: Flats around Dassenberg Hills. HABITAT: Sandveld of Tertiary and Recent origin, 30-170 m. STATUS: *Red Data Book* status: Vulnerable, as a result of agriculture and invasion of its habitat by alien acacias. A few extensive, dense populations still remain. FLOWERS: July to November. FRUITS: Released 1-2 months after flowering.

***Leucospermum arenarium*** Rycroft        Redelinghuys Pincushion    **Plate 69**

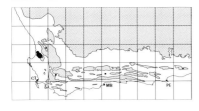

*A low, spreading shrub* up to 0.75 m tall, 1-1.5 m across, with a single main stem. Leaves pointing vertically from a horizontal stem, narrowly oblong-linear, 60-80 mm long, 7 mm wide, usually with 1 (rarely 2 or 3) glandular teeth, twisted, tapering to base, densely covered with crispy hairs, grey. *Flowerhead 50-70 mm across*, depressed-globose, usually solitary, rarely in twos; stalk 0-40 mm long.

*Involucral bracts membranous, tip recurved*, ovate, 8-10 mm long, 6 mm wide, hairless or with soft hairs, margin hairy, red-carmine. Perianth 20-25 mm long, sparsely covered with long hairs, tube 7 mm long. *Style strongly curved inwards, 30-35 mm long*, tapering, pale ivory to yellow-green. Pollen presenter cylindrical, tip pointed.

DISTRIBUTION: Sandveld flats between Aurora and Redelinghuys. HABITAT: Deep, white, Tertiary sands, 120-170 m. STATUS: *Red Data Book* status: Endangered, due to agriculture. It is known only from 2 farms where it occurs as scattered plants. FLOWERS: July to October. FRUITS: Released 1-2 months after flowering.

## *Leucospermum* The Louse Pincushions

The Louse Pincushions (section *Diastelloidea*) are erect, sprawling or decumbent shrubs, the *pointed leaves usually with only 1 glandular tooth. The flowerheads are small (10-30 mm across) and globose, borne in clusters of 2 to 6.* The involucral receptacle is never flat. *The style is typically short* (10-25 mm long), with a conical-ovoid, cylindrical or club-shaped pollen presenter. The perianth colour varies with age, from cream-white changing to pink or yellow, then changing to orange. *All 4 perianth segments separate at the tip and curl back* to form 4 small, round 'lice' surrounding each style, a feature shared with some *Vexatorella* species.

---

*Leucospermum calligerum* (Salisb. ex Knight) Rourke          Arid Pincushion     **Plate 70**

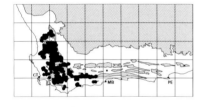

*An erect to almost erect shrub* up to 2 m tall, usually much shorter, 3 m across, with a single stem. *Leaves grey, hairy, with tip pointed (rarely with 2 or 3 glandular teeth)*, lanceolate to elliptic, 12-36 mm long, 4-8 mm wide; stalkless. Flowerhead globose, 20-35 mm across, usually in clusters of 2 to 6, with a sweet scent; stalk 0-30 mm long. Involucral bracts lanceolate, cartilaginous, not conspicuous. Perianth 15-17 mm long, cream flushed with carmine, with long, silky hairs, tube 5 mm long. *Style 21-25 mm long*, slightly curved inwards, tapering, yellow but dull carmine when mature. *Pollen presenter conical-ovoid*, yellow.
DISTRIBUTION: Bokkeveld escarpment and Gifberg to Olifants River to Bredasdorp Mountains in the south; from Bonteberg to the Langeberg; isolated populations at Riversdale Flats, Potberg, Waboomsberg, Malmesbury, Joostenberg. HABITAT: Hot, dry flats and northern slopes, 150-1350 m. STATUS: Usually a social species occurring in extensive stands, but occasionally as isolated clumps. FLOWERS: July to January. FRUITS: Released 1-2 months after flowering.

---

*Leucospermum wittebergense* Compton          Swartberg Pincushion     **Plate 70**

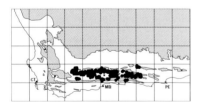

An erect, much-branched shrub 0.5-1.5 m tall, with a single stem. *Leaves crowded and overlapping, densely covered with crispy hairs*, elliptic-lanceolate, 15-25 mm long, 3-6 mm wide, tip pointed, with usually 1 (occasionally 2 or 3) glandular teeth, silver. Flowerhead globose, 20 mm across, usually solitary. Involucral bracts lanceolate, cartilaginous. Perianth 15 mm long, tube 3 mm long, cream but carmine when mature, with long, silky hairs. *Style 12-19 mm long*, straight to slightly curved inwards, pink or carmine. *Pollen presenter club-shaped to cylindrical with a rounded tip*, yellow.
DISTRIBUTION: Witteberg to Swartberg to Kouga Mountains; Grootrivier Mountains; Warmwaterberg; Outeniqua Mountains near Moeras River; Tsitsikamma Mountains. HABITAT: Arid, rocky, sandstone/quartzite slopes, 830-2000 m. STATUS: Usually a social species occurring in extensive stands. FLOWERS: August to January. FRUITS: Released 1-2 months after flowering.
☐ VARIATION: Northwestern forms appear stunted and seldom exceed a height of 0.5 m, whereas southern and eastern forms may exceed 1.5 m.

*Leucospermum royenifolium* (Salisb. ex Knight) Stapf          Eastern Pincushion     **Plate 70**

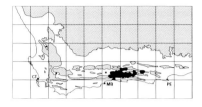

*A sprawling, semi-erect to prostrate shrub with an exposed rootstock,* forming dense mats 1-3 m across, 0.5 m tall. Leaves elliptic, 15-22 mm long, 4-6 mm wide, tip pointed, with usually 1 (occasionally 2 or 3) glandular teeth, occasionally covered with soft hairs when young, *mature leaves hairless.* Flowerhead globose, 10-20 mm across, usually in clusters of 3 to 5 (rarely up to 30), with a sweet scent; stalk 0-10 mm long. Involucral bracts ovate, tip pointed, cartilaginous. Perianth 10-15 mm long, with long hairs, cream to green but pale carmine when mature, tube 4 mm long. *Style 13-16 mm long,* tapering, green-cream but pink-carmine when mature. *Pollen presenter cylindrical, tip rounded.*
DISTRIBUTION: Outeniqua Mountains at Langkloof and Swartberg at Meiringspoort to Kouga Mountains at Scholtzberg. HABITAT: Hot, northern, quartzitic, sandstone slopes, 650-1350 m. STATUS: Usually a social species occurring in extensive stands. FLOWERS: July to December. FRUITS: Released 1-2 months after flowering.

*Leucospermum heterophyllum* (Thunb.) Rourke          Trident Pincushion     **Plate 70**

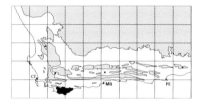

*A prostrate shrub* forming dense mats 1-6 m across, 0.1-0.15 m tall, from a large, woody rootstock. *Leaves variable, oblanceolate to linear-spatulate, mature leaves hairless, young leaves often hairy, twisted, pointing vertically from a horizontal stem, tip usually abrupt with 3 (or occasionally a single) glandular teeth,* 20-30 mm long, 3-6 mm wide; *stalkless.* Flowerhead globose, 20-30 mm across, numerous; stalk 10-20 mm long. Involucral bracts ovate, cartilaginous. Perianth 15 mm long, with long hairs, yellow-green, tube 4 mm long. Style straight, 18-21 mm long, tapering, pale yellow but dull carmine when mature. Pollen presenter conical-ovoid, yellow.
DISTRIBUTION: Elim Flats from Wolvengat to De Hoop. HABITAT: Sandstone or shale conglomerates, 150-200 m. STATUS: Localized in dense patches. *Red Data Book* status: Vulnerable. FLOWERS: August to January, mainly September and October. FRUITS: Released 1-2 months after flowering.

*Leucospermum bolusii* Gand.          Gordon's Bay Pincushion     **Plate 71**

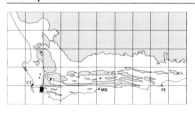

An erect to spreading, rounded shrub up to 1.5 m tall, with a single main stem. *Leaves ovate-elliptic, hairless when mature, 25-45 mm long,* 7-15 mm wide, entire; stalkless. Flowerhead depressed-globose, 20 mm across, in clusters of up to 8, sweetly scented; stalk 10 mm long. *Involucral bracts ovate, membranous, tip pointed, forming a cup-shaped involucre, hairless, margin hairy. Perianth cream-white* but pale pink when mature, 12 mm long, covered with long hairs, tube 5 mm long. Style straight, 15-20 mm long, tapering, cream. *Pollen presenter conical-ovoid,* pale green-yellow.
DISTRIBUTION: Coastal slopes from Gordon's Bay to Kogel Bay. HABITAT: Steep, western, sandstone, gravel slopes, 0-150 m. STATUS: Dense populations of thousands of plants are typical. FLOWERS: September to December. FRUITS: Released 1-2 months after flowering.

**Leucospermum truncatulum** (Salisb. ex Knight) Rourke          Oval-leaf Pincushion     **Plate 71**

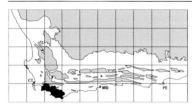

A sparsely branched, slender, erect shrub up to 2 m tall, with a single main stem. *Leaves obovate to elliptic, densely overlapping, 10-25 mm long, 5-10 mm wide, entire, covered with dense, crispy hairs.* Flowerhead globose, 15-20 mm across, usually in clusters of 2 to 8; stalkless. *Involucral bracts papery, forming a distinctly cup-shaped involucre,* lanceolate to ovate, hairless, but with occasional hairs on margin. Perianth 8-10 mm long, covered with long hairs, yellow but pink when mature, tube 4 mm long. Style straight to slightly curved, 14-16 mm long, tapering, yellow but crimson when mature. *Pollen presenter conical-ovoid, distinct from style.*
DISTRIBUTION: Kogelberg, Kleinmond, Groenland, Klein River, Babylonstoring and Bredasdorp Mountains and Soetanysberg, Elim Flats; Caledon Swartberg. HABITAT: Sandy soils, 0-400 m. STATUS: A social species forming dense stands over extensive areas. FLOWERS: August to December. FRUITS: Released 1-2 months after flowering.

**Leucospermum pedunculatum** Klotzsch          White-trailing Pincushion     **Plate 71**

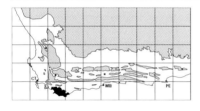

A low, prostrate shrub 0.15-0.3 m tall, forming dense mats up to 3 m across, with stout horizontal branches arising from *an exposed, erect rootstock, 300 mm tall, 100-150 mm in diameter. Leaves bright green,* linear, 30-60 mm long, 2-5 mm wide, hairless or with minute soft hairs, entire, tending to point vertically from a horizontal stem. *Flowerhead usually solitary on short lateral branches, globose, 25-30 mm across*, with a sweet scent; stalk 20-40 mm long. Involucral bracts lanceolate, tip tapering to a narrow point, cartilaginous, with long hairs. *Perianth cream to white but carmine when mature,* 9 mm long, with long hairs, tube 7 mm long. Style straight, 17-20 mm long, pale cream but carmine when mature. Pollen presenter club-shaped to cylindrical.
DISTRIBUTION: From Stanford and Salmonsdam to Agulhas. HABITAT: Deep, white, Recent, Tertiary or sandstone sands, 0-200 m. STATUS: Scattered plants often covering large areas. *Red Data Book* status: Rare. FLOWERS: August to January, peaking in September. FRUITS: Released 1-2 months after flowering.
☐ VARIATIONS: Western forms have bright green leaves and many vigorous branches forming dense mats. Eastern forms tend to have olive-green leaves, a less vigorous habit, with diffuse branches and a taller rootstock.

**Leucospermum prostratum** (Thunb.) Stapf          Yellow-trailing Pincushion     **Plate 71**

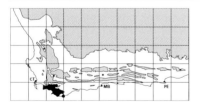

*A prostrate plant with numerous long, slender, rarely branching, trailing stems*, up to 4 m across, the stems arising from an underground rootstock. Leaves linear to oblong, 20-40 mm long, 2-6 mm wide, pointing vertically from a horizontal stem, tip pointed, entire, hairless to sparsely covered with hairs, grey-green; stalkless. *Flowerhead globose, 20-25 mm across*, usually solitary, rarely in clusters of 2 or 3, sweetly scented; stalk 10-30 mm long. Involucral bracts lanceolate, tip pointed, cartilaginous. *Perianth bright yellow but deep orange when mature*, 8-10 mm long, sparsely covered with hairs, tube 3 mm long. Style straight, 12-15 mm long, pale yellow but orange when mature. Pollen presenter cylindrical, tip rounded.

DISTRIBUTION: Kogelberg, Kleinmond, Groenland and Klein River Mountains, Elim Flats; Caledon Swartberg. HABITAT: Deep sands, mainly on coastal flats, 0-500 m. STATUS: Usually encountered as scattered plants. FLOWERS: July to December. FRUITS: Released 1-2 months after flowering.

***Leucospermum secundifolium*** Rourke                    Stalked Pincushion    **Plate 72**

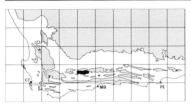

A low, prostrate shrub up to 2 m across, with slender, diffuse stems. *Leaves stalked, pointing vertically from a horizontal stem, elliptic, tip rounded, hairless*, with 1 (rarely 3) glandular teeth, 50-80 mm long, 7-16 mm wide, margin horny. *Flowerhead globose, usually solitary, small*, 10-15 mm across, axillary, bearing 12-30 flowers; stalk 5-15 mm long. Involucral bracts lanceolate, tip tapering to a narrow point. Floral bracts lanceolate to broadly ovate, cartilaginous, densely covered with long hairs, *enlarging to 10 mm long and becoming woody after pollination* (as in *Vexatorella*). Perianth 6 mm long, with long hairs, yellow but carmine when mature, tube 4-5 mm long. Style 14 mm long, tapering slightly, yellow but carmine when mature. Pollen presenter club-shaped, tip rounded.
DISTRIBUTION: Klein Swartberg between the Buffels and Gamka Rivers. HABITAT: Southern slopes, 1200-1400 m. STATUS: Sparse, isolated populations. *Red Data Book* status: Rare. FLOWERS: Mainly December. FRUITS: Released 1-2 months after flowering.
NOTE: This species fits uneasily within this group. It shares many features with *Vexatorella*, but does not have terminal flowers. In its growth form it closely resembles the Hook Pincushions, but its flowers are distinctly like those in this group. A more detailed study may still link it to the Hook Pincushions.

***Leucospermum winteri*** Rourke                    Riversdale Pincushion    **Plate 72**

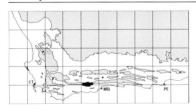

A small, rounded shrub up to 1.3 m tall, up to 2 m across, with a single main stem. *Leaves broadly wedge-shaped to broadly obovate, 40-70 mm long, 20-45 mm wide, mature leaves hairless, tip incised with 5-14 reddish glandular teeth.* Flowerhead globose, 30 mm across, in clusters of 3 to 6; stalk 15-30 mm long. Involucral bracts ovate, with dense hairs. Perianth 12-15 mm long, tip with soft hairs, yellow but pink when mature, tube 8 mm long. *Style 20 mm long*, straight to slightly curved inwards, yellow but crimson-red when mature. *Pollen presenter obovoid to club-shaped.*
DISTRIBUTION: Langeberg from Garcia's Pass to Gouritz River. HABITAT: Summit ridges, 1100-1300 m. STATUS: Found as a population of a few hundred scattered plants. FLOWERS: July to December. FRUITS: Released 1-2 months after flowering.
NOTE: *Leucospermum winteri* differs from other members of this group in having many glandular teeth, and it is clearly related to the Flat Pincushions. However, as it shares many other characteristics with the Louse Pincushions, it has been included in this group. It may have arisen as a hybrid between *L. calligerum* and *L. mundii*.

## *Leucospermum* **The Hook Pincushions**

The Hook Pincushions are characterized by their *minute flowerheads with 4-12 flowers, and knobby recurved styles.* Under magnification, the knobs on the styles can be seen to be minute hooks. The floral bracts are sometimes enlarged to form a cup-shaped false involucre which clasps the perianth segments. These species appear to be pollinated by rats and mice.

*Leucospermum hamatum* Rourke         Ruitersbos Pincushion    **Plate 72**

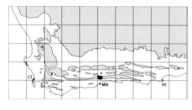

A prostrate, sprawling shrub forming dense mats 1-3 m across, up to 0.3 m tall, with a single main trunk. *Leaves pointing vertically from a horizontal stem, narrowly oblong to oblong-elliptic, flat, with a lobed base,* 45-65 mm long, 8-18 mm wide, usually with 3 glandular teeth, hairless when mature; with a short stalk. *Flowerhead turban-shaped, with 4-7 flowers in a single whorl,* 15-20 mm across; stalk 10-20 mm long. Involucral bracts reduced. *Perianth margin with fine hairs,* 10-14 mm long, with a pouched tube 5-8 mm long. *Style strongly curved inwards, tapered, granular,* 18-20 mm long. Pollen presenter conical, tip pointed.
DISTRIBUTION: Outeniqua Mountains at Klein Moeras River. HABITAT: Rocky outcrops on northern slopes, 750 m. STATUS: Known from a single population which comprises scattered clumps numbering several thousand plants. *Red Data Book* status: Rare. FLOWERS: July to November. FRUITS: Released 1-2 months after flowering.

*Leucospermum harpagonatum* Rourke         McGregor Pincushion    **Plate 72**

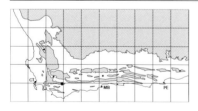

A creeping shrub forming dense mats 1-4 m across, up to 0.2 m tall, with a single main trunk. *Leaves pointing vertically from a horizontal stem, narrowly linear to oblong-elliptic, folded inwards, narrowing to a stalk,* 40-110 mm long, 2-10 mm wide, usually with 1 glandular tooth, hairless when mature. *Flowerhead turban-shaped, with 7-12 flowers in a single whorl,* 25-35 mm across; stalk 10-20 mm long. Involucral bracts linear to awl-shaped. *Perianth margin and outer surface with woolly hairs,* 9-15 mm long, with a pouched tube 5-6 mm long. *Style strongly curved inwards, tapering, granular,* 20-25 mm long. Pollen presenter conical, tip pointed.
DISTRIBUTION: Riviersonderend Mountains at Olifants Doorns near McGregor.
HABITAT: Rocky outcrops on northern slopes, 750-800 m. STATUS: *Red Data Book* status: Endangered. Known from a single population of about 200 plants. FLOWERS: August to November. FRUITS: Released 1-2 months after flowering.

## *Leucospermum* The Flat Pincushions

The Flat Pincushions (section *Crinitae*) are erect or sprawling shrubs characterized by *flat involucral receptacles and turban-shaped flowerheads* 20-40 mm in diameter. The perianth lobes do not curl back after flowering, but remain erect. The *thread-like style* and perianth undergo conspicuous colour changes with age.
 The Flat Pincushions form a cohesive group of *4 species, 2* of which are very variable.

*Leucospermum oleifolium* (P.J. Bergius) R. Br.      Overberg Pincushion    **Plate 73**

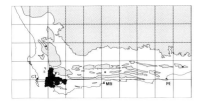

An erect, rounded shrub up to 1 m tall, with a single main stem. *Leaves variable, lanceolate to oblong to ovate, generally entire or with 2-5 glandular teeth*, 40-60 mm long, 8-25 mm wide, hairless or with long hairs; stalkless. Flowerhead turban-shaped, 25-40 mm across, in clusters of up to 5. *Involucral bracts ovate with a pointed tip to lanceolate tapering to a narrow point, membranous to papery*, 9-36 mm long, 5-7 mm wide, variable from inconspicuous to longer than the styles, overlapping conspicuously or marginally, hairy to hairless. Perianth 20 mm long, hairy to hairless, pale yellow-green but crimson when mature, tube 8 mm long. Style straight, 25-30 mm long, thread-like, pale yellow but crimson when mature. Pollen presenter thread-like to cylindrical, slightly thickened at base.
DISTRIBUTION: Slanghoek, Du Toit's Kloof, Riviersonderend, Hottentots-Holland, Kleinmond and Groenland Mountains; Caledon Swartberg. HABITAT: Sandstone sands, 0-1000 m. STATUS: In the southwest this is a social plant occurring in extensive, dense stands, but at the northern and eastern extremes of the distribution range it often occurs as scattered individuals. FLOWERS: August to January, mainly September and October. FRUITS: Released 1-2 months after flowering.
□ VARIATIONS: The length of the involucral bracts varies considerably with altitude, from 9-17 mm at sea level to 15-36 mm at 600 m, the latter with hairy tips. Similarly, forms at lower altitudes tend to be more erect and have more hairy leaves than those at higher altitudes. Formerly, this species was thought to be 8 species, but these are now known to comprise a single continuously variable species. Forms on the Riviersonderend Mountains have narrow flowerheads and may be mistaken for *Mimetes cucullatus* at first glance.

*Leucospermum mundii* Meisn.      Langeberg Pincushion    **Plate 73**

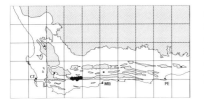

An erect, much-branched shrub 0.5-1 m tall, with a single main stem. *Leaves broadly wedge-shaped to broadly ovate, margin incised by 7-17 glandular teeth*, 50-85 mm long, 20-65 mm wide, hairless or with short, crispy hairs; stalkless to scarcely stalked. Flowerhead turban-shaped, 20-40 mm long, 10-20 mm across, in clusters of 3 to 10; stalk 10-15 mm. Involucral bracts lanceolate to ovate, tip pointed, 5-7 mm long, 3-5 mm wide, cartilaginous, overlapping, with long hairs. Perianth 16-18 mm long, hairy, pale yellow but orange when mature, tube 8-10 mm long. Style straight, 20-28 mm long, pale yellow. Pollen presenter thread-like to cylindrical, with a rounded tip.

DISTRIBUTION: Langeberg from Marloth Nature Reserve to Riversdale. HABITAT: Cool, south-western kloofs on northern slopes, 300-1000 m. STATUS: Encountered as small, dense, isolated populations. FLOWERS: July to November. FRUITS: Released 1-2 months after flowering.
☐ VARIATIONS: Eastern forms have a narrow leaf (15-40 mm wide) which is grey, hairy and wedge-shaped. Western forms have a wide, wedge-shaped to ovate leaf (30-60 mm wide) which is green and without hairs.

***Leucospermum gracile*** (Salisb. ex Knight) Rourke    Hermanus Pincushion    **Plate 73**

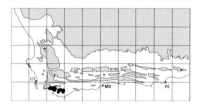

*A low, sprawling shrub*, 0.3-0.4 m tall, forming mats up to 1.5 m across, with a single main stem. *Leaves oblong-linear, rounded to ending abruptly at the base, 2-5 mm wide*, 20-45 mm long, entire or with 3 glandular teeth, pointing vertically from a horizontal stem, with sparse, long or short hairs. Flowerhead turban-shaped, 25-30 mm across; stalk 0-20 mm long. Involucral bracts lanceolate-linear, 8-10 mm long, 1-2 mm wide, cartilaginous, hairy. *Floral bracts oblanceolate, with a rounded-pointed tip. Perianth yellow*, 20-25 mm long, hairy, tube 8 mm long and green. Style straight, thread-like, tapering, 25-30 mm long, yellow but pale green when mature. Pollen presenter cylindrical, tip pointed.
DISTRIBUTION: Klein River, Babylonstoring and Bredasdorp Mountains. HABITAT: Southern slopes on rocky sandstone soils, 100-1000 m. STATUS: A social species occurring in dense, isolated stands. FLOWERS: July to December. FRUITS: Released 1-2 months after flowering.

***Leucospermum saxatile*** (Salisb. ex Knight) Rourke    Karoo Pincushion    **Plate 73**

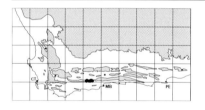

A low, single-stemmed, almost erect to sprawling shrub 0.5-0.7 m tall, 1-1.5 m across. *Leaves linear to narrowly wedge-shaped, margin often curved inwards*, 25-50 mm long, 2-5 mm wide, tip with 1 (rarely 2 or 3) glandular teeth, base narrow, hairless when mature. Flowerhead turban-shaped, 25-30 mm across, usually solitary or in clusters of up to 3; stalk 5-10 mm long. Involucral bracts lanceolate, cartilaginous. *Floral bracts lanceolate, tip thinning to a point. Perianth lime-green* but carmine when mature, 20 mm long, hairy, tube 6 mm long. Style thread-like, 30 mm long. Pollen presenter cylindrical, tip rounded.
DISTRIBUTION: Langeberg from west of Garcia's Pass to Cloete's Pass. HABITAT: Ecotone between arid fynbos and karoo, sandstone soils, 500-670 m. STATUS: Locally abundant, forming dense stands. FLOWERS: July to February. FRUITS: Released 1-2 months after flowering.

## *DIASTELLA* Salisb. **The Silkypuffs**

Members of the genus *Diastella* may be confused with smaller *Leucospermum* species. Their leaves are linear to ovate, usually with a single glandular tooth. The flowerheads are small, globose and terminal (or both terminal and axillary). *One to 3 rows of papery or membranous bracts extend to or beyond the flowers, covering the flowerhead at its base.* The floral bracts are *linear to thread-like and covered with silky hairs.* All 4 perianth segments are free almost to the base. Floral nectaries are usually absent. The fruit is like a typical *Leucospermum* nut.

## A QUICK KEY TO THE SILKYPUFFS

**The Northern Silkypuffs** (Plate 74)
Leaves with 1 to 3 glandular teeth
Flowerheads either terminal or axillary
Perianth parts unequal
Floral nectaries present

**The Southern Silkypuffs** (Plate 74)
Leaves with a single glandular tooth
Flowerheads always terminal
Perianth parts equal
Floral nectaries absent

### *Diastella* **The Northern Silkypuffs**

The Northern Silkypuffs (section *Hypogynae*), the more primitive of the 2 groups, more closely resemble *Leucospermum* species. Unlike the other *Diastella* species, they have *floral nectaries.*

---

*Diastella parilis* Salisb. ex Knight        Worcester Silkypuff    **Plate 74**

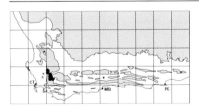

An erect shrub 0.5-0.7 m tall, with a single main stem. Leaves oblong to elliptic, 10-30 mm long, 2-5 mm wide, with 1-3 glandular teeth. Flowerhead 15-20 mm across. *Involucral bracts ovate, margin hairy, pink, turning brown and papery with age.* Perianth pink, with white hairs, tube 2 mm long. Style red, 10 mm long.
DISTRIBUTION: Breede River Valley from Wolseley to Slanghoek. HABITAT: Seeps on sandstone foothills, 250-500 m.
STATUS: Scattered clumps. *Red Data Book* status: Vulnerable. FLOWERS: July to January.
FRUITS: Released 1-2 months after flowering.

***Diastella myrtifolia*** (Thunb.) Salisb. ex Knight — Tulbagh Silkypuff — **Plate 74**

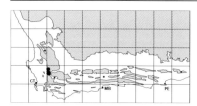

*An erect to almost erect shrub with mat-like, sprawling branches*, 0.5-1 m tall, up to 2 m across. Leaves oblong to elliptic, 10-25 mm long, 2-6 mm wide, with 1-3 glandular teeth. Flowerhead 15 mm across. *Involucral bracts oblong-elliptic, green*, in 2 rows forming a dish below the flowers. Perianth pink, occasionally white, tube 2 mm long. Style 8 mm long. DISTRIBUTION: Elandskloof Mountains. HABITAT: Seeps on sandstone sands, 420-600 m. STATUS: Known from a few small, scattered populations. *Red Data Book* status: Rare. FLOWERS: September to January. FRUITS: Released 1-2 months after flowering.

### *Diastella* The Southern Silkypuffs

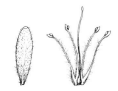

The Southern Silkypuffs (section *Diastella*) differ from the Northern Silkypuffs in *not having floral nectaries.* They are therefore probably unable to secrete nectar. They also differ more markedly from *Leucospermum* than the Northern Silkypuffs do, in that they have only *terminal flowerheads.*

***Diastella proteoides*** (L.) Druce — Flats Silkypuff — **Plate 75**

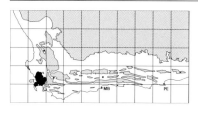

A low, sprawling shrub 0.5 m tall, up to 3 m across. *Stems hairy. Leaves linear, 5-15 mm long, 1-2 mm wide, current year's leaves hairy.* Flowerhead 10 mm across, pink. *Involucral bracts hairy*, 5-10 mm long, sharply pointed and extending beyond the flowers to give a star-like outline to the flowerhead. Perianth 7-10 mm long. Style 10 mm long, basal third hairy. DISTRIBUTION: Cape Flats from Tokai to Eerste River to Paarl and Mamre. HABITAT: Tertiary and Recent sands on flats, 0-150 m. STATUS: Once abundant on the Cape Flats, it now has a *Red Data Book* status of Vulnerable, with most of its southern populations destroyed. FLOWERS: All year round, mainly July to February. FRUITS: Released 1-2 months after flowering.

***Diastella buekii*** (Gand.) Rourke        Franschhoek Silkypuff    **Plate 75**

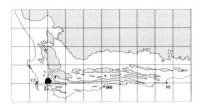

A very low, mat-like shrub 0.15 m tall, up to 1 m across. *Stems not hairy. Leaves hairless, needle-like,* 10-25 mm long, 1-2 mm wide. *Flowerhead overtopped by leaves*, 10-15 mm across. Involucral bracts 5-7 mm long, lanceolate, *outer whorl hairless with hairy margin*, extending beyond the flowers and giving a slightly star-like appearance to the flowerhead. Perianth 8-10 mm long, tube 0.5 mm long. Style 8-12 mm long, hairy immediately above the ovary.
DISTRIBUTION: Berg River Valley from Franschhoek to Paarl. HABITAT: Moist sands, 200-300 m. STATUS: *Red Data Book* status: Endangered. Only 2 populations comprising 2000 plants remain, due to afforestation and viticulture. FLOWERS: August to November. FRUITS: Released 1-2 months after flowering.

***Diastella fraterna*** Rourke        Palmiet Silkypuff    **Plate 75**

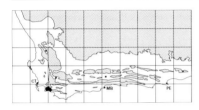

*A low, almost erect shrublet 0.7 m tall and 1 m across*, single-stemmed at base. *Leaves lanceolate to elliptic, 1-4 mm wide*, 8-14 mm long. *Flowerhead white to cream*, 10-15 mm across. *Involucral bracts drying to brown and papery with age*, 6-10 mm long. Perianth 8-10 mm long. Style 12-14 mm long, hairy 6 mm up from base.
DISTRIBUTION: Kogelberg and Kleinmond Mountains. HABITAT: Seeps and streamsides, 0-450 m. STATUS: Occurs as isolated patches of a few dozen plants. *Red Data Book* status: Rare. FLOWERS: Irregular, all year round.
FRUITS: Released 1-2 months after flowering.
☐ VARIATION: In some populations involucral bracts do not become brown and papery with age.

***Diastella divaricata*** (P.J. Bergius) Rourke subsp. ***divaricata***      Peninsula Silkypuff    **Plate 74**

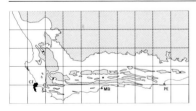

*A low, sprawling shrub* 0.5 m tall, 3 m across, with a single main stem. *Leaves ovate to rounded, 2-10 mm long*, 2-7 mm wide. Flowerhead 10-15 mm across, pink. Involucral bracts as long as perianth. Perianth 6-8 mm long. *Style hairy for 2 mm above the ovary*, 8-10 mm long.
DISTRIBUTION: Cape Peninsula from Silvermine southwards. HABITAT: Sandy flats, 0-600 m.
STATUS: Often forming extensive, dense stands. FLOWERS: All year round. FRUITS: Released 1-2 months after flowering.

***Diastella divaricata*** subsp. ***montana*** Rourke                    Mountain Silkypuff    **Plate 74**

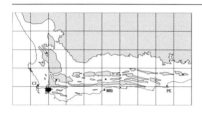

*A low, sprawling shrub* 0.5 m tall and up to 2 m across, single-stemmed at base. *Leaves lanceolate to elliptic, 10-18 mm long*, 1-7 mm wide, tip pointed. Flowerhead 10-15 mm across, pink. Involucral bracts as long as perianth. Perianth 6-8 mm long. *Style hairy for 5 mm above the ovary*, 8-10 mm long. DISTRIBUTION: Wemmershoek Mountains to Villiersdorp and western Riviersonderend Mountains, Hottentots-Holland, Groenland, Kleinmond and Klein River Mountains. HABITAT: Cool, moist, southern sandstone slopes, 300-1200 m. STATUS: Encountered as small, isolated populations. FLOWERS: All year round. FRUITS: Released 1-2 months after flowering.

***Diastella thymelaeoides*** (P.J. Bergius) Rourke subsp. ***thymelaeoides***

Kogelberg Silkypuff    **Plate 75**

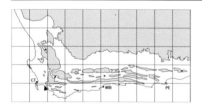

*An erect shrub* up to 1.5 m tall. *Leaves ovate or rounded, 8-14 mm long, 4-9 mm wide. Flowerhead globose, 10-15 mm across*, white, rarely pink. *Involucral bracts clasping base of flowerhead*, 7-15 mm long. Perianth 7-10 mm long. Style 10-12 mm long, hairy at base. DISTRIBUTION: Hottentots-Holland Mountains and northern Kogelberg from the Steenbras to the Kogelberg Dams. HABITAT: Montane, sandstone slopes, 450-900 m. STATUS: Occurs as isolated patches of a few dozen plants. *Red Data Book* status: Rare. FLOWERS: All year round, but mainly August to November. FRUITS: Released 1-2 months after flowering.

***Diastella thymelaeoides*** subsp. ***meridiana*** Rourke                    Hangklip Silkypuff    **Plate 75**

*An erect shrub* up to 1 m tall. *Leaves elliptic, 12-22 mm long, 4-9 mm wide. Flowerhead globose, 20 mm across*, white or pink. *Involucral bracts projecting beyond the perianth, giving a rounded, star-like outline to the flowerhead*, 6-20 mm long, 1-6 mm wide. Perianth 7-10 mm long. Style 10-12 mm long, hairy at base. DISTRIBUTION: Southern Kogelberg from Kogel Bay to Cape Hangklip and Betty's Bay. HABITAT: Sandstone slopes, 0-150 m. STATUS: Occurs as isolated patches of a few dozen plants. *Red Data Book* status: Rare. FLOWERS: All year round, but mainly August to November. FRUITS: Released 1-2 months after flowering.

## *VEXATORELLA* Rourke  **The Vexators**

Although members of the genus *Vexatorella* could be mistaken for a Louse Pincushion (*Leucospermum* section *Diastelloidea*), they can easily be identified by their *terminal flowerheads,* which occasionally comprise a number of headlets. The leaves always have a single tooth at the tip. *The 4 perianth segments separate symmetrically and are fused only in the tube region.* The flowers are sweetly scented. *The floral bracts become woody after flowering* (a feature shared with *L. secundifolium*). *The fruits have a persistent style,* are hairless and are surrounded by an elaiosome that forms a little stalk.

---

*Vexatorella alpina* (Salisb. ex Knight) Rourke          Kamiesberg Vexator    **Plate 76**

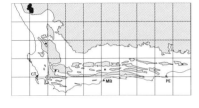

An erect shrub 2-3 m tall, up to 4 m across, dense and robust in stature. *Leaves obovate to elliptic, 30-45 mm long,* 5-13 mm wide. *Flowerhead usually comprises 2-6 stalked headlets*, occasionally only 1, 20-25 mm across, comprising 15-30 flowers, with a strong sweet scent. Flowers cream. Perianth 12-18 mm long, with a dense mat of hairs, tip sparsely covered with shaggy hairs. Style straight, 12-18 mm long. Pollen presenter club-shaped.
DISTRIBUTION: Kamiesberg from Rooiberg to Leliefontein and Sneeukop and Rooiberg near Kamieskroon. HABITAT: Granite soils, 1200-1500 m. STATUS: Sometimes forming dense stands, dominating the flora. *Red Data Book* status: Rare. FLOWERS: September to December.
FRUITS: Released 1-2 months after flowering.

---

*Vexatorella amoena* (Rourke) Rourke          Swartruggens Vexator    **Plate 76**

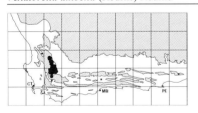

An erect to sprawling, sparsely branched shrub 1-1.5 m tall. *Leaves obovate to elliptic, 15-30 mm long*, 5-13 mm wide. Flowerhead solitary, 12-25 mm across, comprising 18-35 flowers, cream to pink, with a sweet scent; stalk with *a collar of bracts at base.* Perianth 12-18 mm long, densely covered with shaggy hairs, tip densely covered with short hairs. Style straight, 14-16 mm long. Pollen presenter club-shaped.
DISTRIBUTION: Koue Bokkeveld and Swartruggens Mountains from Wuppertal to Karoopoort. HABITAT: Montane, sandstone soils, 1000-1500 m. STATUS: Occurring in dense stands or as scattered plants. FLOWERS: September to November. FRUITS: Released 1-2 months after flowering.

***Vexatorella latebrosa*** Rourke                                                                Robertson Vexator     **Plate 76**

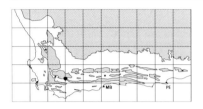

An erect shrub 1-2 m tall, branching from a single main trunk at about 0.45 m. *Leaves linear to spatulate*, 50-60 mm long, 2-3 mm wide. *Flowerhead solitary, comprising 40-50 flowers*, 25-30 mm across, pink to carmine. Perianth 15-18 mm long, with long shaggy hairs. Style straight, 15-18 mm long. Pollen presenter club-shaped.

DISTRIBUTION: Langeberg at Klaasvoogds near Robertson. HABITAT: Fynbos/renosterveld ecotone on shales, 400-900 m. STATUS: Known from a few adjacent stands where it is locally abundant. *Red Data Book* status: Rare. FLOWERS: October and November. FRUITS: Released 1-2 months after flowering.

***Vexatorella obtusata*** (Thunb.) Rourke subsp. ***obtusata***                         Montagu Vexator     **Plate 76**

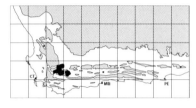

*A prostrate shrub* forming dense mats 1-2 m across. *Leaves linear to spatulate, 9-45 mm long*, 1-6 mm wide. Flowerhead solitary, 15-20 mm across, comprising 5-20 flowers, cream or pink, with a sweet scent. Perianth 10-15 mm long, with a dense mat of hairs, tip with short shaggy hairs. Style straight, 10-13 mm long, yellow-green ageing to deep red. Pollen presenter rounded club-shaped.

DISTRIBUTION: Hex River and Bokkerivier Mountains, Keeromsberg and Kwadouw Mountain to Langeberg at Koo and Waboomsberg. HABITAT: Arid fynbos on sandstone soils, 300-1800 m. STATUS: Locally common in stands of scattered plants. FLOWERS: September to December. FRUITS: Released 1-2 months after flowering.

***Vexatorella obtusata*** subsp. ***albomontana*** (Rourke) Rourke                 Witteberg Vexator     **Plate 76**

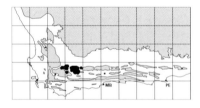

*An erect, upright or rounded shrub* 0.5-1 m tall. *Leaves linear to spatulate, 22-45 mm long*, 1-6 mm wide. Flowerhead solitary, 15-20 mm across, comprising 5-20 flowers, pink to carmine, with a sweet scent. Perianth 10-15 mm long, with a dense mat of hairs, tip with short shaggy hairs. Style straight, 10-13 mm long, yellow-green ageing to deep red. Pollen presenter rounded club-shaped.

DISTRIBUTION: Bonteberg, Witteberg and Anysberg. HABITAT: Quartzite soils, 1000-1500 m. STATUS: Locally common in stands of scattered plants. FLOWERS: August to November. FRUITS: Released 1-2 months after flowering.

*Protea amplexicaulis (x 0.6)* Page 29

*Protea cordata (x 0.7)* Page 30

*Protea humiflora (x 0.6)* Page 30

*Protea decurrens (x 0.3)* Page 31

*Protea subulifolia (x 0.5)* Page 31

**Plate 2** ☐ *Protea* ☐ **The Grassland Sugarbushes**

*Protea caffra* subsp. *caffra (x 0.6)* Page 32

*Protea caffra* subsp. *gazensis (x 0.4)* Page 33

*Protea petiolaris* subsp. *elegans (x 0.4)* Page 33

*Protea simplex (x 0.6)* Page 34

*Protea dracomontana (x 0.7)* Page 35

*Protea parvula (x 1.0)* Page 34

*Protea nubigena (x 1.0)* Page 35

**Plate 4** □ *Protea* □ **The Shaving-brush Sugarbushes**

*Protea inopina (x 0.2)* Page 36

*Protea glabra (x 0.4)* Page 36

*Protea rupicola (x 0.4)* Page 37

*Protea nitida (x 0.3)* Page 37

*Protea enervis (x 1.7)* Page 38

**Plate 6** □ *Protea* □ **The Mountain Sugarbushes**

*Protea angolensis* var. *angolensis (x 0.3)*
Page 39

*Protea angolensis* var. *divaricata (x 0.4)*
Page 39

*Protea rupestris (x 0.4)* Page 39

*Protea madiensis* subsp. *madiensis (x 0.5)*
Page 40

*Protea rubropilosa (x 0.4)* Page 40

*Protea comptonii (x 0.4)* Page 40

*Protea curvata (x 0.7)* Page 41

*Protea laetans (x 0.5)* Page 41

**Plate 8** ☐ *Protea* ☐ **The Savanna Sugarbushes**

*Protea welwitschii* subsp. *hirta (x 0.4)*
Page 43

*Protea welwitschii (x 0.9)* Page 42

*Protea gaguedi (x 0.4)* Page 43

*Protea wentzeliana (x 0.5)* Page 44

*Protea asymmetrica (x 0.5)* Page 44

**Plate 10** ☐ *Protea* ☐ **The King Sugarbush**

*Protea cynaroides*, elliptic-leaf variant
*(x 0.2)* Page 45

*Protea cynaroides*, oval-leaf variant
*(x 0.2)* Page 45

*Protea cynaroides*, small-leaf variant
*(x 0.4)* Page 45

*Protea scolopendriifolia (x 0.3)* Page 46

*Protea scabriuscula (x 0.4)* Page 46

*Protea cryophila (x 0.3)* Page 47

*Protea pruinosa (x 0.3)* Page 47

**Plate 12** □ *Protea* □ **The Spoon-bract Sugarbushes**

*Protea roupelliae* subsp. *roupelliae (x 0.5)* Page 48

*Protea eximia (x 0.4)* Page 48

*Protea compacta (x 0.4)* Page 49

*Protea obtusifolia (x 0.3)* Page 49

*Protea susannae (x 0.3)* Page 50

*Protea burchellii (x 0.5)* Page 50

*Protea longifolia (x 0.6)* Page 51

*Protea pudens (x 0.9)* Page 51

**Plate 14** □ *Protea* □ **The 'True' Sugarbushes**

*Protea aristata (x 0.5)* Page 53

*Protea repens (x 0.4)* Page 52

*Protea lanceolata (x 0.6)* Page 53

*Protea laurifolia (x 0.6)* Page 54

*Protea neriifolia (x 0.5)* Page 55

*Protea lepidocarpodendron (x 0.4)* Page 55

**Plate 16** □ *Protea* □ **The Bearded Sugarbushes**

*Protea lorifolia (x 0.7)* Page 56

*Protea coronata (x 0.4)* Page 56

*Protea speciosa (x 0.5)* Page 57

*Protea stokoei (x 0.5)* Page 57

*Protea grandiceps (x 0.5)* Page 58

*Protea magnifica (x 0.6)* Page 58

*Protea holosericea (x 0.8)* Page 59

**Plate 18** □ *Protea* □ **The Dwarf-tufted Sugarbushes**

*Protea scorzonerifolia (x 0.5)* Page 60

*Protea lorea (x 0.5)* Page 60

*Protea aspera (x 0.6)* Page 61

*Protea scabra (x 1.1)* Page 61

*Protea piscina (x 0.7)* Page 62

*Protea restionifolia (x 0.6)* Page 62

*Protea denticulata (x 0.8)* Page 63

**Plate 20** ☐ *Protea* ☐ **The White Sugarbushes**

*Protea subvestita (x 0.9)* Page 63

*Protea lacticolor (x 0.8)* Page 64

*Protea punctata (x 0.8)* Page 64

*Protea mundii (x 0.6)* Page 65

*Protea aurea* subsp. *aurea (x 0.4)* Page 65

*Protea venusta (x 0.3)* Page 66

*Protea aurea* subsp. *potbergensis (x 0.4)*
Page 65

Plate 22 □ *Protea* □ **The Bishop/Eastern Ground Sugarbushes**

*Protea caespitosa*, Hottentots-Holland variant
*(x 0.5)* Page 67

*Protea caespitosa*, cabbage-leaf variant
*(x 0.5)* Page 67

*Protea tenax (x 0.3)* Page 67

*Protea vogtsiae (x 0.5)* Page 68

*Protea foliosa (x 0.7)* Page 68

*Protea intonsa (x 0.7)* Page 68

*Protea montana (x 0.6)* Page 69

**Plate 24** ☐ *Protea* ☐ **The Western Ground Sugarbushes**

*Protea acaulos (x 0.3)* Page 69

*Protea angustata (x 0.7)* Page 70

*Protea laevis (x 0.5)* Page 70

*Protea convexa (x 0.4)* Page 71

*Protea revoluta (x 0.7)* Page 71

*Protea mucronifolia (x 0.8)* Page 72

*Protea odorata (x 1.6)* Page 72

**Plate 26**  □  *Protea*  □  **The Rose Sugarbushes**

*Protea acuminata (x 0.7)* Page 73

*Protea scolymocephala (x 1.0)* Page 73

*Protea canaliculata (x 0.7)* Page 74

*Protea nana (x 1.2)* Page 74

*Protea witzenbergiana (x 1.2)* Page 74

*Protea pityphylla (x 0.7)* Page 75

*Protea recondita* (leaves removed to show flowerhead) *(x 0.5)* Page 75

**Plate 28** ☐ *Protea* ☐ **The Penduline Sugarbushes**

*Protea effusa (x 0.4)* Page 76

*Protea namaquana (x 0.3)* Page 77

*Protea sulphurea (x 0.2)* Page 76

*Protea pendula (x 0.4)* Page 77

*Aulax pallasia* ♂ *(x 0.4)*
Page 78

*Aulax pallasia* ♀ *(x 0.4)*
Page 78

*Aulax cancellata* ♂ *(x 0.4)*
Page 79

*Aulax cancellata* ♀ *(x 0.8)* Page 79

*Aulax umbellata* ♂ *(x 0.3)*
Page 79

*Aulax umbellata* ♀ *(x 0.3)*
Page 70

**Plate 30** ☐ *Faurea* ☐ **The Beechwoods**

*Faurea galpinii (x 0.4)* Page 80

*Faurea rubriflora (x 0.4)* Page 80

*Faurea macnaughtonii (x 0.3)* Page 80

*Faurea rochetiana (x 0.2)* Page 81

*Faurea delevoyi (x 0.3)* Page 81

*Faurea saligna (x 0.5)* Page 81

**Plate 32** □ *Serruria* □ **The Pin Spiderheads**

*Serruria candicans (x 1.0)* Page 84

*Serruria inconspicua (x 1.0)* Page 84

*Serruria fasciflora (x 0.5)* Page 84

*Serruria viridifolia (x 1.0)* Page 85

*Serruria zeyheri (x 1.0)* Page 85

*Serruria kraussii (x 0.8)* Page 85

**Plate 34**  □  *Serruria*  □  **The Curly Spiderheads**

*Serruria rubricaulis (x 1.0)* Page 86

*Serruria adscendens (x 0.6)* Page 86

*Serruria decipiens (x 0.4)* Page 87

Possible new *Serruria* species, showing
affinity to *S. decipiens (x 1.2)* Page 87

*Serruria glomerata (x 0.5)* Page 87

*Serruria collina (x 0.7)* Page 87

*Serruria nervosa (x 0.7)* Page 88

*Serruria roxburghii (x 1.0)* Page 88

*Serruria bolusii (x 0.8)* Page 88

**Plate 36** ☐ *Serruria* ☐ **The Tulbagh/Stalked Spiderheads**

*Serruria triternata (x 0.5)* Page 89

*Serruria confragosa (x 1.1)* Page 89

*Serruria meisneriana (x 0.6)* Page 90

*Serruria leipoldtii (x 1.2)* Page 90

*Serruria elongata (x 0.2)* Page 90

*Serruria williamsii (x 0.2)* Page 91

*Serruria altiscapa (x 0.1)* Page 91

*Serruria lacunosa (x 0.3)* Page 91

**Plate 38**  □  *Serruria*  □  **The Paw Spiderheads**

*Serruria aitonii (x 1.0)* Page 92

*Serruria reflexa (x 0.3)* Page 92

*Serruria fucifolia (x 1.3)* Page 92

*Serruria dodii (x 0.7)* Page 93

*Serruria pedunculata (x 0.7)* Page 93

*Serruria flava (x 0.7)* Page 94

*Serruria balanocephala (x 0.8)* Page 94

*Serruria acrocarpa (x 0.8)* Page 94

**Plate 40**  □  *Serruria*  □  **The Paw Spiderheads**

*Serruria incrassata (x 0.7)* Page 95

*Serruria cygnea (x 0.2)* Page 95

*Serruria gremialis (x 0.7)* Page 95

*Serruria effusa (x 1.0)* Page 96

*Serruria villosa (x 0.7)* Page 97

*Serruria hirsuta (x 0.4)* Page 96

*Serruria rostellaris (x 0.6)* Page 97

**Plate 42** ☐ *Serruria* ☐ **The Stalkless Spiderheads**

*Serruria rebeloi (x 1.3)* Page 98

*Serruria deluvialis (x 1.2)* Page 97

*Serruria brownii (x 0.9)* Page 98

*Serruria millefolia (x 0.8)* Page 98

*Serruria aemula (x 0.7)* Page 99

*Serruria cyanoides (x 1.3)* Page 99

*Serruria furcellata (x 1.1)* Page 100

*Serruria trilopha (x 1.3)* Page 100

*Serruria gracilis (x 1.6)* Page 101

*Serruria linearis (x 1.0)* Page 100

*Serruria stellata (x 1.3)* Page 101

*Serruria heterophylla (x 1.0)* Page 102

*Serruria phylicoides*, high-altitude form
*(x 0.6)* Page 102

*Serruria phylicoides*, low-altitude form
*(x 0.9)* Page 102

*Serruria rosea (x 0.8)* Page 103

*Serruria florida (x 0.6)* Page 103

**Plate 46** □ *Serruria* □ **The Whip-leaf Spiderheads**

*Serruria decumbens (x 1.5)* Page 104

*Serruria flagellifolia (x 1.2)* Page 104

*Paranomus dregei (x 0.9)* Page 106

*Paranomus esterhuyseniae (x 1.1)* Page 106

*Paranomus centauroides (x 0.9)* Page 107

*Paranomus* sp. nova *(x 1.6)* Page 107

**Plate 48** ☐ *Paranomus* ☐ **The Common Sceptres**

*Paranomus candicans (x 0.6)* Page 108

*Paranomus tomentosus (x 1.1)* Page 108

*Paranomus spicatus (x 0.6)* Page 108

*Paranomus bolusii (x 1.0)* Page 109

*Paranomus bracteolaris (x 0.5)* Page 109

*Paranomus abrotanifolius (x 1.0)* Page 110

*Paranomus lagopus (x 0.5)* Page 109

*Paranomus dispersus (x 0.7)* Page 110

**Plate 50** ☐ *Paranomus* ☐ **The Fine-leaf/Woolly/Elongate Sceptres**

*Paranomus capitatus*, western form *(x 0.8)*
Page 111

*Paranomus capitatus*, eastern form *(x 1.3)*
Page 111

*Paranomus longicaulis (x 0.9)* Page 111

*Paranomus spathulatus (x 0.8)* Page 112

*Paranomus roodebergensis (x 0.7)* Page 113

*Paranomus adiantifolius (x 0.9)* Page 112

*Paranomus reflexus (x 0.4)* Page 113

*Paranomus sceptrum-gustavianus (x 0.4)*
Page 113

**Plate 52**  □  *Sorocephalus*  □  **The Needle-leaf Clusterheads**

*Sorocephalus pinifolius (x 1.4)* Page 115

*Sorocephalus alopecurus (x 1.1)* Page 115

*Sorocephalus palustris (x 1.2)* Page 116

*Sorocephalus clavigerus (x 1.0)* Page 116

*Sorocephalus crassifolius (x 1.5)* Page 117

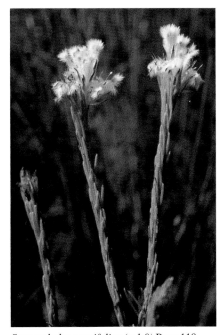

*Sorocephalus tenuifolius (x 1.0)* Page 118

*Sorocephalus teretifolius (x 1.4)* Page 117

**Plate 54** □ *Sorocephalus* □ **The Flat-leaf Clusterheads**

*Sorocephalus imbricatus (x 0.6)* Page 119

*Sorocephalus scabridus (x 1.5)* Page 119

*Sorocephalus lanatus (x 1.0)* Page 120

*Sorocephalus capitatus (x 1.4)* Page 120

*Spatalla prolifera (x 1.0)* Page 122

*Spatalla salsoloides (x 2.8)* Page 122

*Spatalla setacea (x 1.4)* Page 123

*Spatalla nubicola (x 1.1)* Page 123

**Plate 56** ☐ *Spatalla* ☐ **The Unispoons**

*Spatalla parilis (x 0.9)* Page 123

*Spatalla colorata (x 1.2)*
Page 124

*Spatalla squamata (x 1.0)*
Page 124

*Spatalla barbigera (x 1.0)* Page 124

*Spatalla ericoides (x 0.7)*
Page 125

*Spatalla longifolia (x 1.0)* Page 125

*Spatalla curvifolia (x 1.5)* Page 125

*Spatalla racemosa (x 1.6)* Page 126

*Spatalla mollis (x 1.4)* Page 126

**Plate 58** ☐ *Spatalla* ☐ **The Triplespoons**

*Spatalla tulbaghensis (x 1.3)* Page 127

*Spatalla caudata (x 1.0)* Page 127

*Spatalla confusa (x 1.3)* Page 128

*Spatalla thyrsiflora (x 1.3)* Page 128

*Spatalla incurva (x 1.3)* Page 128

*Spatalla argentea (x 1.5)* Page 129

*Spatalla propinqua (x 1.6)* Page 129

**Plate 60** □ *Leucospermum* □ **The Cylindrical Pincushions**

*Leucospermum saxosum (x 1.0)* Page 132

*Leucospermum cuneiforme (x 0.6)* Page 132

*Leucospermum gerrardii (x 0.5)* Page 133

*Leucospermum*
*innovans (x 1.1)*
Page 133

*Leucospermum conocarpodendron* subsp.
*conocarpodendron (x 0.5)* Page 134

*Leucospermum conocarpodendron* subsp.
*viridum (x 0.4)* Page 134

*Leucospermum glabrum (x 0.4)* Page 135

*Leucospermum pluridens (x 0.5)* Page 135

Plate 62 □ *Leucospermum* □ **The Wide-tubed Pincushions**

*Leucospermum praecox (x 0.6)* Page 136

*Leucospermum fulgens (x 0.6)* Page 136

*Leucospermum truncatum (x 0.9)* Page 137

*Leucospermum muirii (x 1.0)* Page 137

*Leucospermum erubescens (x 0.3)* Page 137

*Leucospermum spathulatum (x 0.9)* Page 138

*Leucospermum profugum (x 0.5)* Page 138

*Leucospermum utriculosum (x 0.5)* Page 138

**Plate 64** □ *Leucospermum* □ **The Showy Pincushions**

*Leucospermum tottum* var. *tottum (x 0.3)*
Page 139

*Leucospermum tottum* var. *glabrum (x 0.3)*
Page 139

*Leucospermum vestitum (x 0.4)* Page 140

*Leucospermum lineare (x 0.4)* Page 140

*Leucospermum patersonii (x 0.7)* Page 141

*Leucospermum cordatum (x 0.6)* Page 141

*Leucospermum cordifolium (x 0.4)* Page 140

**Plate 66**  ☐  *Leucospermum*  ☐  **The Fireworks Pincushions**

*Leucospermum catherinae (x 0.3)* Page 142

*Leucospermum formosum (x 0.3)* Page 142

*Leucospermum grandiflorum (x 0.4)*
Page 143

*Leucospermum praemorsum (x 1.0)* Page 144

*Leucospermum gueinzii (x 0.3)* Page 143

*Leucospermum reflexum* var. *luteum (x 0.4)*
Page 144

**Plate 68** □ *Leucospermum* □ **The Sandveld Pincushions**

*Leucospermum hypophyllocarpodendron* subsp. *hypophyllocarpodendron (x 1.0)* Page 145

*Leucospermum hypophyllocarpodendron*
subsp. *canaliculatum (x 0.7)* Page 145

*Leucospermum tomentosum (x 1.8)* Page 146

*Leucospermum rodolentum (x 1.9)* Page 146

*Leucospermum arenarium (x 0.5)* Page 147

*Leucospermum parile (x 0.9)* Page 147

**Plate 70**  □  *Leucospermum*  □  **The Louse Pincushions**

*Leucospermum calligerum (x 2.2)* Page 148

*Leucospermum wittebergense (x 2.0)*
Page 148

*Leucospermum royenifolium (x 2.0)* Page 149

*Leucospermum heterophyllum (x 1.0)*
Page 149

*Leucospermum truncatulum (x 1.7)* Page 150

*Leucospermum prostratum (x 1.4)* Page 150

*Leucospermum pedunculatum (x 0.9)*
Page 150

*Leucospermum bolusii (x 0.9)* Page 149

**Plate 72** ☐ *Leucospermum* ☐ **The Louse/Hook Pincushions**

*Leucospermum secundifolium (x 1.6)*
Page 151

*Leucospermum winteri (x 1.2)* Page 151

*Leucospermum hamatum (x 0.7)* Page 152

*Leucospermum harpagonatum (x 0.5)*
Page 152

*Leucospermum oleifolium (x 0.9)* Page 153

*Leucospermum gracile (x 0.6)* Page 154

*Leucospermum saxatile (x 1.0)* Page 154

*Leucospermum mundii (x 1.1)* Page 153

**Plate 74** ☐ *Diastella* ☐ **The Northern/Southern Silkypuffs**

*Diastella parilis (x 1.4)* Page 155

*Diastella myrtifolia (x 2.0)* Page 156

*Diastella divaricata* subsp. *montana (x 1.8)*
Page 158

*Diastella divaricata* subsp. *divaricata (x 2.0)*
Page 157

*Diastella thymelaeoides* subsp.
*thymelaeoides (x 1.3)* Page 158

*Diastella thymelaeoides* subsp. *meridiana*
*(x 2.1)* Page 158

*Diastella proteoides (x 1.2)* Page 156

*Diastella fraterna (x 2.4)* Page 157

*Diastella buekii (x 2.0)* Page 157

**Plate 76** □ *Vexatorella* □ **The Vexators**

*Vexatorella alpina (x 0.5)* Page 159

*Vexatorella amoena (x 1.5)* Page 159

*Vexatorella obtusata* subsp. *albomontana (x 1.5)* Page 160

*Vexatorella obtusata* subsp. *obtusata (x 1.2)* Page 160

*Vexatorella latebrosa (x 1.3)* Page 160

*Mimetes fimbriifolius (x 0.5)* Page 163

*Mimetes cucullatus (x 0.6)* Page 163

*Mimetes chrysanthus (x 0.4)* Page 162

**Plate 78**  □  *Mimetes*  □  **The Silver Pagodas**

*Mimetes saxatilis (x 0.7)* Page 164

*Mimetes splendidus (x 0.8)* Page 164

*Mimetes argenteus*
*(x 0.5)* Page 164

*Mimetes arboreus (x 0.6)* Page 165

*Mimetes stokoei (x 0.7)* Page 165

*Mimetes hottentoticus*
*(x 0.6)* Page 165

**Plate 80** ☐ *Mimetes* ☐ **The Tube Pagodas**

*Mimetes hirtus (x 0.6)* Page 166

*Mimetes pauciflorus (x 0.5)* Page 166

*Mimetes palustris (x 0.6)* Page 167

*Mimetes capitulatus (x 0.5)* Page 167

*Orothamnus zeyheri (x 1.1)* Page 168

Plate 82 □ *Leucadendron* □ **The Sandveld Conebushes**

*Leucadendron coriaceum* ♂ *(x 1.0)* Page 172     *Leucadendron coriaceum* ♀ *(x 2.5)* Page 172

*Leucadendron brunioides* var. *brunioides* ♂      *Leucadendron brunioides* var. *brunioides* ♀
*(x 0.9)* Page 173                                  *(x 1.1)* Page 173

*Leucadendron brunioides* var.
*flumenlupinum* ♂ *(x 0.9)* Page 173

*Leucadendron brunioides* var.
*flumenlupinum* ♀ *(x 0.7)* Page 173

*Leucadendron stellare* ♂ *(x 0.9)* Page 173

*Leucadendron stellare* ♀ *(x 1.2)* Page 173

*Leucadendron thymifolium* ♂ *(x 1.0)*
Page 174

*Leucadendron thymifolium* ♀ *(x 1.0)*
Page 174

**Plate 84** □ *Leucadendron* □ **The Sandveld Conebushes**

*Leucadendron levisanus* ♂
*(x 0.6)* Page 174

*Leucadendron concavum* ♂
*(x 0.7)* Page 174

*Leucadendron dubium* ♂
*(x 1.1)* Page 175

*Leucadendron levisanus* ♀
*(x 0.6)* Page 174

*Leucadendron concavum* ♀
*(x 0.4)* Page 174

*Leucadendron dubium* ♀
*(x 0.4)* Page 175

*Leucadendron cinereum* ♂
*(x 0.5)* Page 175

*Leucadendron linifolium* ♂
*(x 0.5)* Page 175

*Leucadendron galpinii* ♂
*(x 0.7)* Page 176

*Leucadendron cinereum* ♀
*(x 0.5)* Page 175

*Leucadendron linifolium* ♀
*(x 0.5)* Page 175

*Leucadendron galpinii* ♀
*(x 1.0)* Page 176

**Plate 86** ☐ *Leucadendron* ☐ **The Arid Conebushes**

*Leucadendron remotum* ♂
*(x 0.8)* Page 176

*Leucadendron pubescens* ♂
*(x 0.5)* Page 177

*Leucadendron bonum* ♂
*(x 0.4)* Page 177

*Leucadendron remotum* ♀
*(x 0.5)* Page 176

*Leucadendron pubescens* ♀
*(x 0.4)* Page 177

*Leucadendron bonum* ♀
*(x 0.6)* Page 177

*Leucadendron arcuatum* ♂
*(x 0.6)* Page 178

*Leucadendron crassulaefolium*
♂ *(x 0.4)* Page 178

*Leucadendron sericeum* ♂
*(x 0.5)* Page 179

*Leucadendron arcuatum* ♀
*(x 0.5)* Page 178

*Leucadendron crassulaefolium*
♀ *(x 0.4)* Page 178

*Leucadendron sericeum* ♀
*(x 0.5)* Page 179

*Leucadendron nitidum* ♂
*(x 0.7)* Page 179

*Leucadendron nitidum* ♀
*(x 0.8)* Page 179

**Plate 88** ☐ *Leucadendron* ☐ **The Pauciflor/Kouga Conebushes**

*Leucadendron olens* ♂
*(x 0.4)* Page 180

*Leucadendron ericifolium*
♂ *(x 0.5)* Page 180

*Leucadendron singulare* ♂
*(x 1.4)* Page 181

*Leucadendron olens* ♀
*(x 0.8)* Page 180

*Leucadendron ericifolium*
♀ *(x 1.0)* Page 180

*Leucadendron singulare* ♀
*(x 0.6)* Page 181

*Leucadendron sorocephalodes* ♂ *(x 1.3)*
Page 181

*Leucadendron sorocephalodes* ♀ *(x 0.9)*
Page 181

*Leucadendron verticillatum* ♂
*(x 0.6)* Page 182

*Leucadendron corymbosum* ♂
*(x 0.8)* Page 182

*Leucadendron laxum* ♂
*(x 0.9)* Page 183

*Leucadendron verticillatum* ♀
*(x 0.9)* Page 182

*Leucadendron corymbosum* ♀
*(x 1.0)* Page 182

*Leucadendron laxum* ♀
*(x 0.4)* Page 183

**Plate 90**   □   *Leucadendron*   □   **The Silky-ruff/Silver Conebushes**

*Leucadendron nervosum* ♂ *(x 0.5)*
Page 184

*Leucadendron nervosum* ♀ *(x 0.6)*
Page 184

*Leucadendron dregei* ♂ *(x 0.5)* Page 185

*Leucadendron dregei* ♀ *(x 0.8)* Page 185

*Leucadendron album* ♂ *(x 0.5)* Page 185

*Leucadendron album* ♀ *(x 0.7)* Page 185

*Leucadendron rubrum* ♂ *(x 1.0)* Page 186

*Leucadendron rubrum* ♀ *(x 0.4)* Page 186

*Leucadendron argenteum* ♀ *(x 0.5)*
Page 186

*Leucadendron argenteum* ♂ *(x 0.4)*
Page 186

**Plate 92** ☐ *Leucadendron* ☐ **The Stigmatic Sun Conebushes**

*Leucadendron barkerae* ♂
*(x 0.4)* Page 188

*Leucadendron burchellii* ♂
*(x 0.4)* Page 188

*Leucadendron tradouwense* ♂
*(x 0.4)* Page 188

*Leucadendron barkerae* ♀
*(x 0.4)* Page 188

*Leucadendron burchellii* ♀
*(x 0.7)* Page 188

*Leucadendron tradouwense* ♀
*(x 1.1)* Page 188

*Leucadendron orientale* ♂
*(x 0.4)* Page 189

*Leucadendron pubibracteolatum*
♂ *(x 0.4)* Page 189

*Leucadendron tinctum* ♂
*(x 0.2)* Page 190

*Leucadendron orientale* ♀
*(x 0.5)* Page 189

*Leucadendron pubibracteolatum*
♀ *(x 0.4)* Page 189

*Leucadendron tinctum* ♀
*(x 0.3)* Page 190

**Plate 94** □ *Leucadendron* □ **The Stigmatic/Southwestern Sun Conebushes**

*Leucadendron cordatum* ♂ *(x 0.7)* Page 190

*Leucadendron cordatum* ♀ *(x 0.6)* Page 190

*Leucadendron cadens* ♂ *(x 1.0)* Page 191

*Leucadendron cadens* ♀ *(x 2.3)* Page 191

*Leucadendron gydoense* ♂
*(x 0.6)* Page 191

*Leucadendron sessile* ♂
*(x 0.3)* Page 191

*Leucadendron daphnoides*
♂ *(x 0.3)* Page 192

*Leucadendron gydoense*  ♀
*(x 0.7)* Page 191

*Leucadendron sessile* ♀
*(x 0.5)* Page 191

*Leucadendron daphnoides*
♀ *(x 0.5)* Page 192

**Plate 96** ☐ *Leucadendron* ☐ **The Northwestern Sun Conebushes**

*Leucadendron sheilae* ♂ *(x 0.8)* Page 192

*Leucadendron sheilae* ♀ *(x 0.9)* Page 192

*Leucadendron meyerianum* ♂ *(x 0.6)*
Page 193

*Leucadendron meyerianum* ♀ *(x 1.4)*
Page 193

*Leucadendron roodii* ♂ *(x 0.5)* Page 193

*Leucadendron roodii* ♀ *(x 0.9)* Page 193

*Leucadendron glaberrimum* subsp.
*glaberrimum*  ♂ *(x 1.1)* Page 193

*Leucadendron glaberrimum* subsp.
*glaberrimum*  ♀ *(x 1.2)* Page 193

*Leucadendron glaberrimum* subsp.
*erubescens*  ♂ *(x 0.9)* Page 194

*Leucadendron glaberrimum* subsp.
*erubescens*  ♀ *(x 0.9)* Page 194

*Leucadendron loranthifolium*  ♂ *(x 0.5)*
Page 194

*Leucadendron loranthifolium*  ♀ *(x 0.7)*
Page 194

**Plate 98** ☐ *Leucadendron* ☐ **The Crown Conebushes**

*Leucadendron globosum* ♂ *(x 0.4)*
Page 195

*Leucadendron globosum* ♀ *(x.0.5)*
Page 195

*Leucadendron chamelaea* ♀ *(x 0.5)*
Page 196

*Leucadendron grandiflorum* see Page 195

*Leucadendron chamelaea* ♂ *(x 0.8)*
Page 196

*Leucadendron elimense* subsp. *elimense* ♂ *(x 0.5)* Page 196

*Leucadendron elimense* subsp. *salteri* ♂ *(x 0.5)* Page 196

*Leucadendron elimense* subsp. *vyeboomense* ♂ *(x 0.5)* Page 197

*Leucadendron elimense* subsp. *elimense* ♀ *(x 0.4)* Page 196

*Leucadendron elimense* subsp. *salteri* ♀ *(x 0.6)* Page 196

*Leucadendron elimense* subsp. *vyeboomense* ♀ *(x 0.8)* Page 197

**Plate 100** ☐ *Leucadendron* ☐ **The Delta-seed Conebushes**

*Leucadendron ugilinosum*
subsp. *uliginosum* ♂
*(x 0.1)* Page 197

*Leucadendron ugilinosum*
subsp. *glabratum* ♂
*(x 0.2)* Page 198

*Leucadendron loeriense*
♂ *(x 0.5)* Page 198

*Leucadendron ugilinosum*
subsp. *uliginosum* ♀
*(x 0.4)* Page 197

*Leucadendron ugilinosum*
subsp. *glabratum* ♀
*(x 0.6)* Page 198

*Leucadendron loeriense*
♀ *(x 0.2)* Page 198

*Leucadendron rourkei* ♂
*(x 0.4)* Page 199

*Leucadendron rourkei* ♀
*(x 0.4)* Page 199

*Leucadendron radiatum* ♂
*(x 0.8)* Page 199

*Leucadendron conicum* ♂
*(x 0.5)* Page 200

*Leucadendron salicifolium*
♂ *(x 0.4)* Page 200

*Leucadendron radiatum* ♀
*(x 0.7)* Page 199

*Leucadendron conicum* ♀
*(x 0.3)* Page 200

*Leucadendron salicifolium*
♀ *(x 0.4)* Page 200

*Leucadendron pondoense* ♂ *(x 0.4)*
Page 201

*Leucadendron pondoense* ♀ *(x 0.3)*
Page 201

**Plate 102** ☐ *Leucadendron* ☐ **The Delta-seed/Oilbract Conebushes**

*Leucadendron macowanii* ♂ *(x 0.6)* Page 201

*Leucadendron macowanii* ♀ *(x 0.4)* Page 201

*Leucadendron floridum* ♂ *(x 0.5)* Page 202

*Leucadendron floridum* ♀ *(x 0.8)* Page 202

*Leucadendron microcephalum* ♂
*(x 0.6)* Page 202

*Leucadendron microcephalum* ♀
*(x 0.5)* Page 202

*Leucadendron lanigerum*
var. *lanigerum* ♂
*(x 0.5)* Page 203

*Leucadendron lanigerum*
var. *laevigatum* ♂
*(x 0.5)* Page 203

*Leucadendron modestum* ♂
*(x 0.7)* Page 204

*Leucadendron lanigerum*
var. *lanigerum* ♀
*(x 0.6)* Page 203

*Leucadendron lanigerum*
var. *laevigatum* ♀
*(x 0.6)* Page 203

*Leucadendron modestum* ♀
*(x 0.4)* Page 204

*Leucadendron stelligerum*
♂ *(x 0.5)* Page 204

*Leucadendron stelligerum*
♀ *(x 0.3)* Page 204

**Plate 104** □ *Leucadendron* □ **The Sunshine Conebushes**

*Leucadendron diemontianum*
♂ *(x 0.5)* Page 206

*Leucadendron flexuosum* ♂
*(x 0.6)* Page 206

*Leucadendron salignum* ♂
*(x 0.7)* Page 206

*Leucadendron diemontianum*
♀ *(x 0.4)* Page 206

*Leucadendron flexuosum* ♀
*(x 0.7)* Page 206

*Leucadendron salignum* ♀
*(x 0.8)* Page 206

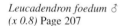

*Leucadendron foedum* ♂
*(x 0.8)* Page 207

*Leucadendron procerum* ♂
*(x 0.5)* Page 207

*Leucadendron discolor* ♂
*(x 0.6)* Page 208

*Leucadendron foedum* ♀
*(x 0.6)* Page 207

*Leucadendron procerum* ♀
*(x 0.8)* Page 207

*Leucadendron discolor* ♀
*(x 0.4)* Page 208

Plate 106 □ *Leucadendron* □ **The Sunshine Conebushes**

*Leucadendron coniferum* ♂
*(x 0.4)* Page 208

*Leucadendron meridianum* ♂
*(x 0.3)* Page 209

*Leucadendron eucalyptifolium* ♂
*(x 0.5)* Page 208

*Leucadendron coniferum* ♀
*(x 0.3)* Page 208

*Leucadendron meridianum* ♀
*(x 0.5)* Page 209

*Leucadendron eucalyptifolium* ♀
*(x 0.6)* Page 208

*Leucadendron xanthoconus* ♂
*(x 0.6)* Page 209

*Leucadendron laureolum* ♂
(leaves removed to show
flowerhead) *(x 0.4)* Page 209

*Leucadendron cryptocephalum*
♂ (leaves removed to show
flowerhead) *(x 0.7)* Page 210

*Leucadendron xanthoconus* ♀
*(x 0.5)* Page 209

*Leucadendron laureolum* ♀
(leaves removed to show
flowerhead) *(x 0.6)* Page 209

*Leucadendron cryptocephalum*
♀ (leaves removed to show
flowerhead) *(x 0.6)* Page 210

**Plate 108** ☐ *Leucadendron* ☐ **The Sunshine Conebushes**

*Leucadendron gandogeri* ♂ *(x 0.5)*
Page 210

*Leucadendron gandogeri* ♀ *(x 0.4)*
Page 210

*Leucadendron strobilinum* ♂ *(x 0.4)*
Page 211

*Leucadendron strobilinum* ♀ *(x 0.5)*
Page 211

*Leucadendron spissifolium* subsp.
*spissifolium* ♂ *(x 0.7)* Page 211

*Leucadendron spissifolium* subsp.
*spissifolium* ♀ *(x 0.7)* Page 211

*Leucadendron spissifolium*
subsp. *fragrans* ♂
*(x 0.2)* Page 211

*Leucadendron spissifolium*
subsp. *phillipsii* ♂
*(x 0.2)* Page 212

*Leucadendron spissifolium*
subsp. *natalense* ♂
*(x 0.3)* Page 212

*Leucadendron spissifolium*
subsp. *fragrans* ♀
*(x 0.4)* Page 211

*Leucadendron spissifolium*
subsp. *phillipsii* ♀
*(x 0.3)* Page 212

*Leucadendron spissifolium*
subsp. *natalense* ♀
*(x 0.3)* Page 212

*Leucadendron spissifolium*
subsp. *oribinum* ♂
*(x 0.3)* Page 212

*Leucadendron spissifolium*
subsp. *oribinum* ♀
*(x 0.5)* Page 212

**Plate  110**  ☐  *Leucadendron*  ☐  **The Needle-leaf Conebushes**

*Leucadendron spirale* see Page 214

*Leucadendron teretifolium*
♂ *(x 1.3)* Page 213

*Leucadendron osbornei* ♂
*(x 0.4)* Page 213

*Leucadendron nobile* ♂
*(x 0.9)* Page 214

*Leucadendron teretifolium*
♀ *(x 1.1)* Page 213

*Leucadendron osbornei* ♀
*(x 0.3)* Page 213

*Leucadendron nobile* ♀
*(x 0.8)* Page 214

*Leucadendron muirii* ♂
*(x 0.6)* Page 214

*Leucadendron comosum*
subsp. *comosum* ♂
*(x 0.4)* Page 215

*Leucadendron comosum*
subsp. *homaeophyllum* ♂
*(x 0.4)* Page 215

*Leucadendron muirii* ♀
*(x 0.5)* Page 214

*Leucadendron comosum*
subsp. *comosum* ♀
*(x 0.3)* Page 215

*Leucadendron comosum*
subsp. *homaeophyllum* ♀
*(x 0.5)* Page 215

*Leucadendron platyspermum*
♂ *(x 0.3)* Page 216

*Leucadendron platyspermum*
♀ *(x 0.2)* Page 216

*Brabejum stellatifolium (x 0.3)* Page 217

*Hakea drupacea (x 0.5)* Page 218

*Hakea gibbosa (x 0.3)* Page 219

*Hakea sericea (x 0.2)* Page 219

*Grevillea banksii (x 0.4)* Page 220

*Grevillea robusta (x 0.2)* Page 220

## *MIMETES* Salisb. **The Pagodas**

The genus *Mimetes* can readily be distinguished from all other Proteaceae by the *large cylindrical flowerhead* (technically a conflorescence) *which comprises an aggregation of tubular, axillary, stalkless headlets* (technically pseudanthia), *each of which contains 3-22* (35 in M. chrysanthus) *flowers and is subtended by a leaf.* The perianth segments are almost entirely free and symmetrical. The style is hairless and is adorned by a distinctively shaped pollen presenter in each species. The leaves have 1-3 glandular teeth. The fruit is ovoid to cylindrical, usually hairless to covered with minute hairs, with a prominent elaiosome at either end joined by a thin ridge down one side.

## A QUICK KEY TO THE PAGODAS

**The Tube Pagodas**
(Page 166, Plate 80)
Involucral bracts conspicuous and brightly coloured
Leaves among headlets small and inconspicuous

**The Golden Pagoda**
(Page 162, Plate 77)
Headlets with 25 to 35 flowers.
Perianth segments fused at base and tip, free in middle

**The Cowl Pagodas**
(Page 163, Plate 77)
Leaf above headlet enlarged and hooded
Headlet tube asymmetrical with involucral bracts on lower side longer than bracts on upper side

**The Silver Pagodas**
(Page 164, Plate 78)
Leaves silver or grey
Leaves among headlets large, horizontal and brightly coloured during flowering
Involucral bracts relatively inconspicuous

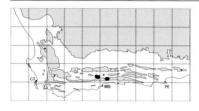

## *Mimetes*  The Golden Pagoda

The Golden Pagoda is a distinct species, not obviously related to any other member of the genus. It is readily distinguished by its *headlets which bear as many as 25-35 flowers.* The *median perianth tube with segments free both at the base and tip* is also diagnostic.

*Mimetes chrysanthus* Rourke                                            Golden Pagoda    **Plate 77**

An erect, sparsely branched shrub up to 2 m tall, with a single main trunk. Leaves lanceolate to elliptic, 30-45 mm long, 10-18 mm wide, hairless when mature; stalk 3-5 mm long. Flowerheads 60-90 mm long, 55-60 mm wide, with a coma, with a faintly sweet scent. *Headlet with 25-35 flowers.* Involucral bracts tightly overlapping, yellow, enlarging up to 4 times and becoming woody after flowering. *Perianth 24-28 mm long, free at base and tip, with a 6-8 mm-long median tube, yellow.* Style yellow, 25-35 mm long. *Pollen presenter 1 mm long, linear, knee-bent at base.*
DISTRIBUTION: Gamka and Perdepoort Mountains. HABITAT: Sandstone soils, 800-1040 m.
STATUS: Known from several isolated patches of a few dozen plants each. *Red Data Book* status: Rare. FLOWERS: March to July, mainly April and May. FRUITS: December.

## *Mimetes* The Cowl Pagodas

The Cowl Pagodas are characterized by the *enlarged sub-tending leaf* which clasps the headlet below it, and the *asymmetrical headlet tube* of which the involucral bracts on the lower side of the headlet are longer than the bracts on the upper side.

*Mimetes cucullatus* (L.) R. Br.  Common Pagoda  **Plate 77**

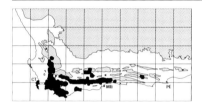

An erect shrub 1-2 m tall, *with many erect stems arising from a large underground rootstock. Leaves oblong-elliptic, hairless, 25-55 mm long,* 5-20 mm wide. Flowerhead cylindrical, 60-100 mm long, 40-70 mm across, topped by a coma of flat, red, reduced leaves. *Headlet with 4-7 flowers, subtended and clasped from above by a red-orange, cowl-shaped leaf.* Style 45-50 mm long, red. Pollen presenter 5-7 mm long, narrowly spindle-shaped, with a thickened ring at base.

DISTRIBUTION: Koue Bokkeveld (near Middelberg) to Kogelberg to Elim Flats; Caledon Swartberg; Cape Peninsula; Potberg; Riviersonderend Mountains, eastern Langeberg to Outeniqua and Kouga Mountains; Klein Swartberg; Rooiberg. HABITAT: Sandstone slopes, 0-1200 m. STATUS: Isolated clumps of a few plants are typical, but extensive stands of scattered plants are sometimes found in the southwest. FLOWERS: All year, mainly August to March. FRUITS: Released 2-6 months after flowering.

□ VARIATIONS: A variable species both in size (dwarf forms with smaller leaves and flowerheads occur sporadically) and in flowerhead colour (red, orange, yellow, cream or, less frequently, yellow-green may occur within populations).

*Mimetes fimbriifolius* Salisb. ex Knight  Tree Pagoda  **Plate 77**

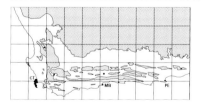

*A tree 2-5 m tall, with a single trunk covered with thick, corky bark. Leaves oblong to elliptic, margin densely covered with hairs,* 40-70 mm long, 12-22 mm wide. Flowerhead cylindrical, 60-80 mm long, 60-70 mm across. *Headlet with 4-7 flowers, subtended and clasped from above by a reddish yellow, cowl-shaped leaf.* Style 55-60 mm long, reddish yellow. Pollen presenter 8-10 mm long, narrowly spindle-shaped, with a thickened ring at base.

DISTRIBUTION: Cape Peninsula. HABITAT: Rocky slopes and flats, sandstone sands, 0-1100 m. STATUS: A striking species growing in clumps of scattered plants around rocky outcrops, often in association with *Leucospermum conocarpodendron.* It is becoming rare in the northern Peninsula. FLOWERS: All year, mainly July to December, with a peak in September. FRUITS: Released ?-6 months after flowering.

## *Mimetes* The Silver Pagodas

In the Silver Pagodas the *leaves between the headlets are much larger and usually more brightly coloured than the involucral bracts. The leaves are distinctly silver* in all species except one, *M. saxatilis*, which has grey leaves.

**Mimetes saxatilis** E. Phillips                                    Limestone Pagoda    **Plate 78**

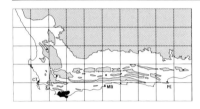

An erect shrub 1-2.2 m tall, with a single main trunk. *Leaves not silvery, hairless when mature,* elliptic to ovate, 35-50 mm long, 17-30 mm wide, with 1 (rarely up to 3) glandular teeth. Flowerheads 50-100 mm long, 50-60 mm across. *Headlet with 12-22 flowers, subtended by a flat green leaf. Involucral bracts conspicuous, yellow. Style yellow, 30-50 mm long. Pollen presenter 4 mm long, ringed at style junction, quadrangular-cylindrical at base, then ovoid with a pointed tip.*
DISTRIBUTION: Elim Flats between Franskraal and Struisbaai. HABITAT: Limestone soils, 0-180 m. STATUS: Encountered as well-scattered stands, often forming dense clumps. FLOWERS: July to December. FRUITS: Released 2-6 months after flowering.

**Mimetes splendidus** Salisb. ex Knight                          Splendid Pagoda    **Plate 78**

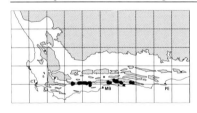

An erect, sparsely branched shrub up to 2.5 m tall, single-stemmed at base. *Leaves with silver hairs,* lanceolate to elliptic, 40-55 mm long, 12-25 mm wide, with 3 or 4 glandular teeth. Flowerhead 80-120 mm long, 60-80 mm across. *Headlet with 10-14 flowers, subtended by a silvery, pink flushed leaf. Involucral bracts ovate,* hairless, yellow. Style 45-55 mm long, yellow. *Pollen presenter 5-7 mm long, ringed at style junction, linear, tip pointed.*
DISTRIBUTION: Western Langeberg, Outeniqua and Tsitsikamma Mountains. HABITAT: Moist, south slopes on peaty soils, 600-1200 m. STATUS: Usually encountered as isolated plants, but a few dense stands of about 40 plants are known. *Red Data Book* status: Rare. FLOWERS: May to September, mainly May to July. FRUITS: Released 2-6 months after flowering.

**Mimetes argenteus** Salisb. ex Knight                            Silver Pagoda    **Plate 78**

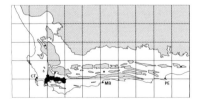

An erect, sparsely branched shrub up to 3.5 m tall, with a single main trunk. *Leaves with silver hairs, held at right angles to branches,* 40-65 mm long, 18-36 mm wide, elliptic, with 1 (rarely 3) glandular teeth. *Flowerhead 100-120 mm across,* 80-150 mm long. *Headlet with 6-9 flowers, subtended by a deep carmine to pale mauve leaf held perpendicular to the stem.* Style 40-45 mm long, yellow. *Pollen presenter 7-8 mm long, knee-bent at style junction, cylindrical with a terminal spur.*
DISTRIBUTION: Hottentots-Holland Mountains from Verkykerskop to Franschhoek to the eastern

Riviersonderend Mountains. HABITAT: Moist, southern, middle slopes, 600-1500 m. STATUS: Usually occurring in scattered stands of a few dozen plants, with a few dense stands of several hundred plants. *Red Data Book* status: Rare. FLOWERS: March to June. FRUITS: Released 2-6 months after flowering.

***Mimetes arboreus*** Rourke                                    Kogelberg Pagoda    **Plate 79**

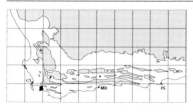

*A large, much-branched shrub* 2-6 m tall, with a single main trunk. *Leaves lanceolate, with silver hairs,* 50-82 mm long, 8-33 mm wide. Flowerhead 80-200 mm long, 80-100 mm across. *Headlet with 8-13 flowers, subtended by an upcurved, orange-pink leaf.* Style 45-55 mm long, yellow. *Pollen presenter 7-8 mm long, knee-bent at junction with style, cylindrical, ending in a small recurved spur.*

DISTRIBUTION: Kogelberg. HABITAT: Moist, montane slopes, 450-1200 m. STATUS: Usually encountered as solitary plants, but a few small groves are known, as well as a single large clump of about 100 trees. *Red Data Book* status: Rare. FLOWERS: April to June. FRUITS: Released 2-6 months after flowering.

***Mimetes hottentoticus*** E. Phillips & Hutch.                Matchstick Pagoda    **Plate 79**

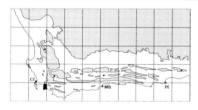

*An erect silvery shrub* 1-3 m tall, with a single basal stem. *Leaves ovate,* 50-75 mm long, 25-40 mm wide. Flowerhead 70-140 mm long, 70-120 mm across. *Headlet with 8-12 flowers, subtended by a flat, silver leaf. Involucral bracts lanceolate. Style 65-70 mm long, red. Pollen presenter 4 mm long, grooved at base, ending in a black cone.*

DISTRIBUTION: Kogelberg on Kogelberg, Dwarsrivier and Kudu Peaks. HABITAT: Upper southern slopes in seeps, 1000-1260 m. STATUS: Known from only 3 populations, with most plants on Kogelberg Peak. *Red Data Book* status: Rare. FLOWERS: January to May, mainly February. FRUITS: Released 2-6 months after flowering.
NOTE: A relatively short-lived plant, usually dying well within 25 years and leaving long-lived seeds in the soil to await the next fire.

***Mimetes stokoei*** E. Phillips & Hutch.                      Mace Pagoda    **Plate 79**

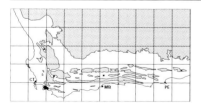

An erect, unbranched plant 1-2 m tall. *Leaves ovate, silver,* 50-80 mm long, 25-40 mm wide. Flowerhead 100-150 mm long, 100 mm wide. *Headlet with 8-12 flowers, subtended by golden yellow leaves. Involucral bracts ovate. Style 50-65 mm long, yellow. Pollen presenter 4 mm long, grooved at base and ending in a black cone.*

DISTRIBUTION: Kleinmond Mountains in the Highlands Forest Reserve. HABITAT: Gentle slopes, moist sandstone soils, 560-600 m. STATUS: Extinct; this species was last recorded flowering in 1967. It was known from 2 clumps, 100 m apart, consisting of about a dozen plants. FLOWERS: All year. FRUITS: Released 2-6 months after flowering.

## *Mimetes* The Tube Pagodas

The Tube Pagodas are distinguished by the *involucral bracts surrounding the headlet being brightly coloured, and the leaves having no display function in the flowerhead.*

---

**Mimetes hirtus** (L.) Salisb. ex Knight                           Marsh Pagoda     **Plate 80**

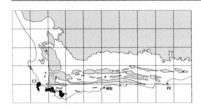

An erect, well-branched shrub 1-2.5 m tall, with a single main trunk. *Leaves lanceolate to broadly lanceolate, 25-45 mm long*, 5-18 mm wide, becoming hairless. Flowerhead topped by a flattened coma of reduced, pink leaves, 80-140 mm long, 80-90 mm wide. *Headlet with 9-14 flowers*, subtended by an inconspicuous green leaf. *Involucral bracts yellow with red tips*, 15-40 mm long, 5-12 mm wide. *Style 50-55 mm long, red*, tapering towards tip. *Pollen presenter 4 mm long, linear; with a prominent ring at the style junction.*
DISTRIBUTION: Cape Peninsula, Kogelberg, Kleinmond and Klein River Mountains to east of Salmonsdam, Elim Flats. HABITAT: Restricted to marshes, seeps and streambanks on black peaty soils, 0-400 m. STATUS: Extinct from Rondebosch to Silvermine, but still locally abundant in dense stands at Cape Point and Betty's Bay. *Red Data Book* status: Vulnerable, owing to housing development at the latter site. FLOWERS: May to November, mainly July and August.
FRUITS: Released 2-6 months after flowering.
NOTE: Relatively short-lived, most plants having grown, set seed and died within 12 years, leaving the long-lived seeds in the soil to await the next fire.

**Mimetes pauciflorus** R. Br.                           Three-flowered Pagoda     **Plate 80**

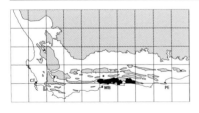

An erect, sparsely branched shrub 2-4 m tall, with a single main trunk. *Leaves ovate, 25-40 mm long, 8-20 mm wide*, young leaves hairy, older leaves with a hairy margin. *Flowerhead with 40-120 densely clustered, upward pointing headlets*, 100-400 mm long, 50-55 mm across, *with a little coma of leaves at the top. Headlet with 3 or 4 flowers*, subtended by an inconspicuous green leaf. *Involucral bracts 10-25 mm long, 5-8 mm wide, 4 or 5 in number*, orange-yellow. Style 45-50 mm long, orange. *Pollen presenter 3-4 mm long, linear to thread-like with a pointed tip and a slightly thickened ring at style junction, orange-red.*
DISTRIBUTION: Outeniqua and Tsitsikamma Mountains between Attaquaskloof and the Kareedouw Pass. HABITAT: Montane, southern, moist slopes, 450-1400 m. STATUS: Found in scattered stands of a few to a few dozen plants. *Red Data Book* status: Rare. FLOWERS: August to November, mainly September. FRUITS: Released 2-6 months after flowering.
NOTE: Relatively short-lived, most plants having grown, set seed and died within 15-20 years, leaving the long-lived seeds in the soil to await the next fire.

*Mimetes palustris* Salisb. ex Knight                    Cryptic Pagoda    **Plate 80**

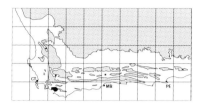

*A low, almost erect shrub,* rarely up to 1 m tall, with a single basal stem. Stems laterally sprawling, well-branched, giving rise to a few erect, unbranched stems. *Leaves lanceolate-elliptic, 15-25 mm long, 5-10 mm wide, tightly clasping stem, densely covered with shaggy hairs. Flowerhead 10-45 mm long, 30-50 mm wide, comprising 5-12 headlets, without a coma.* Headlet with 3-6 flowers, subtended by an inconspicuous grey leaf. Involucral bracts 15-30 mm long, 2-10 mm wide, yellow-green. *Style 30-35 mm long,* yellow fading to orange-red. *Pollen presenter 2 mm long, with style thickened below ring at junction, linear with a pointed tip, yellow with a red flush.*
DISTRIBUTION: Klein River Mountains between Hermanus and Stanford. HABITAT: Swampy, moist slopes, 600-900 m. STATUS: The scattered populations of a few dozen to a few hundred plants are easily overlooked. *Red Data Book* status: Rare. FLOWERS: All year, mainly July to November. FRUITS: Released 2-6 months after flowering.

*Mimetes capitulatus* R. Br.                    Conical Pagoda    **Plate 80**

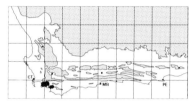

An erect, rounded shrub 2 m tall, with a single main stem. *Stems low, laterally branching with tall, erect, unbranched flowering stems. Leaves lanceolate to ovate, 20-35 mm long, 5-20 mm wide, densely covered with shaggy hairs, tightly clasping stem or spreading. Flowerhead 60-100 mm long, 60-80 mm wide, with 10-13 headlets, without a coma.* Headlet with 11 flowers, subtended by an inconspicuous grey leaf. Involucral bracts 15-40 mm long, 3-14 mm wide, orange-red. Style 45-55 mm long, orange-red. *Pollen presenter 5-7 mm long, thickened below prominent ring at style junction, linear with a rounded to conical tip.*
DISTRIBUTION: Kogelberg, Paardeberg (Kleinmond), Groenland and Klein River Mountains. HABITAT: Swampy, southern slopes of mountain peaks, 600-1200 m. STATUS: Occurs as isolated clumps of plants; only in the Groenland Mountains does the population exceed more than a few dozen, and here it amounts to about a thousand plants. *Red Data Book* status: Rare. FLOWERS: June to December, mainly August. FRUITS: November to February.
□ VARIATIONS: Northern populations lack the low branches, have spreading leaves and bear flowers on most branches. Southern populations have leaves that tightly clasp the stem, flowering branches that are strong and erect, and weaker low branches.

## *OROTHAMNUS* Pappe **The Marsh Rose**

The genus *Orothamnus* is distinct in that the *flowerheads are pendulous and surrounded by large, hairy, pink involucral bracts* which resemble the petals of a rose. The Marsh Rose is most closely allied to the Tube Pagodas, its flowerheads equivalent to the headlets of *Mimetes*. The major difference between *Orothamnus* and *Mimetes* is that the flowerheads of the former are terminal, not axillary as are those of *Mimetes*. The stem continues growing from an axillary bud, thus producing several flowerheads during the flowering season.
The genus is confined to the Kogelberg and the Kleinmond Mountains, with a single population near Hermanus. It comprises only 1 species.

*Orothamnus zeyheri* Pappe ex Hook. f.                    Marsh Rose    **Plate 81**

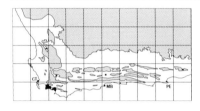

A tall, erect, sparsely branched shrub, reaching 3 m, single-stemmed at base. Leaves 30-50 mm long, 20-30 mm wide, overlapping like tiles, with long hairs, margin hairy, with a smell like ironed washing. Flowerhead terminal, apparently axillary, 40-65 mm long, 40-60 mm across, drooping on a short, downward-curved stalk. *Involucral bracts ovate, 20-40 mm long, 20-40 mm wide, hairy, arranged in 4 or 5 whorls, rose-red.* Flowers 20-45 in number, yellow, only tips visible. Perianth tube very short, segments otherwise free.
DISTRIBUTION: Kogelberg, Kleinmond and Klein River Mountains. HABITAT: Montane, peaty seeps and swamps, 450-850 m. STATUS: Known from a few extremely isolated, dense stands, although single plants may be found on neighbouring ridges. *Red Data Book* status: Rare.
FLOWERS: All year, mainly September. FRUITS: Released a few months after flowering.

## *LEUCADENDRON* R.Br. **The Conebushes**

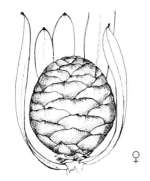

♀

♂

The genus *Leucadendron* is easily identified by having *plants of separate sexes:* the *female plants produce flowerheads that form woody cones in which the fruits are borne*, whereas the flowerheads of the male plants do not form cones. The conspicuous fruiting cones on female plants consist of spirally arranged floral bracts, each of which covers a flower, partially hiding it. After flowering, the bracts become hard and woody, forming the cones. In female flowers the perianth segments are fused into a tube, with only their tips free; and the style is straight or slightly curved, with a large terminal portion, usually with a slit at the top for receiving pollen.

Male plants are usually more branched than female plants and are often slightly larger, with smaller leaves and flowerheads; their flowers are subtended by an inconspicuous floral bract, and the perianth segments are free at the top half of the flower, but often fused into a tube lower down; and the style is always present and serves as a pollen presenter, but other female organs, including the ovary, are reduced.

The identification of conebushes relies very heavily on fruit morphology. Fortunately, many species store their fruits in the female cones for most of the year. In species which do not store their fruit, cones lying on the ground should be collected for identification purposes. Once fruits have been obtained, it is relatively easy to identify the species to which they belong. Depending on the shape of the fruit, conebushes may be separated into two sections: *Alatosperma*, in which the fruits are flat; and *Leucadendron*, in which the fruits are round nuts.

Several other useful characters (required from both male and female plants) include: the size of the cones, the habit of the plant, and the size, shape and hairiness of the leaf. Of these, the multi-stemmed habit versus a single basal stem is by far the most useful and should be carefully noted.

## A QUICK KEY TO THE CONEBUSHES

### FRUIT FLATTENED, STORED IN CONES (SECTION *ALATOSPERMA*)

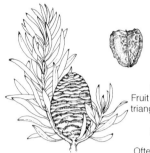

**The Delta-seed Conebushes**
(Page 197, Plate100)
Fruit narrower than 5 mm, triangular in cross-section
Female perianth parts short (2-5 mm), with short, soft hairs
Often very well branched

**The Oilbract Conebush**
(Page 202, Plate 102)
Fruit flat, with median ridge rough and asymmetrical
Involucral bracts large, dark brown and rounded
Cone covered with bootpolish-like resin

### FRUIT A NUT, AT LEAST 1 SIDE ROUNDED, OFTEN RELEASED (SECTION *LEUCADENDRON*)

*FEMALE PERIANTH SEGMENTS FREE OR FUSED, WITH EXPANDING BASES*

**The Arid Conebushes**
(Page 176, Plate 86)
Fruit large, rounded and hairless, released after ripening
Perianth segments hairy at tip

**The Sandveld Conebushes**
(Page 172, Plate 82)
Fruit mottled or with shaggy hairs, tip pointed
Cone small

**The Ridge-seed Conebushes**
(Page 179, Plate 87)
Fruit elongate, grey, with a double ridge on the upper side
Male perianth parts fused into a tube

**The Pauciflor Conebushes**
(Page 180, Plate 88)
Fruit with short or long hairs, with an elaiosome at the base
Female flowerhead with 1 to 3 flowers
Male perianth segments fused into a tube

**The Kouga Conebushes**
(Page 181, Plate 88)
Fruit obovoid, with short hairs
Style shed from fruit
Female perianth segments fused into a tube

## (SECTION *ALATOSPERMA*)

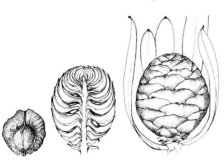
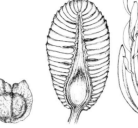

**The Clay and Sunshine Conebushes**
(Pages 203, 205; Plates 103, 104)
Leaves always flat
Fruit wider than 5 mm, flat, winged
Cone bracts curled upwards and overlapping

**The Needle-leaf Conebushes**
(Page 213, Plate 110)
Leaves needle-like in young plants, remaining
needle-like or becoming flattened as they mature
Cone bracts flat and sealed at tips
Fruit wider than 5 mm, flat, winged

## (SECTION *LEUCADENDRON*)

*FEMALE PERIANTH SEGMENTS
FUSED INTO A TUBE;
BASES FORMING A CROSS
AND NOT EXPANDING*

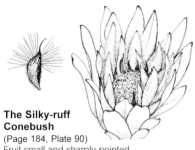

**The Silky-ruff
Conebush**
(Page 184, Plate 90)
Fruit small and sharply pointed,
fringed with hairs 8 mm long
Female perianth segments free
Style retained on fruit

**The Fuse-bract
Conebushes**
(Page 182, Plate 89)
Fruit mottled, sparsely covered
with short hairs
Cone bracts leaf-like and tightly
pressed together

**The Sun Conebushes**
(Page 187, Plate 92)
Fruit large, dark brown, hairless
Cone bracts rounded and
cup-shaped

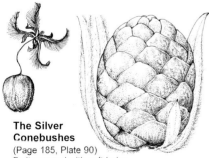

**The Silver
Conebushes**
(Page 185, Plate 90)
Fruit covered with soft hairs
Female perianth segments fused
into a tube, with a plume of hairs at the tip
Style retained on fruit, and together with
perianth segments acts as a parachute
Fruits stored in cones

**The Crown
Conebushes**
(Page 195, Plate 98)
Fruit hairless, rounded on
1 side and keeled on the other,
perimeter with narrow wings
Cone bracts leaf-like and free
Female perianth segments
longer than 7 mm

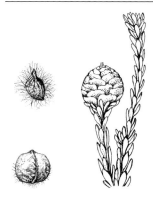

## *Leucadendron* The Sandveld Conebushes

The Sandveld Conebushes (subsection *Villosa*) are characterized by their *mottled, nut-like fruits which are densely to sparsely covered with shaggy hairs and have a pointed tip.* Two of the species (*L. dubium* and *L. concavum*) have almost hairless fruits which are much larger than those of the other species. All tend to be relatively spindly plants with small flower-heads and cones.

Leaf shape and the presence of a rootstock are the most important features used to distinguish between species of Sandveld Conebushes. It is also helpful to subdivide this group on the basis of whether fruits are released and on the leaves' position in relation to the stem:

□ Fruits shed within 2 months of flowering .................................................................................
..................... *L. brunioides, L. concavum, L. coriaceum, L. dubium, L. stellare, L. thymifolium*
□ Fruits retained on the plant ....................... *L. cinereum, L. galpinii, L. levisanus, L. linifolium*

□ Leaves imbricate (clasping the stem and overlapping like tiles on a roof) ...........................
............................................... *L. concavum, L. dubium, L. levisanus, L. stellare, L. thymifolium*
□ Leaves spreading away from the stem .....................................................................................
............................................. *L. brunioides, L. cinereum, L. coriaceum, L. galpinii, L. linifolium*

***Leucadendron coriaceum*** E. Phillips & Hutch.     Rosette Conebush     **Plate 82**

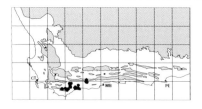

A shrub up to 0.6 m tall, with *thin stems arising from a rootstock. Leaves small, obovate and hairless,* 14 mm long, 6 mm wide, narrowing to base. Involucral leaves similar, forming a neat silvery rosette. Male flowerhead 10 mm long, 17 mm across, solitary, with a yeasty to honey-like smell. Perianth yellow. *Male style with 2 mm-long hairs on basal half.* Female flowerhead 9 mm long, 8 mm across, globose. Cones 15 mm in diameter, fruits released when ripe; bracts narrower than 8 mm. DISTRIBUTION: Rûens northwest of Napier; Potberg; far eastern end of the Riviersonderend Mountains; southern foothills of the Langeberg near Riversdale. HABITAT: Hard, dry, gravelly soil, 130-170 m. STATUS: Known from only 8 stands of a few hundred scattered plants. *Red Data Book* status: Endangered. FLOWERS: September. FRUITS: December.

***Leucadendron brunioides*** Meisn. var. ***brunioides***       Foetid Conebush    **Plate 82**

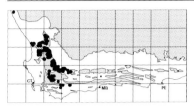

A shrub up to 2 m tall, usually 0.5 m, *with many thin stems arising from a rootstock. Leaves linear, 23 mm long, 1-2 mm wide, hairless.* Male flowerhead up to 11 mm long, 17 mm across, globose, solitary, with a foetid odour. *Male floral bracts oblanceolate, with shaggy hairs.* Female flowerhead 11 mm across, globose, with a foetid odour. Cones 18 mm in diameter, fruits released when ripe.

DISTRIBUTION: Bokkeveld escarpment near Nieuwoudtville, Sandveld, Gifberg, Cederberg, eastern Koue Bokkeveld, Hex River Mountains, Bonteberg, middle and lower Breede River Valley, Riviersonderend Mountains; with isolated populations on the west coast near Kotzesrus and Hondeklip Bay. HABITAT: Deep sandstone sands at bottom of valleys, 100-1000 m.
STATUS: Occurring as scattered plants, often in large populations. FLOWERS: October and November. FRUITS: December and January.
□ VARIATIONS: Northwestern forms have wider leaves. Forms in the far north have fruits which tend to be hairless and male flowerheads which are stalked (like *L. linifolium*).

***Leucadendron brunioides*** Meisn. var. ***flumenlupinum*** I. Williams
                                                        Graafwater Conebush    **Plate 83**

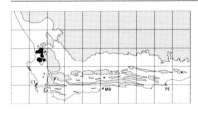

A shrub up to 1.6 m tall, *with many thin stems arising from a rootstock. Leaves linear to oblong, 23 mm long, 2-4 mm wide in female plants.* Male flowerhead up to 11 mm long, 17 mm wide, globose, solitary, with a foetid odour. *Male floral bracts oblanceolate, with shaggy hairs.* Female flowerhead 11 mm across, globose, with a foetid odour. Cones 18 mm in diameter, fruits released when ripe.

DISTRIBUTION: Sandveld from Graafwater to Aurora and Eendekuil. HABITAT: Sandstone soils.
STATUS: Occurring as clumps of scattered plants. *Red Data Book* status: Rare.
FLOWERS: September. FRUITS: December.
NOTE: Closely related to, and intermediate between, *L. brunioides* var. *brunioides* and *L. stellare.*

***Leucadendron stellare*** (Sims) Sweet                       Star Conebush    **Plate 83**

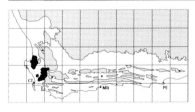

A shrub up to 2 m tall, *with many stems arising from a rootstock. Leaves linear-lanceolate with a narrowed tip, stalkless, tightly clasping the stem,* 8-12 mm long, 2-2.5 mm wide in males, 10-17 mm long, 2-3 mm wide in females. Male flowerhead 15-20 mm across, globose, solitary, with an unpleasant yeasty odour, green-yellow. Female flowerhead 8-10 mm long, 8 mm across, ovoid, solitary, terminal, with a foetid odour. Cones 12 mm in diameter, hairless when mature. *Fruits 4.5 mm long, 4 mm wide*, released when ripe.

DISTRIBUTION: Cape Flats near Durbanville to the Berg River Valley and adjacent flats to Aurora. HABITAT: Level, dry sands over clay, 30-170 m. STATUS: Clumps of scattered plants.
FLOWERS: September and October. FRUITS: January and February.
□ VARIATIONS: Northwestern forms have leaves more oblong and larger (approaching those of *L. brunioides* var. *flumenlupinum* in size) than those of forms in the southeast. Fruits vary from hairless to hairy, and are not always mottled.

**Leucadendron thymifolium** (Salisb. ex Knight) I. Williams    Malmesbury Conebush    **Plate 83**

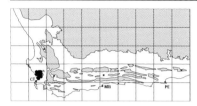

A sparsely branched shrub up to 2 m tall, either single-stemmed or, rarely, *with a few branches arising from a basal stem* (a rootstock, but plants are usually killed by fire). *Leaves elliptic to oblong*, 8 mm long, 3.5 mm wide in males, 8-16 mm long, 4 mm wide in females, clasping the stem. Male flowerhead 10 mm long, 17 mm across, globose, with a yeasty odour. *Floral nectaries present.* Female flowerhead 13 mm across, globose, yellow tinged with purple, with a yeasty odour. *Cones 18 mm in diameter; bracts slightly hairy. Fruits 5.5 mm long, 6 mm wide*, released when ripe.
DISTRIBUTION: Malmesbury Flats from Dassenberg to Klipheuwel. HABITAT: Sands or gravels over clay, 100 m. STATUS: *Red Data Book* status: Endangered, as a result of agriculture, too-frequent fires and invasion by alien plants. It is currently known from 8 populations totalling 700 plants, usually as dense stands of a few to a few hundred plants. FLOWERS: August and September. FRUITS: January and February.

**Leucadendron levisanus** (L.) P.J. Bergius    Cape Flats Conebush    **Plate 84**

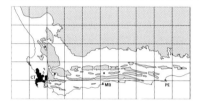

A shrub up to 2 m tall, usually 1 m, *with a single main stem. Leaves oblanceolate to spatulate, 10 mm long, 4 mm wide*, loosely clasping the stem, hairless. Male flowerhead 9 mm long, 16 mm across, globose, with a faint sweet scent, yellow. Female flowerhead 11 mm across, globose. *Cones retaining fruit until released after fire*, 16-19 mm in diameter; bracts 8 mm wide.
DISTRIBUTION: Cape Flats from Fish Hoek to Eerste River to Mamre. HABITAT: Damp, sandy soil on flats, 0-100 m. STATUS: Once one of the most common species in the southern Cape Flats, but now overwhelmed by Cape Town's suburbs. *Red Data Book* status: Endangered. Some of the largest populations occur along road verges and inside race tracks. FLOWERS: October. FRUITS: Retained.
□ VARIATION: Young plants have larger leaves which may be confused with those of the closely related *L. cinereum.*

**Leucadendron concavum** I. Williams    Pakhuis Conebush    **Plate 84**

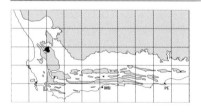

A shrub up to 1.5 m tall, *with a single stem at base. Leaves obovate to circular, with soft hairs, 9 mm long, 5 mm wide in males, 12 mm long, 7.5 mm wide in females*, loosely clasping the stem. Male flowerhead 13 mm long, 20 mm across, odourless, flowers cream-white. Floral nectaries absent (plants are wind-pollinated). Female flowerhead 19 mm long, 13 mm across, globose, flowers in a white, woolly tuft at tip. *Cones with dense hairs*, 21 mm long, 25 mm wide, globose; bracts 15 mm wide. *Fruits released when ripe*, slightly hairy.
DISTRIBUTION: Cederberg at Pakhuis Pass. HABITAT: Sandy plateau, 1000 m. STATUS: Known from 2 populations of about 1000 plants occurring in dense patches. *Red Data Book* status: Rare. FLOWERS: September. FRUITS: November.

*Leucadendron dubium* H. Buek ex E. Phillips & Hutch.  Cederberg Conebush  **Plate 84**

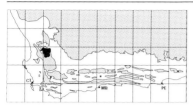

A shrub up to 1.3 m tall, *with a single basal stem and many slender branches. Leaves elliptic, with soft hairs, closely overlapping and clasping the stem, 5-9 mm long, 3.5 mm wide.* Male flowerhead 9 mm long, 12 mm across, odourless. Floral nectaries absent (plants are wind-pollinated). Female flowerhead 12 mm long, 10 mm across, globose, with 6 flowers at tip, odourless. *Perianth with dense hairs. Cones with dense hairs, fruits released when ripe, 20 mm in diameter*; bracts 15 mm wide.
DISTRIBUTION: Cederberg. HABITAT: Level sandstone soils, 1000-2000 m. STATUS: Occurs in dense, isolated stands. FLOWERS: August and September. FRUITS: November.

*Leucadendron cinereum* (Sol. ex Aiton) R. Br.  Scraggly Conebush  **Plate 85**

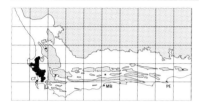

A shrub up to 1 m tall, *with a single main stem. Leaves linear-oblanceolate, narrowed to base, tip with a red gland, 27 mm long, 5.5 mm wide in males, 47 mm long, 5.5 mm wide in females*, slightly twisted. *Male flowerhead stalkless*, 11 mm long, 17 mm across, solitary, terminal, yellow, with a faint sweet scent. Female flowerhead 13 mm across, globose. *Perianth segments overlapping like tiles.* Cones retaining fruit until released after fire, 22 mm in diameter.
DISTRIBUTION: Hopefield and Cape Flats from Aurora to Kraaifontein. HABITAT: Level, sandy soil, 15-100 m. STATUS: Usually occurring as many dense, isolated stands comprising a few plants to several dozen. FLOWERS: October. FRUITS: Retained.
☐ VARIATIONS: Southern forms have smaller leaves. There is a north-south gradient from very hairy to sparsely hairy leaves.

*Leucadendron linifolium* (Jacq.) R. Br.  Line-leaf Conebush  **Plate 85**

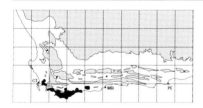

A shrub up to 2 m tall, densely branched, *with a single main stem. Leaves variable, linear-oblanceolate, twisted*, narrowing to base, 7-27 mm long, 1-3 mm wide in male plants, 15-35 mm long, 2-2.5 mm wide in female plants. *Male flowerhead stalked*, 10-12 mm across, solitary, terminal, with a yeasty odour. Female flowerhead 12-14 mm across, globose, with an unpleasant yeasty odour. *Cones retaining fruit until released after fire, 13-24 mm in diameter.*
DISTRIBUTION: Eastern parts of the Cape Flats from Eerste River to Strand; Bot River to Elim and Bredasdorp and to Potberg; Riversdale Flats at Jakkalsfontein. HABITAT: Level, waterlogged, sandy soil over clay, 5-120 m. STATUS: Dense isolated stands occur in suitable habitat.
FLOWERS: September and October. FRUITS: Retained.
☐ VARIATIONS: Forms with the largest leaves occur between Bot River and Hermanus. Occasionally male flowerheads are not stalked.

**Leucadendron galpinii** E. Phillips & Hutch.                    Hairless Conebush    **Plate 85**

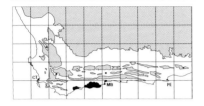

*A tall, greyish shrub reaching heights of 2-3 m*, with a single main stem. *Leaves linear-oblanceolate, tapered to base, twisted*, hairless, up to 39 mm long, 3 mm wide in males, up to 57 mm long, 4 mm wide in females. *Male flowerhead with a 7 mm-long stalk,* 15 mm across, with a yeasty odour. Female flowerhead 17 mm across, globose, silver, with a foetid odour. *Cones retaining fruit until released after fire, 32 mm long, 22 mm in diameter*, globose, with silky hairs, silver.

DISTRIBUTION: De Hoop, Riversdale Flats to Gouritz River Mouth; a curious record from Great Brak River near Mossel Bay. HABITAT: Sandy soils, 0-200 m. STATUS: *Red Data Book* status: Vulnerable, as its lowland habitats are suitable for agriculture. Typically occurring in dense stands dominating the vegetation. FLOWERS: October and November. FRUITS: Retained.

### *Leucadendron* The Arid Conebushes

The Arid Conebushes (subsection *Membranacea*) are characterized by their *biconvex, hairless, dark brown, nut-like fruits* which are released after they have ripened. The fruits are almost identical to those of the Sun Conebushes, but tend to retain the style. Plants of this group are further distinguished by having the *perianth segments of the mature female flowers free, with hairs on the perianth tips and a membranous texture at the base.*

All 4 species are confined to the arid northwestern mountain ranges. The leaf shape and the size of the female flowers are important in distinguishing between species.

**Leucadendron remotum** I. Williams                    Nieuwoudtville Conebush    **Plate 86**

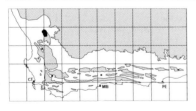

A shrub up to 1.7 m tall, single-stemmed, but branching from near the base. *Leaves 29 mm long, 6.5 mm wide in males, 42 mm long, 8 mm wide in females, oblanceolate-linear, greyish green, erect, the basal end clasping the stem.* Male flowerhead 10 mm long, 16 mm across, solitary, terminal, flattened above, brown in bud, yellow, with a faint smell. *Male style hairless.* Female flowerhead with yellow flowers clustered at a domed tip, surrounded by *shiny brown, overlapping involucral bracts with a pointed tip. Ovary hairy towards the tip. Style longer than 10 mm.* Cones 30 mm long, 25 mm in diameter, bracts purplish brown, tips pointed.

DISTRIBUTION: Bokkeveld escarpment north of Oorlogskloof. HABITAT: Level sandy plains, 800-940 m. STATUS: The scattered to dense plants dominate local communities. *Red Data Book* status: Rare. FLOWERS: August and September. FRUITS: November.

*Leucadendron bonum* I. Williams                    Gideonskop Conebush    **Plate 86**

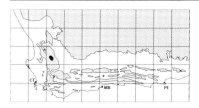

An erect shrub up to 1.6 m tall, with a single main stem. *Leaves spatulate, with soft, silver hairs,* up to 55 mm long, 20 mm wide in males, up to 62 mm long, 26 mm wide in females. Male flowerhead 20 mm long, 21 mm across, yellow, densely woolly in bud, with a faint honey scent. Female flowerhead 18 mm across, globose, with a faint honey scent. *Involucral bracts numerous, tip pointed,* 40 mm long, yellow, *with long hairs, opening in sunny weather and closing when rainy.* Style shorter than 10 mm. Cones 20 mm in diameter, globose, hairy.

DISTRIBUTION: Koue Bokkeveld at Gideon's Kop and Hondverbrand. HABITAT: Level, dry, sandy soil, among rocks, 1950-2000 m. STATUS: Known from 2 populations and 3 dense stands totalling fewer than 250 plants. *Red Data Book* status: Endangered. FLOWERS: October. FRUITS: January.

NOTE: Somewhat intermediate between *L. pubescens* and *L. arcuatum.*

*Leucadendron pubescens* R. Br.                    Grey Conebush    **Plate 86**

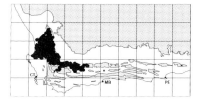

*An erect, dense shrub 0.6-2.5 m tall, greyish green, with a single stem. Leaves oblanceolate, narrowed to base, twisted, hairless or with silvery hairs,* usually showing a marked difference between male and female, 16-28 mm long, 3-7 mm wide in males, 25-57 mm long, 7-15 mm wide in females. Male flowerhead 6-10 mm long, 9-18 mm across, with a sweet scent. Female flowerhead 10-20 mm across, globose, with a yeasty odour. *Involucral bracts with soft hairs, tip pointed. Perianth with soft hairs. Style shorter than 10 mm. Cones covered with silvery hairs, 32-40 mm in diameter, globose.*

DISTRIBUTION: Bokkeveld escarpment from Oorlogskloof, Gifberg, Cederberg, Piketberg, Olifants River, Sandveld, Koue Bokkeveld, Hex River, Bonteberg and Kwadouw Mountains; Witteberg; Touwsberg. HABITAT: Sandstone and quartzite soils, 60-1700 m. STATUS: Extremely common, usually occurring in dense stands. FLOWERS: June to October, mainly July. FRUITS: September to January, mainly October.

□ VARIATIONS: Very variable (previously regarded as up to 6 species) with smaller leaves in northern forms, and populations with hairless leaves common. The following forms may be discerned but do not warrant separate status: a conspicuous crowded involucre at Citrusdal; dwarf plants with silvery leaves on Tafelberg (Cederberg); very pointed leaves on Touwsberg; extremely large leaves (especially in male plants) at Karoopoort; silver leaves in the Koue Bokkeveld and at Ezelbank.

***Leucadendron arcuatum*** (Lam.) I. Williams                    Red-edge Conebush     **Plate 87**

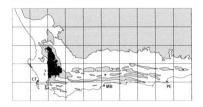

A sprawling or erect shrub up to 1.3 m tall, *with numerous stems arising from a rootstock. Leaves variable, obovate to spatulate, margin red and thickened,* hairless, 55-80 mm long, 19-45 mm wide, yellow below flowerhead. *Male flowerhead globose,* 17-26 mm long, 22-35 mm across, cream, with a sweet scent. Female flowerhead 14-33 mm across, with cream flowers, with a sweet scent. *Involucral bracts narrowly triangular, hairless,* shorter than 30 mm. Style shorter than 10 mm. Cones up to 35 mm in diameter, globose; bracts not tightly pressed together, but densely covered with hairs below.

DISTRIBUTION: Cederberg, Olifants River, Koue Bokkeveld, Groot Winterhoek Mountains, Elandskloof; Hex River Mountains, Keeromsberg, Kwadouw Mountains. HABITAT: Stony sandstone soils, 800-1700 m. STATUS: Isolated patches of a few scattered plants are typical of this species, although some populations are extensive. FLOWERS: September and October. FRUITS: January.

☐ VARIATIONS: Leaf size and habit are very variable in this species. A dwarf form may occur on Saronsberg near Tulbagh. Populations from the Hex River Mountains and Keeromsberg probably constitute a new species, *L. crassulaefolium* (Salisbury ex Knight) I. Williams (Erect Red-edge Conebush). Its characteristic features are the single-stemmed habit, the large, tree-like shrub to 3 m tall, and the broad, round leaves. However, it does not appear to have any distinct floral characters, and cannot be distinguished from *L. arcuatum* in herbarium material.

## *Leucadendron* The Ridge-seed Conebushes

The Ridge-seed Conebushes (subsection *Carinata*) have fruits which are *elongated, grey, smooth nuts, with a double ridge down the upper surface, giving the fruit a double-keeled appearance.* The female perianth segments are free and do not form a tube. The male *perianth segments form a tube* which is fused to the lower part of the style. Because of this, there are no floral nectaries. Both species in this section release their fruits when ripe.

**Leucadendron sericeum** (Thunb.) R. Br.                    Wabooms Conebush     **Plate 87**

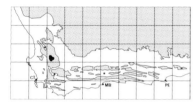

A shrub up to 1 m tall, branching at ground level from a single stem. *Leaves narrowly oblanceolate, with soft hairs (but not silver), up to 9 mm long, 2 mm wide in the males, up to 15 mm long, 2.5 mm wide in females. Involucral leaves the same as foliage leaves.* Male flowerhead solitary or in groups, up to 8 mm long, 11 mm across, with a strong scent. Female flowerhead 19 mm long, 13 mm across, globose, with yellow flowers clustered at tip, solitary or clustered, with a strong sweet scent. Cones up to 17 mm long, 15 mm in diameter, ovoid; bracts densely covered with hairs, tip pointed.
DISTRIBUTION: Koue Bokkeveld at Wabooms River. HABITAT: Level sandstone sands, 900-920 m. STATUS: *Red Data Book* status: Endangered. Known from only 4 populations numbering 2500 plants. FLOWERS: May to September. FRUITS: August to January.
NOTE: Closely related to *L. nitidum.*

**Leucadendron nitidum** H. Buek ex Meisn.                    Bokkeveld Conebush     **Plate 87**

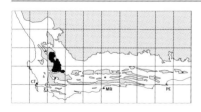

A creeping or erect shrub 0.3-2 m tall, branching at ground level from a single stem. *Leaves narrowly oblanceolate, densely covered with fine hairs, silvery, 9-15 mm long, 2-4 mm wide in males, 11-20 mm long, 2-5 mm wide in females. Involucral leaves twice as large as foliage leaves, yellow, crowded.* Male flowerhead 9-15 mm long, 15-20 mm across, depressed-globose, with a strong, sweet scent.
Female flowerhead variable, 15-20 mm long, 12-18 mm across, ovoid, flowers clustered at tip, with a strong sweet scent. Cones depressed-globose, up to 20 mm long, 25 mm in diameter; bracts densely covered with hairs.
DISTRIBUTION: Cederberg, Koue Bokkeveld and Swartruggens Mountains.
HABITAT: Sandstone and quartzite sands, 1000-2000 m. STATUS: Locally common.
FLOWERS: May to November. FRUITS: June to January.
☐ VARIATIONS: Leaves and flowers variable in size. A low, spreading form with small, inconspicuous involucral leaves occurs in the extreme south on mountain summits.

## *Leucadendron* The Pauciflor Conebushes

The Pauciflor Conebushes (subsection *Uniflora*) are very closely related to the Ridge-seed Conebushes, especially in the male and female floral structure. However, Pauciflor Conebushes have *fruits which are nuts with sparse, short hairs. The female flowerheads bear only 1-3 flowers at their tip.* The female perianth segments are free and do not form a tube. The male flowerheads contain fewer than 12 terminal flowers. *The male perianth segments form a tube* which is fused to the lower part of the style. Because of this, there are no floral nectaries and both species are apparently wind-pollinated. Both species release their fruits when ripe.

*Leucadendron olens* I. Williams                         Yellow Conebush    **Plate 88**

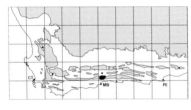

An erect shrub up to 1.2 m tall, single-stemmed at base. *Leaves linear-lanceolate,* tip pointed, 7-11 mm long, 1.2-2 mm wide, hairless. Male flowerhead 9 mm long, 8 mm across, globose, solitary, terminal, yellow, very sweetly scented, bearing 8-12 flowers. *Female flowerhead bearing 2 or 3 yellow flowers, with large forked stigmas,* 5 mm across, terminal, conical-ovoid. Floral nectaries absent. Cones 17 mm long, 8 mm in diameter, conical-ovoid, hairless, with red-tipped bracts.
DISTRIBUTION: Outeniqua Mountains at Groot Doring River. HABITAT: Dry, stony, northern slopes, 590-800 m. STATUS: Known only from 2 dense populations. *Red Data Book* status: Vulnerable, as invasive alien *Hakea* species pose a serious threat to its existence. FLOWERS: June. FRUITS: August.

*Leucadendron ericifolium* R. Br.                    Erica-leaf Yellowbush    **Plate 88**

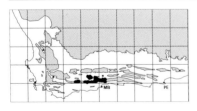

An erect shrub up to 1.3 m tall in males, 3 m tall in females. *Leaves dimorphic, basal leaves ericoid,* up to 27 mm long, hairless; *upper leaves linear,* narrowing to the base, 8 mm long, 1-2 mm wide in males, up to 39 mm long and 4 mm wide in females. *Male flowerheads very numerous,* 7 mm long, 3 mm across, each bearing 12 flowers; stalk 4-14 mm long. *Female flowerhead bearing a single flower,* 12 mm long, 8 mm across, ovoid; stalkless. Floral nectaries absent. Cones 14 mm long, 8 mm in diameter, ovoid, single-fruited; bracts with soft, silver hairs.
DISTRIBUTION: Langeberg and Outeniqua Mountains from Tradouw Pass to George; Rooiberg. HABITAT: Fynbos/renosterbos ecotone, 300-700 m. STATUS: Thought to be extinct in 1972, but several more populations have been found since then. Although occurring only in isolated but dense stands, it has been listed as an agricultural weed on certain herbicide labels since 1984. FLOWERS: July. FRUITS: November.

## *Leucadendron* The Kouga Conebushes

The Kouga Conebushes (subsection *Aliena*) comprise 2 species with a sprawling growth habit. Both bear an *obovoid nut with short hairs* which is released when ripe, and are further characterized by *shedding the style from the fruit*. Both are largely confined to the Uniondale area. The Kouga Conebushes are closely related to the Silver Conebushes, as is apparent from the fused female perianth.

*Leucadendron singulare* I. Williams                     Kammanassie Conebush     **Plate 88**

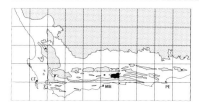

A low, sprawling shrub up to 0.3 m tall, arising from a single stem. *Leaves oblanceolate-linear, narrowing towards the base, densely covered with short hairs, silvery*, 16 mm long, 2.5 mm wide. Involucral leaves crowded, larger than other leaves. Male flowerhead 12 mm across, globose. Female flowerhead 14 mm long, 18 mm across, globose. Cones 17 mm in diameter, globose, with soft hairs.

DISTRIBUTION: Summit ridges along the Kammanassie Mountains. HABITAT: Crevices on summits, 2000-2150 m. STATUS: Known only from several scattered populations. *Red Data Book* status: Rare. FLOWERS: October. FRUITS: February.

*Leucadendron sorocephalodes* E. Phillips & Hutch.                     Woolly Conebush     **Plate 88**

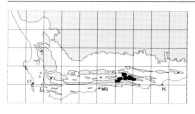

A low, spreading shrub, lower than 0.3 m, up to 2 m wide, arising from a single stem at ground level. *Leaves ericoid, thick, fleshy*, 12 mm long in males, up to 18 mm long and 1.5 mm wide in females, narrowly linear, numerous, hairless. *Involucral bracts numerous, lanceolate, tip pointed, brown, conspicuous.* *Male flowerhead woolly, cream-white*, 12 mm long, 20 mm across, depressed-globose, with a strong sweet scent. *Female flowerhead with woolly, cream flowers at tip*, 17 mm long, 13 mm across, globose, with a strong sweet scent. Cones 15 mm in diameter, globose, floral bracts hidden by conspicuous, dark brown involucral bracts with a pointed tip. Fruits somewhat club-shaped.

DISTRIBUTION: Outeniqua, Kouga and Baviaanskloof Mountains. HABITAT: Among sandstone rocks, 1300-1700 m. STATUS: Poorly known and seldom collected. *Red Data Book* status: Vulnerable, due to too-frequent fires. FLOWERS: August. FRUITS: December.

## *Leucadendron* The Fuse-bract Conebushes

The Fuse-bract Conebushes (subsection *Cuneata*) are distinguished by their *pointed, mottled nutlets which are sparsely covered with short hairs, their fused perianth segments, and their cone bracts which are tightly pressed together with tips spreading*, so that the nutlet looks somewhat like a miniature pineapple. All 3 species are found on level ground in the southwestern coastal plain, and shed their fruits annually. Two of the species (*L. corymbosum* and *L. laxum*) are characterized by a 'corymbose' growth form in which a cluster of short stems is produced at the base of the plant, forming a low, round bush from which long, slender, erect flowering stems emerge.

*Leucadendron verticillatum* (Thunb.) Meisn.　　　　Klapmuts Conebush　**Plate 89**

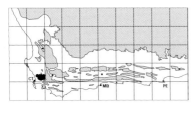

A shrub up to 2 m tall, slender, erect, branching from a single basal stem. *Leaves narrowly oblanceolate, twisted, densely covered with silver hairs, tip with a small, brown point*, narrowing to the base, 22 mm long, 3.5 mm wide in males, up to 25 mm long, 4.5 mm wide in females. Male flowerhead 7 mm long, 11 mm across, turban-shaped, with a faint yeasty smell. Female flowerhead 8 mm across, with up to 12 flowers towards the tip, with a faint unpleasant odour. *Perianth segments tightly pressed together*. Cone 14-16 mm in diameter, globose to vase-shaped; *bracts hairy*, tip rounded. DISTRIBUTION: Cape Flats around Hercules Pillar, Muldersvlei and Fisantekraal. HABITAT: Level, sandy soils over clay, 130-150 m. STATUS: *Red Data Book* status: Endangered. Only 5 dense, extremely isolated populations remain, totalling 2000 plants. FLOWERS: September and October. FRUITS: February.

*Leucadendron corymbosum* P.J. Bergius　　　　Swartveld Conebush　**Plate 89**

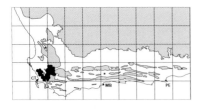

A shrub up to 2 m tall, *with erect stems and many short branchlets clustered at the base*, arising from a single stem at ground level. *Leaves needle-like*, those on tall stems up to 20 mm long, 1.8 mm wide, erect, flattened on the inside; those on branchlets up to 15 mm long, 1 mm wide, closely spaced. *Male flowerhead 12 mm across*, globose, yellow, *solitary at the ends of numerous short branches to give a flattened appearance*, with a foetid odour. *Floral bracts 1.5 mm long with 1 mm-long bristles*. Female flowerhead 8 mm long, 10 mm across, depressed-globose, *flowers somewhat hidden by curling, spatulate floral bracts*, with a foetid odour. Cones up to 18 mm long, 11 mm in diameter, urn-shaped; bracts tightly pressed together, densely covered with hairs at the base. DISTRIBUTION: Cape Flats from Bellville to Paarl, Berg River Valley from Paarl to Saron; Breede River Valley from Tulbagh to Worcester; Riverlands near Malmesbury. HABITAT: Level, wet, clay subsoils in valleys, 100-300 m. STATUS: Despite a tendency to be weedy along road verges and locally abundant, this species has a *Red Data Book* status of Vulnerable due to agriculture, especially viticulture. FLOWERS: September and October. FRUITS: January and February.

***Leucadendron laxum*** I. Williams                               Bredasdorp Conebush     **Plate 89**

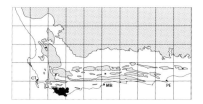

A shrub up to 1.5 m tall, *with slender, erect stems and many short branchlets clustered at the base,* arising from a single stem at ground level. *Leaves needle-like*, up to 13 mm long, 1 mm wide in males, up to 18 mm long, 1.5 mm wide in females, smaller on branchlets, hairless. *Male flowerhead 6 mm long, 9 mm across*, depressed-globose, solitary or in clusters of 3 at the ends of short groups of branches, with a foetid odour; stalk 5 mm long. *Floral bracts 1.5 mm long with bristles shorter than 1 mm.* Female flowerhead solitary, with 12 flowers at the flattened tip. Cones 20 mm long, 14 mm in diameter, ovoid, hairy, *with the points of the tightly pressed bracts elevated.*
DISTRIBUTION: Elim Flats from Hermanus to Bredasdorp and Soetanysberg.
HABITAT: Level, damp ground at the bottom of valleys, 20-200 m. STATUS: Occurs in dense stands. *Red Data Book* status: Endangered, as its habitat is being drained and farmed. FLOWERS: September and October. FRUITS: March.
NOTE: Closely related to *L. corymbosum.*

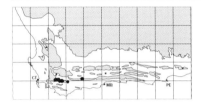

### *Leucadendron* **The Silky-ruff Conebush**

The Silky-ruff Conebush (subsection *Nervosa*) has a *small, sharply pointed nutlet* similar to that of the Silver Conebushes, but the fruit is characterized by being *fringed with 8 mm-long hairs* (thus somewhat resembling the fruit of *Protea*). The female perianth segments are free and hairless, and the style persists on the fruit. This species is most closely related to the Silver Conebushes.

*Leucadendron nervosum* E. Phillips & Hutch.          Silky-ruff Conebush     **Plate 90**

A shrub up to 1.5 m tall, with a single stem at ground level. *Branches hairy. Leaves elliptic, leathery*, 47 mm long, 18 mm wide in males, 60 mm long, 20 mm wide in females, hairless when mature. *Involucral leaves yellow, smaller towards centre, covered with long, white, shaggy hairs.* Male flowerhead 24 mm long, 22 mm across, conical, terminal, with reddish bracts. Female flowerhead 21 mm across, globose, almost hidden by involucral leaves. Style densely covered with hairs at base. Involucral bracts numerous, conspicuous, lanceolate, brown. *Cones conical, densely covered with soft hairs*, 28 mm long, 25 mm in diameter, retaining fruit until released after fire.
DISTRIBUTION: Riviersonderend Mountains and Grootberg in the Langeberg.
HABITAT: Northern slopes, 1100-1350 m. STATUS: Known from several natural, dense stands, but it has been extensively planted in parts of the Riviersonderend Mountains. *Red Data Book* status: Rare. FLOWERS: September. FRUITS: Retained.

## *Leucadendron* The Silver Conebushes

The Silver Conebushes (subsection *Leucadendron*) have *fruits consisting of a soft-haired nut, with the plumed female perianth segments fused into a tube which cannot slip off the persistent style,* thus forming a parachute for seed dispersal. Fruits are stored in the cones for several years.

Leaf morphology is used to distinguish between species.

### *Leucadendron dregei* E. Mey. ex Meisn.                Summit Conebush    **Plate 90**

*A sprawling shrub* up to 0.6 m tall, with a single basal stem. *Leaves linear-oblanceolate, hairless, thick and fleshy*, 25 mm long, 3 mm wide in males, 45 mm long, 5.5 mm wide in females. Male flowerhead 16 mm long, 18 mm across, terminal, solitary or in clusters of up to 7, greenish yellow, with a strong banana smell. Female flowerhead 25 mm long, 24 mm wide, covered with starry green flowers, with 42 brown, lanceolate, overlapping bracts. *Perianth segments surrounding ovaries and later fruits free, fused only at base.* Cones 35 mm long, 30 mm in diameter, red, globose with a pointed tip, retaining fruits until released after fire.
DISTRIBUTION: Swartberg from Touwsberg to Meiringspoort. HABITAT: Southern slopes near summits, 1500-2000 m. STATUS: Scattered plants in extensive populations. *Red Data Book* status: Rare (previously Vulnerable), as it grows very slowly and is being burned too frequently.
FLOWERS: November and December. FRUITS: Retained.

### *Leucadendron album* (Thunb.) Fourc.                Linear-leaf Conebush    **Plate 90**

A silvery shrub up to *2* m tall, with a single basal stem. *Leaves linear to linear-oblanceolate with short, silvery hairs*, 28-42 mm long, 2-3 mm wide in males, 45-59 mm long, 2-4 mm wide in females. Involucral leaves larger than foliage leaves. Male flowerhead 8 mm long, 15 mm across, turban-shaped, greenish yellow, with a faint, pleasant scent. *The posterior perianth segment has a fleshy base.* Female flowerhead 26 mm across, globose, exceeded but not hidden by the involucral leaves, upper half bearing hairy flowers that form greenish yellow stars. *Perianth segments with short plumes, fused, surrounding ovaries and later fruits, and sliding up and down the persistent style.* Cones 33-41 mm long, 28-34 mm in diameter, ovoid, silvery pink, retaining fruits until released after fire.
DISTRIBUTION: Swartberg and Langeberg, Outeniqua and Tsitsikamma Mountains from Swellendam to Uitenhage. HABITAT: Well-drained sandstone slopes, 1100-2000 m.
STATUS: Locally abundant, forming dense stands, especially on the Swartberg.
FLOWERS: December. FRUITS: Retained.
□ VARIATION: Swartberg forms have wider leaves.

***Leucadendron rubrum*** Burm. f.                      Spinning Top    **Plate 91**

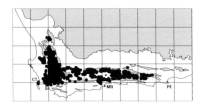

A shrub up to 2.5 m tall, with a single basal main stem, male plants denser and more branched than female. *Leaves oblanceolate, with soft hairs, hairless when mature, green,* up to 34 mm long, 5 mm wide in males, up to 70 mm long and 8 mm wide in females, narrowed and twisted at the base. *Male flowerhead narrow, without involucral leaves,* 11 mm long, 5 mm across, in clusters of up to 16 flowers each, yellow, terminal. *Female flowerhead ovoid with a pointed tip from which the stigmas of the flowers protrude in a tuft,* 40 mm long, 20 mm across, purplish green. Cones 55 mm long, 35 mm in diameter, top-shaped with colourful pointed bracts. *Fruits with persistent style along which the fused perianth segments, with their long plumes, slide.*
DISTRIBUTION: Bokkeveld escarpment, Gifberg and Cederberg to Hottentots-Holland and Riviersonderend Mountains; to Swartberg; to Langeberg, Outeniqua, Kouga and Baviaanskloof Mountains; to Touwsberg; to Rooiberg; to Kammanassie Mountains; to Piketberg; to Table Mountain; and to Cape Flats at Fisantekraal. HABITAT: Dry slopes on granite or sandstone, 250-1500 m. STATUS: Typically occurring in extensive, dense stands, occasionally encountered as scattered plants. FLOWERS: August and September. FRUITS: Retained.
☐ VARIATIONS: Despite its wide distribution there appears to be little variation. Some local forms with hairy leaves (Botterberg) and fewer, shorter involucral bracts (Swartberg Pass) are recorded. A silver-leaved form occurs at Doring River in the Outeniqua Mountains.

***Leucadendron argenteum*** (L.) R. Br.                      Silver Tree    **Plate 91**

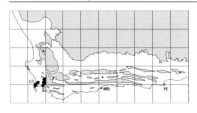

*A tree up to 10 m tall,* with a stout trunk and thick bark. *Leaves silver, margin fringed with long hairs,* up to 150 mm long, 20 mm wide, lanceolate. Male flowerhead 40 mm long, 50 mm across, surrounded and exceeded by the leaves, with a faint, pleasant scent. Female flowerhead 50 mm long, 40 mm across, globose, solitary, silvery or lead-coloured with pink tinge. Cones 90 mm long, 60 mm in diameter, ovoid, tip pointed. *Fruits sparsely covered with long hairs, with persistent style along which the fused perianth segments, with their long plumes, slide.*
DISTRIBUTION: Table Mountain from Lion's Head to Wynberg and Orangekloof; possibly also Helderberg, Simonsberg, Paarl Mountain. HABITAT: Moist slopes on granite clays, 100-500 m. STATUS: Occurring in conspicuous stands, the largest being at Wynberg and Kirstenbosch. All non-Peninsula stands are thought to have been planted, but this is debatable. *Red Data Book* status: Rare. FLOWERS: September. FRUITS: Retained.

## *Leucadendron* **The Sun Conebushes**

The Sun Conebushes (subsection *Nucifera*) are characterized by *large, dark brown, biconvex, hairless nuts*, and in this respect they resemble the Arid Conebushes. The *perianth segments in the mature female flowers are fused into a tube, narrow below and spreading,* with hairs on the upper part of the segments; they do not fall apart into separate segments (as do those of the Arid Conebushes). All species release their fruits when ripe.

The 16 species are classified into 3 groupings on the basis of the morphology of the stigma of the male flowers and the male floral bracts (see key). All the species in this subsection have a single basal trunk, and do not resprout from an underground rootstock.

**Key to the Sun Conebushes**
1    Pollen presenter in male floret truncate and separated by a deep cleft into 2 lobes with a pseudostigmatic surface .................. Stigmatic Sun Conebushes (*L. barkerae, L. burchellii, L. tradouwense, L. orientale, L. pubibracteolatum, L. tinctum, L. cordatum*)
1a  Pollen presenter in male flower almost cylindrical, long and club-shaped ............. go to 2

2    Male floral bracts hairless ................................ Southwestern Sun Conebushes (*L. cadens, L. gydoense, L. sessile, L. daphnoides*)
2a  Male floral bracts hairy ........................................ Northwestern Sun Conebushes (*L. sheilae, L. meyerianum, L. glaberrimum, L. loranthifolium, L. roodii*)

□ The Stigmatic Sun Conebushes comprise 7 species, which can readily be distinguished by the *stigma of the male flower being truncate and forked, the two lobes being separated by a deep cleft and each having a pseudostigmatic pollen presenter*. These species occur from Worcester eastwards to Port Elizabeth, thus comprising the eastern component of the Sun Conebushes. *L. cordatum, L. orientale, L. pubibracteolatum* and *L. tradouwense* may perhaps be considered distinct forms of *L. tinctum,* but they appear to differ in sufficient characters to warrant specific status. The formation of the flowerhead bud and the development of the involucral bracts are useful characters in distinguishing between the species.

□ The Southwestern Sun Conebushes comprise 4 species which are characterized by an *almost cylindrical pollen presenter and hairless male floral bracts*. The leaves and cones tend to be large. These species are distributed in an arc on the Witteberg, southern Cederberg, Du Toit's Kloof and Hottentots-Holland Mountains. They are most easily distinguished from one another by the plant's habit, the shape and size of the leaves, and the involucral bracts.

□ The Northwestern Sun Conebushes comprise 5 species which are characterized by *hairy male floral bracts and almost cylindrical male stigmas*. The leaves and cones also tend to be small. These species are all centred in the Cederberg and associated Hex River Mountains, Gifberg and Nieuwoudtville Mountains in the northwest of the fynbos biome. They are very variable, and are best distinguished from one another by a combination of leaf shape and size, the shape of the involucral bracts and the colour of the flowers.

***Leucadendron barkerae*** I. Williams                                                  Swartberg Conebush     **Plate 92**

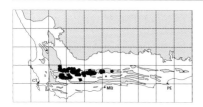

A stout, erect shrub up to 2 m tall, branching at base from a single main stem. *Leaves elliptic, almost glaucous, with fine hairs, occasionally with glandular teeth*, 50 mm long, 13 mm wide in males, 70 mm long, 22 mm wide in females, tip with a red, recurved, fine point, with cartilaginous margin. Involucral leaves larger, yellow. Male flowerhead 33 mm long, 44 mm across, flattened above, flowers spreading widely when open, with a fruit-like smell. *Male floral bracts linear with lateral hairs, tightly clasping base of flowerhead, very distinctive in bud.* Female flowerhead 26 mm across, with flowers at flattened tip, *bracts overlapping and not recurved*, with a fruity smell. Cones 40 mm long, 33 mm in diameter, releasing fruits when ripe; bracts closely overlapping at the base. *Fruits with ridged margin.*
DISTRIBUTION: Bonteberg to Witteberg, Swartberg; Waboomsberg; Warmwaterberg; Langeberg at Koo. HABITAT: Dry areas bordering karoo, 1100-1350 m. STATUS: Known from extremely isolated, discrete stands, each of a few hundred plants. FLOWERS: September and October. FRUITS: December.

***Leucadendron burchellii*** I. Williams                                             Riviersonderend Conebush     **Plate 92**

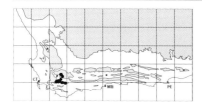

An erect shrub up to 1.6 m tall, with a single basal stem. *Leaves elliptic, hairless, dark green* with purplish margin, 58 mm long, 17 mm wide in males, 60 mm long, 20 mm wide in females, tip with a red, recurved, blunt point. *Involucral leaves closely clasping base of flowerhead and overlapping*, hiding the female flowerhead except from above, yellow and red. Male flowerhead 35 mm long, 42 mm across, *flowers spreading widely when open*, with a lemon scent. *Male perianth slightly hairy.* Female flowerhead 27 mm across, with flowers clustered at tip, sides *with overlapping, recurved involucral bracts*, with a lemon scent. Cones 45 mm long, 35 mm in diameter, globose, releasing fruit when ripe; bracts quadrangular, hairy across middle, not tightly pressed.
DISTRIBUTION: Riviersonderend Mountains from Jonaskop to McGregor, with unconfirmed records from the Langeberg behind Koo. HABITAT: Northern slopes, stony or sandy sandstone soils, 800-1000 m. STATUS: Currently known from 2 discrete, dense populations, but probably more common. FLOWERS: August. FRUITS: December.

***Leucadendron tradouwense*** I. Williams                                                  Tradouw Conebush     **Plate 92**

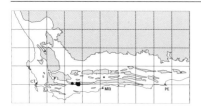

An erect shrub up to 2 m tall, with a single basal stem. *Branches hairless. Leaves erect*, 57 mm long, 13 mm wide in males, 67 mm long, 18 mm wide in females, oblanceolate, tip with a fine, red point, hairless. Involucral leaves 20% larger than foliage leaves, yellow. Flowerheads turn to follow the sun. Male flowerhead 25 mm across, globose, with a strong pleasant smell. Involucral bracts red, recurved. *Male floral bracts hairless.* Female flowerhead 15 mm across, globose, with a pleasant smell; *bracts recurved, not oily. Cones globose or ellipsoid, 1.3-1.6 times as long as wide*, 37-47 mm long, 28 mm in diameter; *bracts broad, tip rounded, hairless above, hairy below, not oily.*
DISTRIBUTION: Langeberg from Tradouw Pass to Grootvadersbos. HABITAT: Steep, southern slopes, sandstone soils, 160-180 m. STATUS: Known from 2 discrete, dense stands, one of which contains most of the 2500 known plants. A population seen in 1932 above Swellendam has not been relocated. *Red Data Book* status: Vulnerable. FLOWERS: June. FRUITS: September.

*Leucadendron orientale* I. Williams          Van Staden's Sunbush    **Plate 93**

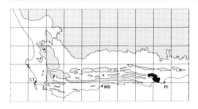

A shrub up to 1.3 m tall, with a few stout branches arising from a single main stem. *Leaves lanceolate to oblanceolate, hairless, erect, grass-green*, up to 90 mm long, 18 mm wide in males, 100 mm long, 23 mm wide in females, glaucous, tip with a recurved, dark red, fine point, margin red and cartilaginous. *Involucral leaves crowded*, overlapping, turning yellow at flowering. Male flowerhead 30 mm long, 35 mm across, cylindrical, with flowers on upper surface, with a strong, pleasant smell. Involucral bracts red, recurved, oily. *Male floral bracts with few hairs.* Female flowerhead 20 mm long, 30 mm across, closely surrounded by involucral leaves, with a strong, pleasant scent. *Involucral bracts numerous (about 94), oblanceolate, recurved*, outer bracts hairy, inner bracts oily. Cones 50 mm long, 40 mm in diameter; bracts thin and hairless above, densely covered with hairs below. Fruits released when ripe.
DISTRIBUTION: Groot Winterhoek, Baviaanskloof and Elandsberg Mountains. HABITAT: Heavy sandstone soils, 150-850 m. STATUS: Poorly known from a few populations. *Red Data Book* status: Vulnerable, as a result of afforestation and invasion by alien vegetation. FLOWERS: June and July. FRUITS: November.

*Leucadendron pubibracteolatum* I. Williams       Purple-leaf Conebush    **Plate 93**

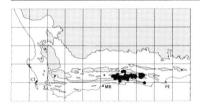

An erect shrub up to 1.3 m tall, with a few branches arising from a single main stem. *Leaves oblanceolate-elliptic, hairless, orientated downward at base and curving upward at tip*, 64 mm long, 21 mm wide in males, 75 mm long, 24 mm wide in females, glaucous, purplish grey, tip with a sunken, fine point. Involucral leaves similar to foliage leaves, but denser, spreading, yellow. Male flowerhead 35 mm long, 35 mm across, cylindrical, with flowers at top, sides with overlapping red bracts, with a sweet, fruity scent. *Male floral bracts with soft hairs.* Female flowerhead 35 mm long, 35 mm across, cylindrical, with flowers at top, with a sweet scent. *Involucral bracts (about 89) reddish, recurved, not shiny or oily*. Cones 50 mm long, 45 mm in diameter, globose; *bracts recurved*, almost quadrangular, tip pointed, densely covered with hairs below. *Fruits with ridged perimeter, released when ripe.*
DISTRIBUTION: Outeniqua, Kouga and Baviaanskloof Mountains from George to Joubertina and Scholtzberg; Slypsteenberg in the eastern Swartberg; Kammanassie Mountains. HABITAT: Stony, sandstone slopes, 300-1000 m. STATUS: Relatively poorly known, occurring in a few isolated stands of 2 or 3 to several hundred plants. Apparently extinct at many of its historical localities. FLOWERS: July and August. FRUITS: November.
□ VARIATION: A variable species, but poorly documented as many populations are no longer available for evaluation. It grades into *L. tinctum* in the west.
NOTE: A possible new species has been discovered from Karoopoort and Hex River to Tweedside near Touws River. It is most similar to *L. pubibracteolatum* in its erect habit and in having very many red involucral bracts forming a base below the flowerheads. However, as in *L. tinctum*, these bracts are oily. The leaves are erect and most similar to those of *L. orientale* in size and shape. As in the other Stigmatic Conebushes, many of these diagnostic features do not preserve in herbarium specimens, so this form will probably not be taxonomically recognized.

**Leucadendron tinctum** I. Williams                    Spicy Conebush    **Plate 93**

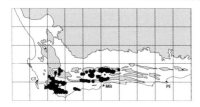

*A bushy, spreading shrub* 1-1.3 m tall, with a single main stem. *Branches hairy. Leaves oblong-lanceolate, hairless, glaucous, orientated downward at base and curving upward at tip,* up to 90 mm long, 24 mm wide in males, 115 mm long, 45 mm wide in females, tip with a recurved, fine point; stalkless. Involucral leaves larger, crowded, forming a large yellow or red bowl. Male flowerhead 30 mm long, 35 mm across, involucral bracts oily, yellow, recurved, with a strong pepper smell. *Male floral bracts hairless.* Female flowerhead 24 mm long, 27 mm across, tip with a floret cluster 10 mm across, *with a strong spicy smell.* Cones 38-47 mm long, 36-41 mm in diameter, globose, *nearly as wide as long, maroon; bracts quadrangular, not recurved, hairless and oily above,* densely covered with hairs across the middle. *Fruits with rounded perimeter.*
DISTRIBUTION: Potberg, Elim and Bredasdorp Flats to Kleinmond, Groenland, eastern Hottentots-Holland Mountains and Stettyns Mountains; Matroosberg in the Hex River Mountains; Langeberg at Gysmanshoek, Garcia's and Robinson Passes; Swartberg Pass; Rooiberg. HABITAT: Stony sandstone soils, 20-300 m. STATUS: Frequently encountered (especially in the southwest) as isolated stands of several hundred plants. FLOWERS: July. FRUITS: November.
☐ VARIATIONS: A variable species in growth and colour forms. Most of the geographically distinct variations have been given specific status. It grades into *L. pubibracteolatum* in the east.

**Leucadendron cordatum** E. Phillips                    Droopy Conebush    **Plate 94**

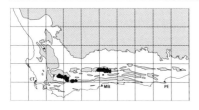

*An erect or sprawling (over rocks) shrub* up to 1 m tall, with a single main stem. *Leaves elliptic or oblong,* 50 mm long, 25 mm wide, with a red, recurved, sunken, glandular tooth, hairless, glaucous, margin cartilaginous. *Involucral leaves larger than foliage leaves, exceeding the flowerhead in length,* up to 75 mm long, 57 mm wide in males, 90 mm long, 53 mm wide in females, crowded, yellow, red or purple, heart-shaped at base. *Flowerheads pendulous on sharply down-curved branch tips.*
Male flowerhead 26 mm long, 25 mm across, cylindrical, flattened above, with a peppery smell. Involucral bracts oily, tip rounded, hairless, overlapping like tiles below. Female flowerhead 20 mm long, ovoid, with flowers clustered at tip, with a peppery smell. Cones 30 mm in diameter, globose; bracts brown, hairless above and densely covered with hairs across the middle. Fruits released when ripe.
DISTRIBUTION: Langeberg between Koo and Barrydale; Swartberg near Klaarstroom.
HABITAT: Rocky sandstone soils, 500-1900 m. STATUS: Known from a few isolated stands of several hundred plants. FLOWERS: June and July. FRUITS: November.
☐ VARIATIONS: Forms at the centre of the distribution range are erect, but sprawling forms occur at its edge. The Montagu form has the largest, broadest involucral bracts. A population which has forms with both nodding and erect flowerheads and both erect and sprawling habits occurs on the Swartberg Pass, although these may be hybrids of *L. cordatum* and *L. tinctum.*

***Leucadendron cadens*** I. Williams                    Witteberg Sunbush    **Plate 94**

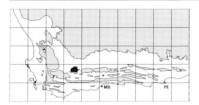

*A prostrate shrub spreading to 0.5 m across from a single main stem. Leaves narrowly oblanceolate, pointing almost vertically from a horizontal stem,* up to 22 mm long, 4 mm wide in males, up to 34 mm long, 7 mm wide in females, tip with a blunt gland, thick, hairless, tinged with red, erect. Involucral leaves inconspicuous. Male flowerhead up to 16 mm long, 15 mm across, solitary, yellow, with flowers spreading at the tip, with a faint spicy smell. *Involucral bracts circular. Male floral bracts 11 mm long, hairless. Perianth tube 9.5 mm long.* Female flowerhead 14 mm long, 11 mm across, ovoid, with flowers clustered at the tip. *Floral nectaries substantially reduced. Cones 27 mm long,* 25 mm in diameter, globose; bracts hairless above but with soft hairs below, shiny, reddened, tip somewhat spreading.
DISTRIBUTION: Witteberg. HABITAT: Among quartzite boulders, 1500-1650 m.
STATUS: Known from several populations scattered in clumps over a distance of 20 km. *Red Data Book* status: Rare. FLOWERS: October. FRUITS: January.

***Leucadendron gydoense*** I. Williams                    Gydo Conebush    **Plate 95**

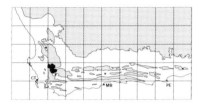

A well-branched shrub up to 1.3 m tall, with a single main stem. *Stems slender, hairless, red. Leaves narrowly oblanceolate,* 45 mm long, 8 mm wide, hairless, tip with a recurved, blunt point, margin narrowly cartilaginous, tapering to the base. *Involucral leaves similar to foliage leaves, not crowded,* turning yellow in male plants and turning pale green in female plants at flowering. Male flowerhead 14 mm long, 30 mm across, depressed-globose, yellow, hairless, with a strong spicy or fruity smell. *Male floral bracts hairless*, with hairy margin. Female flowerhead 19 mm long, 12 mm across, ovoid, with flowers clustered at the tip, sides with overlapping involucral bracts, with a faint spicy smell. Cones 32 mm long, 27 mm in diameter, globose; bracts broad, ovate, red, hairless and resinous.
DISTRIBUTION: Koue Bokkeveld from Gydo Pass to Witsenbergvlakte and Groot Winterhoek Mountains; Hex River Mountains. HABITAT: Sandstone soils, 910-1350 m. STATUS: Locally frequent, in discrete patches. FLOWERS: October. FRUITS: February.

***Leucadendron sessile*** R. Br.                    Western Sunbush    **Plate 95**

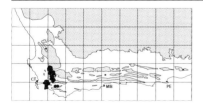

A shrub up to 1.5 m tall, with a single main stem. *Leaves narrowly elliptic*, up to 64 mm long, 13 mm wide in males, up to 80 mm long, 19 mm wide in females, hairless, not shiny, tip with a red, recurved, fine point, narrowed to base. *Involucral leaves similar to foliage leaves, crowded,* yellow or red, much exceeding the flowerheads. Male flowerhead 23 mm long, 35 mm across, depressed-globose, with a lemon scent. *Involucral bracts brown or purplish brown, not recurved, visible.* Female flowerhead 21-28 mm long, 14-18 mm across, elongate-globose, with flowers clustered at the tip, with a sweet scent. Cones 36-44 mm long, 29-31 mm in diameter; bracts broadly elliptic, hairless above with soft hairs below.
DISTRIBUTION: Elandskloof; Slanghoek to Stettyns Mountains; Hottentots-Holland Mountains

from Jonkershoek to Kogelberg. HABITAT: Granite clays on mountain slopes, 10-600 m.
STATUS: Forming extensive, dense, but discrete and well-isolated stands. FLOWERS: July and
August. FRUITS: December.
NOTE: The distribution of this species appears to be divided by the existence of *L. daphnoides.*

***Leucadendron daphnoides*** (Thunb.) Meisn.                                Du Toit's Kloof Conebush     **Plate 95**

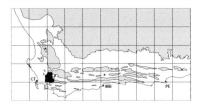

An erect shrub up to 1.5 m tall, with a single main
stem. *Leaves hairless, lanceolate or elliptic,* up
to 60 mm long, 15 mm wide, leathery, glaucous,
narrowing to a blunt, recurved, fine point, margin
cartilaginous. *Involucral leaves closely overlapping
around the lower portion of the flowerhead, hiding
the involucral bracts, broader and shorter than
foliage leaves, becoming yellow then ivory-white
and finally red with age.* Male flowerhead 25 mm long, 43 mm across, depressed-globose,
with a citrus scent. *Male floral bracts with spatulate tip.* Female flowerhead 25 mm long, 23 mm
across, globose, with flowers clustered above, with a citrus scent. *Perianth 21 mm long.* Cones up to
70 mm long, 45 mm in diameter; bracts hairless and thin above, densely covered with hairs below,
old perianths visible.
DISTRIBUTION: Slanghoek and Du Toit's Kloof Mountains and Stettyns Mountains in a triangle
from Bain's Kloof to Wemmershoek and Villiersdorp. HABITAT: Granite slopes, 250-1000 m.
STATUS: The well-isolated stands are usually extensive and dense. *Red Data Book* status:
Vulnerable, as many of the best stands are being lost to forestry. FLOWERS: July to September.
FRUITS: October to December.
☐ VARIATION: Male floral bracts vary from hairless to having long hairs.

***Leucadendron sheilae*** I. Williams                                      Lokenberg Conebush     **Plate 96**

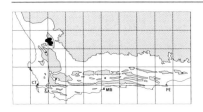

*A small shrub* up to 1 m tall, with a single main stem.
*Branches hairless, green becoming reddish. Leaves
narrowly oblanceolate, grass-green,* 26 mm long,
3.5 mm wide in males, 29 mm long, 4.5 mm wide in
females, glaucous, hairless. Involucral leaves slightly
larger, not concealing the flowerhead, crowded. *Male
flowerhead small, greenish, with a foetid odour,*
10 mm long, 15 mm across, flattened above. *Female*
flowerhead small, globose, with green flowers clustered at the tip, 8 mm long, 6.5 mm across.
*Floral bracts hairy below, ovate, tip rounded. Involucral bracts hairless, with a varnished appear-
ance, reddish brown.* Cones 16 mm in diameter, globose; bracts sparsely covered with hairs below.
DISTRIBUTION: Bokkeveld escarpment from Oorlogskloof, Lokenberg and Kobee Pass.
HABITAT: Hard sandstone sands on flat summits, 800-870 m. STATUS: Fairly large, isolated, but
not dense populations are known. FLOWERS: August. FRUITS: November.

*Leucadendron meyerianum* H. Buek ex E. Phillips & Hutch.

Van Rhynsdorp Conebush    **Plate 96**

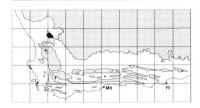

A shrub up to 2 m tall and 3 m wide, *with many slender, purplish branches* arising from a single main stem. *Leaves linear, metal-grey*, 30 mm long, 1.5 mm wide, hairless. Involucral leaves similar to foliage leaves. *Male flowerhead small*, 12 mm long, 16 mm across, turban-shaped, with flowers on upper surface. Involucral bracts reddened, imbricate, with a faint odour. *Female flowerhead small*, 10 mm long, 7 mm across, ovoid, with 7 flowers clustered at the tip. Cones 18 mm in diameter, globose, hairless, reddish brown.
DISTRIBUTION: Bokkeveld escarpment around Nieuwoudtville north of the Oorlogskloof River. HABITAT: Level, sandstone sands, 830 m. STATUS: Usually encountered as small populations of a few dozen plants. FLOWERS: August. FRUITS: December.

*Leucadendron roodii* E. Phillips

Gifberg Conebush    **Plate 96**

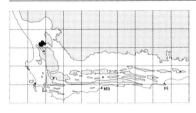

A shrub up to 1.5 m tall, with a single main stem. *Leaves elliptic, hairless*, leathery, 44 mm long, 15 mm wide in males, up to 57 mm long, 17 mm wide in females. Male flowerhead 18 mm long, 20 mm across, globose, with a foetid odour. *Involucral bracts red, pouch-like.* Female flowerhead 17 mm long, 15 mm across, globose, with flowers at tip, with a foetid odour. Cones 17-22 mm in diameter, globose, reddish brown; bracts with a fine point, sparsely covered with hairs.
DISTRIBUTION: Gifberg. HABITAT: Level, sandy, sandstone soils, 660-670 m. STATUS: A single population comprising clumps totalling about 5000 plants is known over a distance of 20 km. *Red Data Book* status: Rare, as its habitat is being lost to agriculture. FLOWERS: August and September. FRUITS: November.
NOTE: Closely related to *L. loranthifolium.*

*Leucadendron glaberrimum* (Schltr.) Compton subsp. ***glaberrimum***

Common Oily Conebush    **Plate 97**

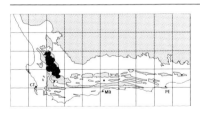

*An erect or spreading shrub* 0.3-1.3 m tall, with a single main stem. *Leaves oblanceolate, hairless or with soft hairs, leathery*, 20-30 mm long, 5-6.5 mm wide in males, 28-38 mm long, 6-10 mm wide in females, green, tip with a red, recurved, fine point. *Involucral leaves inconspicuous.* Male flowerhead 9-12 mm long, 12-17 mm across, depressed-globose, with a pleasant smell. *Male floral bracts 4 mm long, linear, oily, hairy below, hairless above. Male flowers yellow.* Female flowerhead 10-11 mm long, 7-8 mm across, ovoid, with 8 yellow flowers at tip, with a pleasant smell. *Involucral bracts fringed,* lanceolate, numbering 9-15. Cones 20 mm in diameter, globose; bracts few, oily, tip with a fine point, densely covered with hairs below.
DISTRIBUTION: Cederberg to Koue Bokkeveld, Skurweberg, Hex River Mountains. HABITAT: Montane, steep, sandy or stony slopes, 900-1770 m. STATUS: Large but isolated populations are usually encountered. FLOWERS: August to October. FRUITS: December to February.
□ VARIATIONS: Erect forms occur at the centre of the distribution range, with sprawling forms at its edge. A hairy-leaved form occurs on the Baviaansberg.

**Leucadendron glaberrimum** subsp. *erubescens* I. Williams     Red Oily Conebush     **Plate 97**

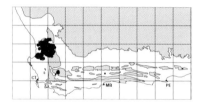

*An erect shrub up to 0.8 m tall,* with a single main stem. *Leaves oblanceolate, hairless, 30-32 mm long, 6.5-7.5 mm wide in males, 39 mm long, 7.5 mm wide in females, not shiny, often purplish, barely narrowed to base,* tip with a red, recurved, fine point. *Involucral leaves slightly larger than foliage leaves. Male flower-head 13 mm long, 20 mm across, with a foetid, yeasty odour. Male floral bracts 5.2 mm long,* linear, oily, hairy below, hairless above. Male flowers yellow. *Female flowerhead 11 mm long, 7 mm across, ovoid, with 8 yellow flowers at tip. Involucral bracts numbering 18,* fringed, lanceolate. *Cones 26 mm in diameter,* globose; bracts few, oily, tip with a fine point, densely covered with hairs below.
DISTRIBUTION: Elandskloof; Olifants River, Groot Winterhoek Mountains, Skurweberg; Piketberg. HABITAT: Montane, steep, sandy or stony slopes, 300-1000 m. STATUS: Large but isolated populations. FLOWERS: August and September. FRUITS: November to February.
☐ VARIATION: A hairy-leaved form occurs at Visgat.

**Leucadendron loranthifolium** (Salisb. ex Knight) I. Williams     Green-flower Sunbush     **Plate 97**

*A shrub up to 2 m tall, with a single main stem. Leaves glaucous, margin cartilaginous,* 38-70 mm long, 12-27 mm wide, variable in shape, tip with a blunt, red, recurved gland, hairless. Involucral leaves crowded. *Male flowerhead green, depressed-globose,* 14-23 mm long, 21-38 mm across, with an unpleasant odour. *Involucral bracts ovate. Male floral bracts linear, densely covered with crispy hairs. Female flowerhead green,* 14-18 mm long, 10-15 mm across, globose, with flowers at tip, with a foetid odour. Cones 20-30 mm long, 24-30 mm in diameter, globose, tip depressed; bracts broad, hairless, sticky, densely or sparsely covered with hairs across the middle.
DISTRIBUTION: Gifberg, Cederberg, Sandveld; a single isolated population in the Hex River Valley. HABITAT: Sandy or stony sandstone soils, 80-1000 m. STATUS: The dense or sparse populations of several dozen to hundreds of plants occur as well-isolated patches. FLOWERS: July to September. FRUITS: November.
☐ VARIATIONS: A variable species with many distinct forms, but difficult to subdivide. Narrow-leaved forms occur in the centre of the distribution range; northern and western forms have large, elliptical leaves; northeastern and southern forms have leaves narrowed to the base. A form with young bracts and leaves densely covered with velvety hairs occurs at Wuppertal. A form with crowded involucral leaves occurs at Algeria and Witelskloof.

## *Leucadendron* The Crown Conebushes

The Crown Conebushes (subsection *Ventricosa*) have *hairless nuts, inflated on 1 side and keeled on the other*, with a narrowly ridged perimeter. The mature *female perianth segments are fused, and longer than 7 mm.* The cones have *bracts quite free* from one another and leaf-like, from an elongated receptacle. All species release their fruits after a 5-month ripening period; the male head resembles a crown. All grow on plains between mountains.

*Leucadendron grandiflorum* (Salisb.) R. Br.     Wynberg Conebush     **Page 222**

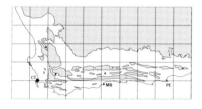

Distinguished from *L. globosum* by its *pale green, smaller (12-14 mm wide), twisted leaves, an unpleasant odour and smaller male flowerheads, bracts and flowers.*
DISTRIBUTION: Wynberg Hill.
HABITAT: Probably shale soils. STATUS: Extinct. Known only from a drawing, of a probably abnormally lanky plant grown in Europe.

*Leucadendron globosum* (Kennedy ex Andrews) I. Williams     Grabouw Conebush     **Plate 98**

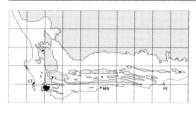

A shrub with a single main stem, males up to 1.3 m, females up to 2 m tall. *Stems hairy. Leaves ovate, dark green*, up to 60 mm long, 30 mm wide, tip round with a recurved gland, hairless. Involucral leaves up to 70 mm long, 33 mm wide, oblong, crowded, yellow. Male flowerhead 25 mm long, 50 mm across, depressed-globose, with a strong spicy smell. Female flowerhead 20 mm long, 23 mm across, globose, with numerous flowers clustered on domed upper surface, sides with closely overlapping *recurved involucral bracts.* Cones up to 50 mm in diameter, globose; bracts wedge-shaped, numerous, recurved above, sparsely covered with hairs below.
DISTRIBUTION: Grabouw to Houhoek in the Elgin Valley. HABITAT: Loamy soils, steep southern slopes, 220-300 m. STATUS: *Red Data Book* status: Endangered, due to loss of habitat to fruit orchards. Formerly it occurred in many isolated populations of several dozen plants. Today fewer than 75 plants are known, mainly from 3 viable populations.
FLOWERS: September and October. FRUITS: February.
NOTE: Resembles *L. tinctum* in bud by having a small rosette of recurved involucral bracts.

***Leucadendron chamelaea*** (Lam.) I. Williams                    Witsenberg Conebush    **Plate 98**

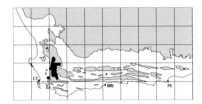

*An erect shrub* up to 2.3 m tall, branching from the base of a single main stem. *Leaves linear-oblanceolate,* 40 mm long, 6 mm wide in males, up to 45 mm long, 6 mm wide in females, hairless, tip with a small, blunt point, narrowed to base. Involucral leaves 20 mm longer in females, narrow, pale, crowded, forming a cup. *Male flowerhead 20 mm across,* depressed-globose, solitary on clustered branch tips, with a pungent odour. Female flowerhead 17 mm long, 21 mm across, globose, with a pungent odour. *Floral bracts in 5 spirals.* Cones 37 mm long, 35 mm in diameter, globose, hairless; *bracts numerous, obovate, not overlapping, green* becoming brown when mature. DISTRIBUTION: Koue Bokkeveld from Leeurivier to Ceres; Witsenbergvlakte; Berg River Valley at Groot Drakenstein; Breede River Valley from Worcester to Wolseley. HABITAT: Level sandstone sands, 150-1000 m. STATUS: Despite having weedy properties and still being common, this species has a *Red Data Book* status of Endangered, due to rapid loss of habitat to agriculture. Large isolated stands can still be found in the Breede River Valley, but it was last recorded in the Berg River Valley in 1934. FLOWERS: September. FRUITS: January.

***Leucadendron elimense*** E. Phillips subsp. ***elimense***                Elim Conebush    **Plate 99**

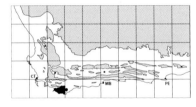

A sparsely branched shrub up to 1.5 m tall, with a single main stem. *Leaves elliptic, 13-49 mm long, 5-19 mm wide in males, 14-57 mm long, 7-21 mm wide in females, closely spaced,* tip with a recurved, red, fine point, hairless, margin narrowly cartilaginous. Involucral leaves crowded, yellow, overlapping base of flowerhead, 20 in number. Male flowerhead 19 mm long, up to 46 mm across, depressed-globose, with a pungent odour. Female flowerhead 20 mm across, globose, flowers closely packed on upper surface, sides closely overlapped by *recurved involucral bracts* and leaves, with a pungent odour. Cones 35 mm in diameter, globose; bracts ovate, numerous, hairless above, with sparse hairs below.
DISTRIBUTION: Elim Flats from Gansbaai to Bredasdorp. HABITAT: Shallow soil with ferricrete over clay, 10-170 m. STATUS: *Red Data Book* status: Vulnerable, due to agriculture. A few discrete populations totalling 2000 plants remain. FLOWERS: July to September. FRUITS: February.
☐ VARIATIONS: Leaf size varies considerably within a population. However, forms in the north and east tend to have smaller leaves, and those in the south and southeast have larger ones.

***Leucadendron elimense*** subsp. ***salteri*** I. Williams                Caledon Conebush    **Plate 99**

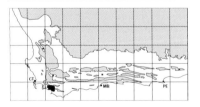

Similar to *L. elimense* subsp. *elimense,* but: *Leaves 55-67 mm long, 15-25 mm wide in males, 61-78 mm long, 19-26 mm wide in females, widely spaced.*
DISTRIBUTION: Bot River Valley, Hemel en Aarde Valley; Rûens near Shaw's Pass. HABITAT: Level gravel soils over clay, 30-330 m. STATUS: *Red Data Book* status: Endangered, due to agriculture. Only 2 major populations, comprising several discrete patches totalling 1500 plants, remain. FLOWERS: August and September. FRUITS: February.
NOTE: Resembles *L. globosum* in having the solitary flowerheads clustered on branch tips.

***Leucadendron elimense*** subsp. ***vyeboomense*** I. Williams          Vyeboom Conebush          **Plate 99**

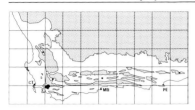

Similar to *L. elimense* subsp. *elimense*, but: *Leaves lanceolate, 43 mm long, 11 mm wide, similar in both sexes*, tip pointed, hairless.
DISTRIBUTION: Northern end of Viljoen's Pass and eastwards to Theewaterskloof Dam.
HABITAT: Level sandy to loamy soils, 330-400 m.
STATUS: *Red Data Book* status: Endangered, as a result of losing its habitat to agriculture and alien plants. Surviving as 4 adjacent stands totalling 20 plants. FLOWERS: September and October.
FRUITS: February.
NOTE: Resembles *L. chamelaea* and may be either intermediate between *L. chamelaea* and *L. elimense* or a hybrid population between the 2 species.

## *Leucadendron* The Delta-seed Conebushes

The Delta-seed Conebushes (subsection *Trigona*) have *fruits that are less than 5 mm wide* with narrow wings or *are almost triangular in cross-section. The mature female perianth has soft hairs and the lobes abut one another without overlapping.* With the exception of *L. floridum*, all species retain their fruits in the cones. A subgroup, the Stream Conebushes (*L. conicum, L. macowanii, L. pondoensis, L. salicifolium*), has *broad cone bracts, an exposed stigma in the female bud and a female perianth forming a tube. All these species grow in damp places.*
    Note that some forms of *L. xanthoconus* (subsection *Alata*) have fruits typical of this subsection.

***Leucadendron uliginosum*** R. Br. subsp. ***uliginosum***          Outeniqua Conebush          **Plate 100**

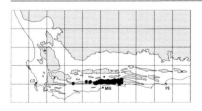

A silvery shrub up to 2.3 m tall, with a single main stem, bushy below with slender, erect, *hairless branches. Leaves linear-oblong, with adpressed, silky, silver hairs*, 35 mm long, 6 mm wide, tip with a small, sunken, fine point, narrowing to base, twisted. On erect stems leaves not twisted, smaller, with a small nodal swelling. Involucral leaves numerous, crowded, edges rolled inwards, yellow, up to 39 in number, forming a star-like cup. Male flowerhead 16 mm long, 15 mm across, globose, with a faint lemon scent. Involucral bracts few, hairy, ovate, with soft hairs. *Male floral bud hairless at tip.* Perianth free, overlapping. Female flowerhead 18 mm long, 12 mm across, ovoid, with a faint smell. Cones 21-33 mm long, 16-24 mm in diameter, globose; *bracts with silver hairs*, numerous. *Fruits narrowly winged.*
DISTRIBUTION: Outeniqua and Tsitsikamma Mountains from Cloete's Pass to Prince Alfred's Pass, with an outlier in the Langeberg above Swellendam. HABITAT: Stony sandstone soils, 500-1000 m. STATUS: Occurs in dense, continuous stands. FLOWERS: November.
FRUITS: Retained.

*Leucadendron uliginosum* subsp. *glabratum* I. Williams    Tsitsikamma Conebush    **Plate 100**

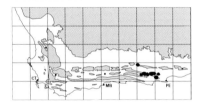

A green shrub up to 4 m tall, with a single main stem and erect branches arising from a bushy base. *Leaves green, with soft hairs, hairless when mature, 20 mm long, 4 mm wide in males, 26 mm long, 4 mm wide in females,* linear, tip with a small, sunken fine point, narrowing to base, twisted. Involucral leaves numerous, crowded, ivory-coloured, forming a star-like cup. Male flowerhead 9-10 mm across, globose, with a faint banana smell. Involucral bracts few, lanceolate, with soft hairs, brown. Perianth free, overlapping. Female flowerhead 14 mm long, 11 mm across, ovoid, green-yellow, with a faint banana smell. Cones 16-24 mm long, 16-20 mm in diameter, globose, red or brown; bracts hairless, numerous. Fruits narrowly winged.
DISTRIBUTION: Outeniqua, Tsitsikamma and Kouga Mountains around the Langkloof.
HABITAT: Sandstone slopes, 500-1000 m. STATUS: Occurs in dense, continuous stands.
FLOWERS: December. FRUITS: Retained.

*Leucadendron loeriense* I. Williams    Loerie Conebush    **Plate 100**

*A red-tinged shrub* up to 2.5 m tall, densely branched below from a single stem, with a few erect stems. *Leaves with erect, velvety hairs, 30-35 mm long, 3-6 mm wide,* narrowly oblong, dark green, tip with a fine point, narrowed to base, slightly twisted. Involucral leaves 16 in number, crowded, lanceolate, green-white, hairless on inner surface, forming a star-like cup. Male flowerhead 15 mm long, 12 mm across, conical. Involucral bracts ovate, hairless, with hairy margin, 6 in number. Female flowerhead 13 mm long, 10 mm across, ovoid, involucral leaves sometimes not coloured. Cones 25 mm long, 20 mm in diameter, globose; bracts reddened and hairless above, densely covered with hairs across middle. *Fruits broadly winged.*
DISTRIBUTION: Elandsberg, Baviaanskloof and Winterhoek Mountains. HABITAT: Sandstone soils, 450-1200 m. STATUS: Known from a few dense stands at widely separated localities. *Red Data Book* status: Rare. FLOWERS: December and January. FRUITS: Retained.
NOTE: Forms previously classified as *L. uliginosum* subsp. *glabratum* from the Kouga Mountains and northward appear to be of this species and require herbarium records for assessment.

*Leucadendron rourkei* I. Williams                    Uniondale Conebush    **Plate 100**

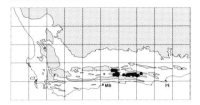

A shrub up to 5 m tall, bushy below, slender above, with a single stem below. *Leaves hairless, up to 18 mm long, 3.5 mm wide in males, up to 24 mm long, 4.5 mm wide in females, oblanceolate*, narrow and twisted at base, young leaves with soft hairs. *Involucral leaves inconspicuous*, crowded, green. Male flowerhead 12 mm long, 9 mm across, globose-elongate, numerous, with a yeasty odour. Involucral bracts lanceolate, edges rolled inward, brown, with soft, white hairs, few in number. Female flowerhead 10 mm long, 9 mm across, globose, solitary at ends of numerous short branches. *Perianth 3.5 mm long.* Cones 19-27 mm long, 16-21 mm in diameter, globose; bracts broad, pale and thin above, hairy across middle. Fruits narrowly winged.

DISTRIBUTION: Kammanassie and Kouga Mountains and eastern Swartberg. HABITAT: Steep, southern slopes, on shale or stony soils, 1370-1700 m. STATUS: Poorly known from a few dense, isolated populations, mostly from a restricted area. *Red Data Book* status: Rare. FLOWERS: December and January. FRUITS: Retained.

□ VARIATION: The young leaves of Kouga forms are sparsely covered with hairs.

*Leucadendron radiatum* E. Phillips & Hutch.              Langeberg Conebush    **Plate 101**

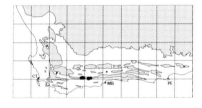

*A dense, robust shrub up to 0.6 m tall*, with a single, short, stout stem. *Leaves sharply twisted, 23 mm long, 5 mm wide*, oblanceolate, tip with a blunt, fine point, tapering to base, thick, leathery, sparsely covered with hairs, hairless when mature, dark green. Involucral leaves crowded, with soft hairs, purplish, exceeding flowerhead in length only in female. Male flowerhead 12 mm across, globose, with a faint sweet scent. *Involucral bracts pale or pink*, with soft hairs, tip pointed, 10 in number. Female flowerhead 11 mm across, globose. Cones 22 mm long, 21 mm in diameter, globose, purple; bracts hairless above, hairy below. Fruits narrowly winged.

DISTRIBUTION: Langeberg from Grootberg to Kampscheberg, possibly at Witelsberg. HABITAT: Southern summit slopes, 910-1700 m. STATUS: Small, dense clumps, in 3 known populations totalling 500 plants. *Red Data Book* status: Rare. FLOWERS: October to December. FRUITS: Retained.

***Leucadendron conicum*** (Lam.) I. Williams        Garden Route Conebush    **Plate 101**

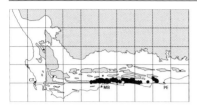

*A shrub or small tree*, 3-6 m tall, with a single main trunk. *Leaves narrowly oblanceolate, dark green*, 38 mm long, 5.5 mm wide in males, 49 mm long, 6 mm wide in females, narrowed to tip with a fine, red point, thin, with soft hairs, hairless when mature. Involucral leaves few, same colour as stem leaves and thus not conspicuous. *Male flowerhead with soft hairs*, 15 mm across, globose, conical in bud,
solitary at ends of numerous small branches, with a fruity smell. *Involucral bracts conspicuous, with soft hairs outside*, linear, edges rolled inward, 9 in number, yellow or purplish inside. Female flowerhead 18 mm long, 12 mm across, ellipsoid, with a faint smell. Perianth 2.5 mm long. Cones 35 mm long, 29 mm in diameter, globose, sparsely covered with hairs, hairless when mature, bracts in 2 spirals. Fruits triangular in cross-section, hairy, sharply edged.
DISTRIBUTION: Langeberg from Witte-els Peak, Outeniqua and Tsitsikamma Mountains, Elandsberg to Loerie; Garden Route Flats. HABITAT: Damp valleys, kloofs and streams, 300-1000 m. STATUS: Occurring in dense, extensive stands. FLOWERS: October and November. FRUITS: Retained.
☐ VARIATION: A form with a reddish tint to the leaves and with pink involucral bracts occurs in the Outeniqua Mountains.

***Leucadendron salicifolium*** (Salisb.) I. Williams      Common Stream Conebush    **Plate 101**

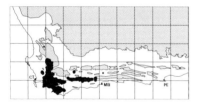

A shrub up to 3 m tall, with a single main stem. *Leaves linear, hairless*, 60 mm long, 5 mm wide, twisted strongly below, slightly sickle-shaped. Involucral leaves few, crowded, yellow-cream. *Male flowerhead 13 mm long, 9 mm across*, hairless, at ends of numerous short branches, with a faint fruity smell, dispersing pollen when knocked (plants are wind-pollinated). Involucral bracts hairless, 7 in
number, tip pointed, forming a conspicuous yellow cup. Female flowerhead 14 mm long, 10 mm across, ovoid, green, with a faint fruity smell. Floral nectaries reduced. Cones 30-40 mm long, 25-30 mm in diameter, hairless; bracts broad and laterally lobed (never bilobed or hairy). Fruits triangular in cross-section, with a narrowly winged or ridged perimeter.
DISTRIBUTION: Olifants River Mountains at Dasklip Pass, Witsenbergvlakte, Elandskloof, Slanghoek, Du Toit's Kloof and Hottentots-Holland Mountains, Kogelberg, Groenland, Kleinmond, Klein River and Bredasdorp Mountains, Elim Flats; Riviersonderend Mountains and Langeberg to the Gouritz River; Paardeberg (Malmesbury); Anysberg. HABITAT: Sandstone sands and seeps near streams, 0-1000 m. STATUS: Occurring in dense, extensive stands. FLOWERS: July to September. FRUITS: Retained.

*Leucadendron pondoense* A.E. van Wyk          Pondoland Conebush          **Plate 101**

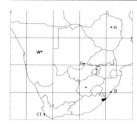

A shrub up to 6 m tall, with a single main stem. *Leaves 35-60 mm long, 2.5-4 mm wide in males, 50-70 mm long, 3-4 mm wide in females*, leathery, with soft, silver hairs, hairless when mature, slightly sickle-shaped, tip with a fine, red point, base tapered to a 2 mm-long stalk. Involucral leaves absent. *Male flowerhead densely covered with silver hairs*, globose, 10 mm across, odourless. *Involucral bracts inconspicuous, linear, 8 in number, with soft hairs on outer surface.* Female flowerhead 12-15 mm long, 8-9 mm across, ellipsoid, odourless. Perianth 3-3.5 mm long, ovary with dense hairs. Cones 25-35 mm long, 15-20 mm in diameter, hairless at tip, with dense hairs below. *Fruits not retained*, triangular in cross-section, with a few hairs, sharply edged.
DISTRIBUTION: Pondoland, from Port St Johns to Port Edward. HABITAT: Riverbeds, 20-250 mm.
STATUS: Grows in dense stands. *Red Data Book* status: Rare. FLOWERS: September to December.
FRUITS: Released after about 12 months.

*Leucadendron macowanii* E. Phillips          Acacia-leaf Conebush          **Plate 102**

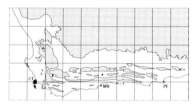

A shrub up to 2.3 m tall, with a single main stem. *Leaves narrowly oblanceolate, 53 mm long, 7 mm wide in males, up to 77 mm long, 9 mm wide in females*, twisted, sparsely covered with soft hairs at base, tip with a recurved fine point, rim slightly raised. *Involucral leaves absent.* Male flowerhead 15 mm long, 14 mm across, ovoid, terminal on numerous short branches, odourless, releasing pollen when knocked (plant is wind-pollinated). *Involucral bracts 14 in number, inconspicuous*, outer bracts leaf-like, lanceolate, becoming brown, hairless, with hairy margin. Female flowerhead 23 mm long, 25 mm across, elongate-ovoid, terminal on stout branches, hairless, reddened on sunny side, with large exposed stigmas, odourless. *Cones hairless*, 30 mm long, 25 mm in diameter, elongate-globose; bracts broad, laterally lobed. Fruits triangular in cross-section, sparsely covered with hairs.
DISTRIBUTION: Cape Peninsula at Smitswinkel Bay and Wynberg. HABITAT: Damp sands near streams, 60-200 m. STATUS: *Red Data Book* status: Endangered, due to agriculture and urbanization which eliminated the Wynberg population, and to invasion by alien acacias which are encroaching the only remaining stands at Smitswinkel Bay. Attempts have been made to establish this species in neighbouring areas within the Cape of Good Hope Nature Reserve.
FLOWERS: May to July. FRUITS: Retained.

**Leucadendron floridum** R. Br.                    Flats Conebush    **Plate 102**

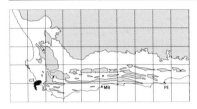

A silvery shrub up to 2 m tall. *Branches hairy.*
*Leaves with silky hairs, tip with a fine point*, 27 mm
long, 5 mm wide, linear, rounded at base. Involucral
leaves 6 in number, similar to foliage leaves, edges
curled. Male flowerhead 14 mm long, 11 mm across,
conical, with a faint fruity smell. Involucral bracts
conspicuous, yellow, hairy margin, lanceolate, 11 in
number. Female flowerhead 13 mm long, 9 mm across,
ovoid, not hidden, with a faint fruity smell. *Perianth fused, tubular.* Stigma 0.5 mm long. Cones
26 mm long, 20 mm in diameter, globose, hairless, with spiral shape, withering and releasing fruit
when ripe. Fruits triangular in cross-section, ridged.
DISTRIBUTION: Cape Flats from Rondebosch to Kuils River, Cape Peninsula around most
vleis. HABITAT: Damp, waterlogged soils and near streams, 10-200 m. STATUS: *Red Data
Book* status: Endangered, due to urbanization and the draining of swamps. Once common as
dense, isolated stands, it is now known from only 2 populations totalling 500 plants.
FLOWERS: September and October. FRUITS: March.
NOTE: Resembles *L. uliginosum*, but has hairy branches.

## *Leucadendron* **The Oilbract Conebush**

The Oilbract Conebush (subsection *Brunneo-
bracteata*) has fruits which are 7-8 mm wide and
have a *sharply ridged perimeter*, a pointed tip, and a
*rough, asymmetrical median ridge*. It also has *dark
brown involucral bracts* which are covered with an
oily, brown, bootpolish-like resin, especially in the
bud stage.

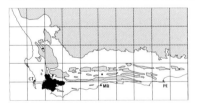

**Leucadendron microcephalum** (Gand.) Gand. & Schinz    Oilbract Conebush    **Plate 102**

A shrub up to 1.5 m tall in males, 2 m tall in
females, with a single stem. Leaves up to 90 mm
long, 20 mm wide, oblong, tip with a blunt, fine
point, narrowed to base, hairless. Involucral leaves
similar to foliage leaves, but crowded, exceeding
flowerheads by far. Male flowerhead 15 mm long,
18 mm across, with a faint fruity smell. *Involucral
bracts conspicuous, with a dark brown oily stain,*
*obovate, concave, large*, 16 mm long, 9 mm wide, hairless, surrounding flowerhead on all sides,
outermost bracts recurved. Female flowerhead 16 mm long, 11 mm across, globose, with a faint
fruity smell. Involucral bracts similar to those of male, almost completely enveloping the
flowerhead. Cones 42 mm long, 33 mm in diameter; retaining fruit until released after fire;
bracts broad, hairless, brown, with a varnished appearance. *Fruits with a double ridge on 1 side.*
DISTRIBUTION: Kogelberg, Kleinmond, Klein River, Groenland, Hottentots-Holland, Du
Toit's Kloof and Riviersonderend Mountains; Caledon Swartberg. HABITAT: Stony sandstone
soils, 0-1330 m. STATUS: Usually encountered as dense populations of hundreds or thousands
of plants, especially extensive near Villiersdorp. FLOWERS: July. FRUITS: Retained.

## *Leucadendron* The Clay Conebushes

The Clay Conebushes (subsection *Alata*) have *winged fruits which are wider than 5 mm* and are retained on the plant until after a fire; *a female perianth tube which has hairless, free segments overlapping one another*; and leaves which are never needle-like. They may be distinguished from the closely related Sunshine Conebushes by their leaves being rough, not smooth, and *their preference for heavy clay soils.*

***Leucadendron lanigerum*** H. Buek ex Meisn. var. ***lanigerum***

Common Shale Conebush　　**Plate 103**

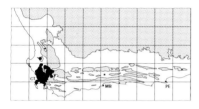

A shrub up to 1.5 m tall, with many stems arising from *a persistent rootstock.* Branches reddish. *Leaves oblanceolate-linear, hairless, gritty to the touch, slightly twisted*, up to 30 mm long, 5 mm wide in males, up to 38 mm long, 5 mm wide in females, tip with a blunt, fine point. Involucral leaves not crowded, becoming pale yellow. Male flowerhead 13 mm long, 11 mm across, globose, with a foetid to yeasty odour. Involucral bracts lanceolate, hairless with hairy margin, dusky. Female flowerhead 7-15 mm long, 7-12 mm across, globose, with a foetid odour. Cones 24 mm long, 21 mm in diameter, globose; bracts hairy, dimpled.

DISTRIBUTION: Cape and Malmesbury Flats from Strand and Diep River to Bain's Kloof and Dassenberg; a possible population on Piketberg. HABITAT: Level clays, 180-200 m.

STATUS: Scattered plants over extensive areas. *Red Data Book* status may have to be upgraded to Endangered due to habitat loss. FLOWERS: July to September. FRUITS: Retained.

NOTE: Easily confused with *L. salignum*, but has rough, not smooth, leaves.

***Leucadendron lanigerum*** var. ***laevigatum*** Meisn.　　Worcester Shale Conebush　　**Plate 103**

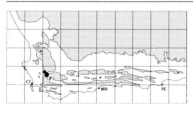

*A shrub up to 1.6 m tall, with a single main stem.* Branches reddish. *Leaves smoother than those of the typical variety*, oblanceolate-linear, slightly twisted, up to 30 mm long, 5 mm wide in males, *up to 40 mm long, 7 mm wide in females,* tip with a blunt, fine point. Involucral leaves not crowded, becoming pale yellow. Male flowerhead 13 mm long, 11 mm across, globose, with a foetid to yeasty odour. Involucral bracts lanceolate, hairless with a hairy margin, dusky. *Female flowerhead 12 mm long, 9 mm across*, globose, with a foetid odour. *Cones 22 mm long, 16 mm in diameter, ovoid;* bracts hairy, dimpled.

DISTRIBUTION: Breede River Valley from Tulbagh to Wolseley, with a dubious record from east of Ceres. HABITAT: Level clays, 300 m. STATUS: Scattered plants over extensive areas. FLOWERS: July to September. FRUITS: Retained.

□ VARIATION: Occasional plants with red flowers may be encountered.

***Leucadendron modestum*** I. Williams                          Rough-leaf Conebush     **Plate 103**

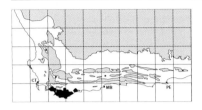

A shrub up to 0.6 m tall, *single-stemmed at base.* Branches red. *Leaves narrowly oblanceolate*, 18 mm long, 4 mm wide in males, 25 mm long, 5 mm wide in females, tip with a blunt, red, fine point, hairless, gritty to the touch. Involucral leaves longer than foliage leaves and flowerheads, linear. Male flower-head 13 mm across, globose, with a foetid odour. Involucral bracts ovate, 14 in number, hairless, margin hairy, dusky. Female flowerhead 10 mm long, 8 mm across, ovoid, with a faint odour. Cones 23 mm long, 15 mm in diameter, globose; bracts with long hairs.

DISTRIBUTION: Elim Flats from Stanford and Bredasdorp to Agulhas; Napier; Bot River Valley; Potberg. HABITAT: Level gravel or clay soils, 0-165 m. STATUS: Encountered as dense, isolated stands. FLOWERS: August. FRUITS: Retained.

NOTE: Closely related to *L. lanigerum*, but smaller all round, with proportionately wider leaves.

***Leucadendron stelligerum*** I. Williams                          Agulhas Conebush     **Plate 103**

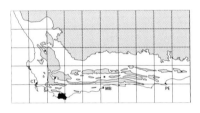

A shrub up to 1.3 m tall, with a single main stem. Branches reddish. *Leaves 23 mm long, 7 mm wide in males, 28 mm long, 8 mm wide in females, not twisted*, oblanceolate, tip with a blunt, fine point, sparsely covered with soft hairs, thick, gritty to the touch. *Involucral leaves partly concealing the flowerhead in a star-like cup*, longer than foliage leaves, crowded. Male flowerhead 19 mm long, 16 mm across, ovoid, often in clusters terminally on short branches, with a foetid odour. Involucral bracts 7-10 in number, ovate, brown, hairy. Female flowerhead 13 mm long, 10 mm across, ovoid, with a foetid odour. Cones 23 mm long, 15 mm in diameter, almost globose, hidden by involucral leaves; old flowers persisting; bracts small and densely covered with short hairs.

DISTRIBUTION: Elim Flats from Wolwengat to Voëlvlei. HABITAT: Gravel, ferricrete and clay soils, 50-100 m. STATUS: *Red Data Book* status: Endangered. Known from 3 populations totalling 1000 plants, occurring in dense, isolated clumps. FLOWERS: July and August. FRUITS: Retained.

## *Leucadendron* The Sunshine Conebushes

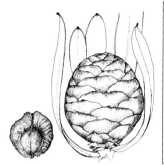

The Sunshine Conebushes are closely related to the Clay Conebushes, belonging to the same subsection (*Alata*). They too have *winged fruits which are wider than 5 mm* and are retained on the plant until after a fire; *a female perianth tube which has hairless, free segments overlapping one another*; and leaves which are never needle-like. Sunshine Conebushes differ from Clay Conebushes in that they have *smooth leaves*, and grow typically in sandy soils. However, *L. meridianum* occurs in calcareous soils, and *L. cryptocephalum* and *L. laureolum* are also found in clay gravels. *Leucadendron salignum* varies in its requirements.

This is a closely knit group, which is subdivided here into 3 groupings purely to aid with their identification. Foliage leaves do not include the involucral leaves (those immediately surrounding the flowerhead).

### Key to the Sunshine Conebushes

1  Plants resprouting from underground rootstocks ...............................................................
..................................................................... *L. flexuosum, L. salignum, L. spissifolium*
   The second and third species are both widespread, the third with several distinct subspecies. Both of these species are variable and best distinguished from each other by
   the hairless, brown, exposed bracts of the cones of *L. spissifolium* and the silvery bracts
   with short hairs on the cones of *L. salignum*.

1a Plants with a single basal stem. Killed by fire ..................................................... go to 2

2  Longest foliage leaves of female plants shorter than 60 mm ................................................
............................... *L. diemontianum, L. foedum, L. procerum, L. discolor, L. meridianum*
   With the exception of *L. meridianum*, all these species occur in the northwestern and
   western areas of the fynbos biome (west of a line from Stellenbosch to the Hex River,
   excluding the Cape Peninsula). Flower colour and leaf hairiness and size are useful
   features in distinguishing the species in this group.

2a Longest foliage leaves of female plants longer than 60 mm .................................................
.......... *L. cryptocephalum, L. xanthoconus, L. eucalyptifolium, L. coniferum, L. gandogeri,*
                                                                         *L. laureolum, L. strobilinum*
   All these species occur mainly on the southern mountains (including the Cape Peninsula)
   and the coastal flats, with only *L. laureolum* overlapping with the distribution of the previous group. Leaf shape and size and cone size are useful features for distinguishing
   species in this group.

***Leucadendron diemontianum*** I. Williams                    Visgat Conebush    **Plate 104**

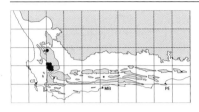

*A shrub with a single main stem and a cluster of branches at base,* and spindly, erect stems up to 1.6 m tall in males, up to 2.2 m tall in females. *Leaves elliptic-linear, clasping stem* so that it appears leafless, 24 mm long, 3.5 mm wide in males, 36 mm long, 6 mm wide in females, tip with a blunt, fine point, hairless, thick, not twisted, dark green or purplish. Involucral leaves broader than foliage leaves, lanceolate, yellow but red when mature, 7-9 in number, overlapping. *Male flowerhead 12 mm across,* up to 15 mm long, ovoid, with a yeasty odour, dropping off rapidly. Involucral bracts ovate, 8 in number, hairless, with hairy margin, brown above when mature. Female flowerhead 10 mm long, 8 mm across, globose, with a yeasty odour. *Cones 13-24 mm long, 13-18 mm across,* concealed by involucral leaves, ellipsoid; bracts indented across middle, hairy below.
DISTRIBUTION: Groot Winterhoek foothills at Visgat, Onderboskloof and Rosendal, and at Heuningvlei in the northern Cederberg. HABITAT: Gentle slopes, sandstone sands, 650-1000 m. STATUS: Known from 3 isolated populations totalling 250 plants. *Red Data Book* status: Rare. FLOWERS: June. FRUITS: Retained.

***Leucadendron flexuosum*** I. Williams                    Worcester Conebush    **Plate 104**

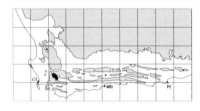

*A slender, spindly shrub* up to 2.5 m tall, without basal shoots, *with a stout rootstock. Leaves oblanceolate-linear, hairless,* 25-27 mm long, 4 mm wide in males, 30-40 mm long, 4 mm wide in females, tip with a blunt, red, fine point, tapering to base. Involucral leaves larger than foliage leaves, yellow but red when mature, almost concealing female flowerhead. *Male flowerhead 14 mm across,* ovoid, with a faint yeasty odour. Involucral bracts small, ovate, 12 in number, brown, with silver hairs. Female flowerhead 10 mm long, 9 mm across, ovoid, with a faint yeasty odour. *Cones 21 mm long,* 19 mm across, globose; bracts grey, densely covered with short hairs, depressed in middle.
DISTRIBUTION: Breede River Valley at Hartebeest River. HABITAT: Level alluvial soils with round stones, 180-200 m. STATUS: *Red Data Book* status: Endangered. Known from a single population which has been reduced to 500 plants by agriculture. FLOWERS: *April and May.* FRUITS: Retained.
NOTE: Similar to *L. lanigerum* var. *laevigatum,* but can be distinguished by its smooth leaves and its earlier flowering season. Very similar to *L. salignum,* but spindly.

***Leucadendron salignum*** P.J. Bergius                    Common Sunshine Conebush    **Plate 104**

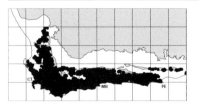

*A multi-stemmed shrub with a persistent rootstock,* up to 2 m tall, usually much less. *Leaves oblanceolate-linear, hairless, not shiny,* 20-47 mm long, 3-5 mm wide in males, 48-58 mm long, 4-6 mm wide in females, tip with a fine point, twisted below. Male involucral leaves not concealing flowerhead, slightly longer than foliage leaves, few in number, yellow or red. Female involucral leaves ivory-coloured, varying from narrow and not concealing flowerhead to broad and concealing flowerhead. Male flowerhead 10-16 mm long, 10-14 mm across, globose, with a sweet or a yeasty smell. *Floral bracts hairy.* Involucral bracts ovate or triangular, hairless, with hairy, dusky margin. Female flowerhead

9-15 mm long, 9-12 mm across, ovoid, with a sweet or a yeasty smell. Cones 17-23 mm in diameter, globose; *bracts with soft hairs*, swollen in middle.
DISTRIBUTION: Widespread from Bokkeveld escarpment to Cape Peninsula to Elim Flats to Riversdale Flats; to Swartberg to Kouga Mountains and Elandsberg; to Langeberg to Tsitsikamma Mountains; Suurberg; Soetwaterberg. HABITAT: Varied, a wide range of soil types, 0-2000 m. STATUS: The most widespread and most common species of the family in the Cape. Usually encountered as extensive populations of scattered plants, but occasional individuals occur even in apparently unfavourable habitats. FLOWERS: April to November. FRUITS: Retained.
☐ VARIATIONS: A very variable species, but with comparatively little variation in southern popula- tions. Far northern forms have smaller, narrower leaves. Individuals with red flowers occur (inter- mixed with yellow-flowered individuals) in the northwest. Forms with larger leaves occur on the northern slopes of the Langeberg and Outeniqua Mountains; eastern populations of this form often have colourful leaves, especially at lower altitudes. A form with occasional male individuals with broad involucral leaves occurs in the Langkloof.
NOTE: Similar to *L. laevigatum* which has rough leaves and, in female plants, involucral leaves not concealing the flowerhead. Also similar to *L. spissifolium*, but the latter has hairless cones.

***Leucadendron foedum*** I. Williams        Hopefield Conebush    **Plate 105**

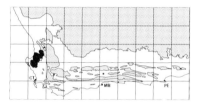

*A shrub up to 2.5 m tall, with a single main stem, male plants rounded,* female plants narrow and sparsely branched. Leaves 27 mm long, 5.5 mm wide in males, 33 mm long, 7 mm wide in female plants, oblanceo- late, hairless, narrowed at tip to a fine point with a tuft of hairs. *Involucral leaves oblanceolate, pale green,* hairless, few in number, not concealing flowerhead. Male flowerhead 19 mm across, globose, with an
unpleasant odour, *flowers yellow. Floral bracts almost hairless. Involucral bracts variable, ovate, with soft hairs and a fringe,* brown, numbering about 20. Female flowerhead 15 mm long, 12 mm across, ellipsoid, with a foetid odour. Cones 22-29 mm long, 21-24 mm in diameter, elongate- globose; *bracts not indented,* with silky hairs, swollen.
DISTRIBUTION: Lower reaches of the Berg River from Hopefield to Het Kruis north of Piketberg; a dubious record from Paarl. HABITAT: Sandy soils, 30-100 m. STATUS: Scattered, often dense stands of several dozen to several hundred plants. FLOWERS: September. FRUITS: Retained.

***Leucadendron procerum*** (Salisb. ex Knight) I. Williams     Ivory Conebush    **Plate 105**

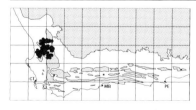

*An erect shrub up to 3 m tall,* with a single main stem, male plants more rounded than female plants. *Leaves oblanceolate,* 26-37 mm long, 10 mm wide in males, 37-47 mm long, 11 mm wide in females, hairless tip with a fine point tufted with hairs when young. *Involucral leaves pale green to ivory-coloured, crowded,* larger than foliage leaves, conspicuous. Male flowerhead up to 22 mm long, 20 mm across, globose,
with a foetid odour, *flowers red.* Floral bracts densely covered with hairs. Involucral bracts ovate, 20 in number, brown, with soft hairs and a fringe. Female flowerhead 16 mm long, 12 mm across, ovoid, green, with a foetid odour. Cones 20-30 mm long, 18-24 mm in diameter, ellipsoid; *bracts ovate, indented (dimpled) in middle,* sparsely covered with hairs.
DISTRIBUTION: Bokkeveld escarpment at Botterkloof Pass, Gifberg, Cederberg to Olifants River Mountains at Redelinghuys, northern Sandveld. HABITAT: Sandstone sands, 300-670 m. STATUS: Localized in dense populations of several dozen to hundreds of individual plants. FLOWERS: August. FRUITS: Retained.
NOTE: Closely related to *L. foedum.*

***Leucadendron discolor*** E. Phillips & Hutch.      Piketberg Conebush    **Plate 105**

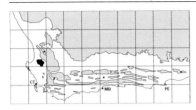

An erect shrub up to 2 m tall, rarely up to 4 m, with a single main stem at base. *Leaves broadly obovate,* 30-35 mm long, 15-17 mm wide in males, 40-48 mm long, 17-20 mm wide in females, tip with a sunken, fine point, margin cartilaginous, narrowed to base, young leaves hairy with a tuft of hairs at the tip. Male involucral leaves similar to foliage leaves, yellow with red tint. Female involucral leaves larger, con-

cave, pale green, overlapping and enclosing flowerhead. *Male flowerhead 38 mm long, including 10 mm-long stalk, 25 mm across, reddened in bud*, oblong, with a foetid odour. Involucral bracts triangular, brown, hairless but with a fringe, grouped at base of stalk. *Floral bracts hairless. Female flowerhead 26 mm long, 16 mm across*, ovoid, with a foetid odour. Cones 43 mm long, 24 mm in diameter, ellipsoid; bracts narrow, with soft hairs above.
DISTRIBUTION: Piketberg. HABITAT: Rocky sandstone soils, 450-500 m. STATUS: Locally common, occurring in dense isolated stands with occasional scattered plants.
FLOWERS: September. FRUITS: Retained.

***Leucadendron eucalyptifolium*** H. Buek ex Meisn.      Gum-leaf Conebush    **Plate 106**

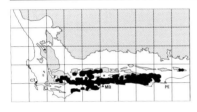

A shrub up to 5 m tall, becoming tree-like, from a single main stem. *Leaves linear-lanceolate, with soft hairs, hairless when mature, tip with a blunt, fine point*, up to 105 mm long, 8 mm wide, narrowed to base, twisted. Involucral leaves few in number, simi-lar to foliage leaves but longer, yellow. *Male flowerhead 24 mm long, 16 mm across*, conical, with a faint smell. Involucral bracts variable, broadly lanceolate, edges

rolled inwards, hairy above, hairless below, yellow, forming a conspicuous cup around flowerhead. Female flowerhead 23 mm long, 12 mm across, ovoid, silvery green with yellow flowers, with a fruity smell. Cones up to 45 mm long, 20 mm in diameter, ovoid; bracts broad, hairy across middle, with transparent hairless margin.
DISTRIBUTION: Potberg; Riversdale Flats, Langeberg, Outeniqua, Tsitsikamma and Kouga Mountains and Elandsberg; Swartberg; Waboomsberg; Warmwaterberg; Touwsberg; Rooiberg; Riviersonderend Mountains; Soetwaterberg; with a doubtful historical record from Grahamstown. HABITAT: Sands, mainly sandstone-derived, 160-1400 m. Often at forest margin. STATUS: Frequent everywhere, occurring in dense, extensive stands in the centre of its distribution range or as discrete populations at the edge of its range. FLOWERS: July to October. FRUITS: Retained.

***Leucadendron coniferum*** (L.) Meisn.      Dune Conebush    **Plate 106**

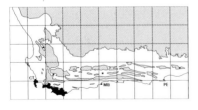

A shrub or small tree up to 4 m tall, with a stout trunk. *Leaves narrowly oblanceolate, tip with a sharp, fine point, hairless when mature*, up to 77 mm long, 7 mm wide in males, 83 mm long, 9.5 mm wide in females, twisted. Involucral leaves yellow, few in number, broadened and hairy below, the inner 6 bract-like. Male flowerhead 28 mm long, 18 mm across, globose, barren towards tip, odourless (possibly wind-

pollinated). *Male stigma hoof-shaped, constricted below tip.* Involucral bracts ovate, hairless but with short hairs on margin, dusky. Female flowerhead 27 mm long, 14 mm across, silvery green with yellow flowers, odourless. Cones 39-49 mm long, 29-31 mm in diameter, ellipsoid; bracts broad, rounded with a small notch, hairless.

DISTRIBUTION: Cape Peninsula south of Karbonkelberg; flats from Kogelberg, Kleinmond, Groenland and Klein River Mountains and Elim Flats to Soetanysberg and Ryspunt.
HABITAT: Wind-blown sands, 0-300 m. STATUS: Dense, isolated stands are typical of this species.
FLOWERS: August and September. FRUITS: Retained.

***Leucadendron meridianum*** I. Williams                    Limestone Conebush     **Plate 106**

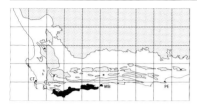

*A densely branched shrub* up to 2 m tall, with a single main stem. *Leaves with silver hairs to hairless*, 40 mm long, 7 mm wide, oblanceolate-linear, twisted at base, tip with a red, short, recurved, fine point. Involucral leaves crowded, 8 in number, longer than foliage leaves, lanceolate, bract-like, yellow, completely enclosing flowerhead except at flowering. Male flowerhead 12 mm across, almost globose, yellow, with a few barren bracts at tip, with a lemon scent. Involucral bracts ovate, 12 in number, with sparse hairs. *Perianth hairless. Abortive male stigma club-shaped.* Female flowerhead 16 mm long, 12 mm across, almost globose, with a faint smell. *Cones with silver hairs, 28 mm long, 22 mm in diameter*, almost globose. Fruits flat, winged.
DISTRIBUTION: Elim, Bredasdorp and Riversdale Flats from Gansbaai to Gouritz River Mouth.
HABITAT: Limestone soils, 0-200 m. STATUS: Occurring in dense stands over large areas.
FLOWERS: July. FRUITS: Retained.

***Leucadendron xanthoconus*** (Kuntze) K. Schum.          Sickle-leaf Conebush     **Plate 107**

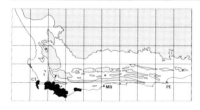

A dense shrub 1-2 m tall, with a single main stem. *Leaves linear-oblong, twisted at base, with silver hairs, hairless when mature, somewhat sickle-shaped*, tip with a fine point, up to 65 mm long, 6 mm wide. Involucral leaves variable, crowded, yellow, far exceeding the flowerhead. Male flowerhead 13 mm long, 10 mm across, ellipsoid, topmost bracts barren. Perianth hairless. Involucral bracts ovate, brown, fringed. Female flowerhead 18 mm long, 11 mm across, ovoid. Cones 30 mm long, 22 mm in diameter, ovoid; *bracts bilobed, hairy.* Fruits either triangular in cross-section or winged.
DISTRIBUTION: Cape Peninsula; Hottentots-Holland and Groenland Mountains, Kogelberg, Kleinmond, Klein River Mountains to Bredasdorp Mountains, Elim Flats; Caledon Swartberg; Riviersonderend Mountains; Potberg. HABITAT: Lower slopes on sandstone soils, 0-670 m.
STATUS: Abundant in extensive stands. FLOWERS: August. FRUITS: Retained.
□ VARIATIONS: Fruits vary in the size of the wing: forms with narrowest fruits (triangular in cross-section) occur in the centre of the distribution range, with fruits at the edge of the range having the broadest wings. The cones are also largest in the latter forms.
NOTE: Forms in the centre of the distribution range may be identified as Delta-seed Conebushes.

***Leucadendron laureolum*** (Lam.) Fourc.          Golden Sunshinebush     **Plate 107**

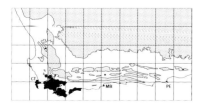

A large, yellowish, rounded shrub up to 2 m tall in male plants, females sparsely branched, bare-stemmed and greenish. *Leaves oblong*, up to 75 mm long, 15 mm wide in males, up to 95 mm long, 17 mm wide in females, tip with a blunt, recurved, fine point, with soft hairs, hairless when mature, margin narrow and cartilaginous. *Involucral leaves almost concealing flowerhead in males, yellow-green and totally*

*concealing flowerheads in females*, oblong, outer leaves longer than foliage leaves, inner leaves becoming shorter and broader. Male flowerhead 23 mm long, 21 mm across, globose, silky at tip, with a faint grapefruit smell. *Involucral bracts brown, hairless*, ovate, 13 in number, fringed with short hairs, recurved towards tip. Female flowerhead 27 mm long, 14 mm across, elongate-globose. *Cones with a spiral of 8 shallow grooves, 38-46 mm long, 32-37 mm in diameter*; bracts broad, rounded with a small notch, hairless. *Fruits winged on sides and above.*
DISTRIBUTION: Cape Peninsula; Paarl Mountain; Hottentots-Holland Mountains, Kogelberg, Kleinmond, Groenland, Klein River and Babylonstoring Mountains, Elim Flats; Riviersonderend Mountains; Caledon Swartberg; Bredasdorp to Potberg. HABITAT: Varied (granite, sands, limestone), but most frequently on deep sands, 0-1000 m. STATUS: Occurring in extensive, dense communities. FLOWERS: June. FRUITS: Retained.

*Leucadendron cryptocephalum* L. Guthrie                Concealed Conebush    **Plate 107**

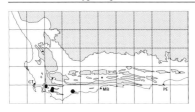

*A bushy shrub up to 1 m tall*, with a single main stem. *Leaves narrowly lanceolate, pale green*, up to 85 mm long, 11 mm wide, with soft hairs, hairless when mature, tip with a blunt, fine point, initially tufted with hairs, broad at base. *Involucral leaves crowded, almost concealing male flowerhead and completely enclosing female flowerhead*, broad at base, longer than foliage leaves, yellow. Male flowerhead 15 mm across, globose, odourless. Involucral bracts circular, hairless, with hairy margin, 12 in number, brown. Female flowerhead 20 mm long, 13 mm across, elongate-ovoid, odourless. Cones up to 40 mm long, 25 mm in diameter, elongate-ovoid; bracts hairy.
DISTRIBUTION: Groenland Mountains at Viljoen's Pass; Caledon; Babylonstoring Mountains at Shaw's Pass; Potberg at Klipfontein. HABITAT: Northern slopes, gravels over clays, 100-300 m. STATUS: *Red Data Book* status: Endangered, due to agriculture. Only 3 populations numbering some 1300 plants remain; the Groenland Mountains and Caledon populations appear to be extinct. FLOWERS: *March to May.* FRUITS: Retained.
NOTE: Similar to *L. laureolum*, but about 20% smaller. The leaves are paler, and it flowers earlier.

*Leucadendron gandogeri* Schinz ex Gand.                Broad-leaf Conebush    **Plate 108**

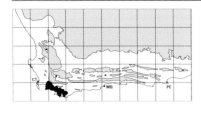

A rounded shrub up to 1.6 m tall, with a single main stem. *Leaves oblanceolate or elliptic, hairless, large*, 42-85 mm long, 18-20 mm wide in males, 60-105 mm long, 20-26 mm wide in females, tip with a red, recurved, fine point, leathery, margin cartilaginous, young leaves soft and hairy. *Involucral leaves crowded, not concealing flowerheads*, yellow, often tinged with orange or red. Male flowerhead up to 24 mm across, globose, with a lemon scent. *Involucral bracts about 20, hairless, fringed, brown*, ovate, recurved. Female flowerhead 25 mm long, 18 mm across, hairless, green bracts with yellow flowers protruding, with a faint smell. *Cones hairless*, 42-64 mm long, 33-45 mm in diameter, globose; bracts often notched, with brown edges clearly outlined.
DISTRIBUTION: Hottentots-Holland Mountains, Kogelberg, Kleinmond, Groenland, Babylonstoring, Klein River and Bredasdorp Mountains, Elim Flats. HABITAT: Stony mountain slopes on sandstone soils, 0-1350 m, more typically higher, moister altitudes. STATUS: Usually occurs in isolated, but extensive, dense stands. FLOWERS: August and September. FRUITS: Retained.
☐ VARIATIONS: Leaves vary. A large-leaved form occurs at Betty's Bay; a form with broad, elliptical, reddish leaves occurs in the Hottentots-Holland Mountains; a form with large leaves, long involucral bracts, very large cones and very large fruits with a rough lower surface occurs in the Groenland Mountains.

*Leucadendron strobilinum* (L.) Druce                    Peninsula Conebush    **Plate 108**

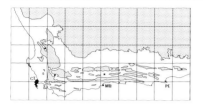

A shrub up to 2.6 m tall, branching from near the base from a single, 150 mm-diameter stem. *Stems stout, purplish, with soft hairs. Leaves elliptic, dark green, hairless, with hairy margin especially when young,* up to 67 mm long, 20 mm wide in males, up to 80 mm long, 23 mm wide in females, tip with a red, recurved, fine point. *Involucral leaves cream-coloured,* crowded, larger than foliage leaves, not concealing flowerheads. *Male flowerhead depressed-globose,* 18-25 mm long, 24-36 mm across, silver-white in bud, with a strong yeasty odour. Involucral bracts ovate, 20 in number, hairless, with hairy margin, recurved above, dusky, oily. Female flowerhead 30-40 mm long, 18-25 mm across, ovoid, flowers numerous, with a strong yeasty odour. Cones 40-65 mm long, 30-41 mm in diameter, ovoid, hairless; *bracts numerous,* sparsely covered with hairs below. Fruits flat.
DISTRIBUTION: Table Mountain to Kommetjie on the Cape Peninsula. HABITAT: Southern, damp, rocky slopes, 500-1100 m. STATUS: Dense, isolated clumps are usually encountered, with the total population estimated at 5000 plants. Very rare south of Constantiaberg. *Red Data Book* status: Rare. FLOWERS: September and October. FRUITS: Retained.

*Leucadendron spissifolium* (Salisb. ex Knight) I. Williams subsp. ***spissifolium***
                                                        Common Spear-leaf Conebush    **Plate 108**

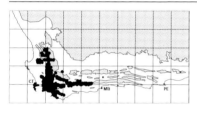

A shrub up to 1.3 m tall, *with many stems arising from a persistent rootstock. Leaves oblanceolate or linear-oblanceolate, hairless, slightly twisted,* 25-63 mm long, 1-7 mm wide in males, 27-81 mm long, 3-17 mm wide in females, tip with a fine, red point, shiny, green. Involucral leaves crowded, ivory-white to pale green, broader than foliage leaves, conspicuous. Male flower-head up to 18 mm across, globose, with a lemon scent. *Involucral bracts lanceolate, brown, with hairy margin,* 20 in number, hairless, recurved. Female flowerhead 16-20 mm long, 13-15 mm across, ovoid, with a lemon scent. Cones 36 mm long, 26 mm in diameter, usually hairless, red when exposed, dead flowers visible; bracts rounded with a slight notch.
DISTRIBUTION: Gifberg, Cederberg, Koue Bokkeveld and Olifants River Mountains; Piketberg; Cape Peninsula, Cape Flats; Groot Winterhoek Mountains to Langeberg at Kampscheberg; Waboomsberg; to Kogelberg to Elim; to Riviersonderend Mountains; Caledon Swartberg; Anysberg. HABITAT: Damp sandstone soils, southern slopes, 0-1500 m. STATUS: Occurs in isolated patches of a few scattered plants which are frequently encountered. FLOWERS: August to October. FRUITS: Retained.
□ VARIATIONS: In any area some populations sometimes have small leaves, others large leaves. Northern forms have sparse, leaf-hugging, long, downy hairs on the leaves. Eastern forms have linear-oblong leaves with long, fine hairs.

*Leucadendron spissifolium* subsp. *fragrans* I. Williams
                                                        Fragrant Spear-leaf Conebush    **Plate 109**

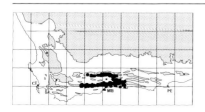

Similar to *L. spissifolium* subsp. *spissifolium,* but: *Leaves 30-45 mm long, 2-2.3 mm wide in male plants, 40-50 mm long, 2-2.5 mm wide in females, linear, channelled, tip with a fine point, twisted, hairless. Involucral bracts lanceolate, tip pointed. Cone bracts hairless.*
DISTRIBUTION: Langeberg and Outeniqua Mountains from Gysmanshoek to Woodville Forest Reserve;

Kammanassie Mountains; Swartberg. HABITAT: Summit and southern slopes, sandstone soils, 500-1800 m. STATUS: Common as isolated patches of a few scattered plants. FLOWERS: September to November. FRUITS: Retained.

***Leucadendron spissifolium*** subsp. ***phillipsii*** (Hutch.) I. Williams
Kareedouwvlakte Spear-leaf Conebush    **Plate 109**

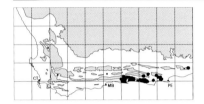

Similar to *L. spissifolium* subsp. *spissifolium*, but: Shrub up to 0.6 m tall. *Leaves up to 50 mm long, 5 mm wide in males, up to 57 mm long, 6.3 mm wide in females, linear to linear-oblanceolate, tip with a fine point, twisted, with soft hairs, hairless when mature. Involucral bracts ovate. Cone bracts hairy across middle.*
DISTRIBUTION: Tsitsikamma Mountains and Elandsberg from Knysna to Van Staden's Mountains. HABITAT: Damp places and southern mountain slopes, 0-300 m. STATUS: Common as isolated patches of a few scattered plants. FLOWERS: October and November. FRUITS: Retained.
☐ VARIATIONS: A form with broad and thickened leaves occurs in the east. Burchell (1814) recorded 2 m-tall specimens in the Tsitsikamma Mountains.

***Leucadendron spissifolium*** subsp. ***natalense*** (Thode & Gilg) I. Williams
Natal Spear-leaf Conebush    **Plate 109**

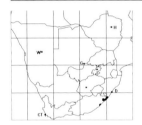

Similar to *L. spissifolium* subsp. *spissifolium*, but: Shrub up to 0.75 m tall. *Leaves oblanceolate, tip with a fine point, twisted below, hairless, 46 mm long, 8 mm wide. Involucral leaves conspicuous, tip pointed, bract-like. Cone bracts hairy across middle.*
DISTRIBUTION: Port St Johns to Port Shepstone; Dwesa. HABITAT: Grassland in damp sandstone sands, 30-500 m. STATUS: Isolated patches of a few scattered plants. FLOWERS: September to November. FRUITS: Retained.

***Leucadendron spissifolium*** subsp. ***oribinum*** I. Williams    Oribi Spear-leaf Conebush    **Plate 109**

Similar to *L. spissifolium* subsp. *spissifolium*, but: *Leaves up to 31 mm long, 3 mm wide in male plants, up to 45 mm long, 4 mm wide in females, linear-oblanceolate, tip with a pale, fine point, sickle-shaped, twisted, hairless. Male flowerhead without involucral leaves.*
DISTRIBUTION: Oribi Gorge near Port Shepstone and near Port Edward. HABITAT: Steep grassy slopes above cliffs, 0-350 m. STATUS: Rare, known from 3 localities. *Red Data Book* status: Uncertain. FLOWERS: October and November. FRUITS: Retained.

## *Leucadendron*  The Needle-leaf Conebushes

The Needle-leaf Conebushes (subsection *Compressa*) all have *seedlings with smooth and needle-shaped leaves.* As the plants mature, these leaves either remain needle-shaped or become flattened, so that more than 1 leaf shape occurs on a plant. *The cone bracts may be partly or completely pressed together,* and *the fruits are compressed and winged.*

Identification of the 6 species is best accomplished by comparing leaf shape, the size of male flowerheads and cones, and the size of the retained fruits.

*Leucadendron teretifolium* (Andrews) I. Williams                Needle-leaf Conebush    **Plate 110**

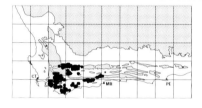

A dense, dark green shrub up to 1 m tall, spreading near the ground from a single main stem. *Leaves needle-like, small,* 8 mm long, 1 mm wide in males, 22 mm long, 1.3 mm wide in females, tip with a fine point, more crowded towards the flowerhead. *Male flowerhead 14 mm long including stalk, numerous,* 7 mm across, flowers in a spike, with a faint yeasty odour. Pollen shed in showers (plant is wind-pollinated). Female flowerhead 20 mm long including stalk, 12 mm across, greenish, not hidden. *Involucral bracts with long pointed tips,* 10 mm long, 2 mm wide, hairy, brown, clasping the stalk. Cones up to 35 mm long, 24 mm in diameter; bracts tightly pressed together, rounded with a small notch, hairless.
DISTRIBUTION: Elim Flats, Klein River Mountains; northern and southern foothills of Riviersonderend Mountains; Potberg; Bonteberg; Witteberg; Waboomsberg; Langeberg near Riversdale. HABITAT: Bokkeveld- and Witteberg-derived soils, 0-1350 m. STATUS: Typically occurring in extremely dense isolated stands. FLOWERS: August and September. FRUITS: Retained.

*Leucadendron osbornei* Rourke                Laingsburg Conebush    **Plate 110**

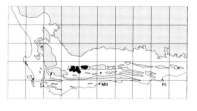

A robust shrub up to 4 m tall, with a single main stem, branching from near the base into several stout, erect stems. *Leaves needle-like,* 15-28 mm long, 1.5-2 mm in diameter, slightly shorter in male plants, hairless, tip rounded with a fine point, slightly grooved on upper surface. Involucral leaves pale green to ivory-coloured, not concealing flowerhead, slightly crowded. Male flowerhead 20-35 mm long, 10 mm across, with a 10-mm stalk, *flowers in a spike.* Involucral bracts 3 mm long, 1 mm wide. *Female flowerhead 20 40 mm long, 12-14 mm across, elongate-ovoid,* growing in length as flowers open, with a stalk 10-15 mm long, with more than 20 involucral bracts 8-12 mm long. Cones 30-70 mm long, 24-40 mm in diameter; bracts hairless.
DISTRIBUTION: Elandsberg, Anysberg, Touwsberg, Matjiesgoedberg. HABITAT: Gravelly or sandy soils, 800-1600 m. STATUS: Surprisingly common and widespread, considering it was discovered only in 1993. FLOWERS: October. FRUITS: Retained.

***Leucadendron spirale*** (Salisb. ex Knight) I. Williams                    Wolseley Conebush        **Page 222**

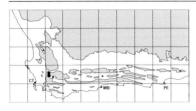

A shrub up to 1 m tall, with a single main stem. *Leaves ericoid, tip roundly pointed, 4-9 mm long,* 1 mm wide, straight, erect, sparsely covered with soft hairs, overlapping in young stems. Male flowerhead 6-8 mm long, ellipsoid. *Male floral bracts rudimentary.* Female flowerhead not known. Cones 20 mm in diameter, oblong-globose; *bracts bilobed, hairless, overlapping below.*

DISTRIBUTION: Breede River Valley from Wolseley to Breede River Station. HABITAT: Riverine and swampy areas, 300 m. STATUS: Extinct; last recorded in 1933. FLOWERS: November. FRUITS: Retained.

***Leucadendron nobile*** I. Williams                    Karoo Conebush        **Plate 110**

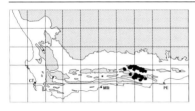

A shrub up to 4 m tall, with a single main stem, branching from the base into several stout, erect stems. *Leaves needle-like,* 41 mm long, 1.2 mm in diameter in males, up to 58 mm long, 1.5 mm in diameter in females, hairless, tip with a fine point, slightly grooved on upper surface. Involucral leaves pale green to ivory-coloured, not concealing flowerhead, slightly crowded. Male flowerhead 40 mm long, 10 mm across, stalked, with *flowers in a spike,* with an unpleasant odour. Involucral bracts 5 mm long, 1 mm wide. *Female flowerhead 28 mm long, 12 mm across, elongate-ovoid,* with a musty odour, growing in length as flowers open, stout stalk 8 mm long, with more than 30 7 mm-long involucral bracts. Cones 40-90 mm long, 24-40 mm in diameter, with bracts arranged in 3 abutting spirals; bracts hairless.

DISTRIBUTION: Kouga, Baviaanskloof and Willowmore Mountains. HABITAT: Gravelly or sandy soils, 760-1000 m. STATUS: Restricted to a few isolated populations. Relatively poorly known. *Red Data Book* status: Rare. FLOWERS: October to March, mainly December. FRUITS: Retained.

***Leucadendron muirii*** E. Phillips                    Silver-ball Conebush        **Plate 111**

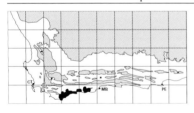

A shrub up to 2 m tall, spreading from a single main stem, dense in male plants, scraggly in females. *Mature leaves obovate-spatulate, thick and fleshy, with rounded tip,* up to 30 mm long, 13 mm wide in males, up to 40 mm long, 13 mm wide in females, tip with a red, sunken, fine point, hairless. Basal and juvenile leaves needle-like. Male flowerhead up to 40 mm long, including *20 mm-long stalk,* up to 15 mm across, ellipsoid, terminal or in clusters of up to 11 axillary flowerheads, greenish yellow, with a yeasty odour. *Involucral bracts with sharply pointed tips.* Female flowerhead 30 mm long, including 12 mm-long stalk, 15 mm across, ellipsoid, green, with a yeasty odour. Involucral bracts 5-15 mm long, 3 mm wide, hairless, dark brown. *Cones ashy grey,* 30-45 mm long, 30 mm in diameter, ellipsoid, hairless; bracts tightly pressed together below, 13 mm long, 13 mm wide, narrowing to base. *Fruits flattened to wings,* 5-8 mm long, 5-6.5 mm wide.

DISTRIBUTION: Elim, Bredasdorp and Riversdale Flats from Die Poort to Still Bay. HABITAT: Limestone soils, 0-200 m. STATUS: Scattered plants are encountered in extensive populations. FLOWERS: November and December. FRUITS: Retained.

*Leucadendron comosum* (Thunb.) R. Br. subsp. *comosum*

Common Ridge-cone Conebush    **Plate 111**

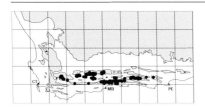

An erect shrub up to 1.7 m tall, with a single main stem. *Leaves dimorphic*, hairless; *lower leaves needle-like*, curved inwards with a shallow upper groove, 1 mm wide, up to 38 mm long in males, up to 44 mm long in females; *upper leaves broadened*, narrowly oblanceolate, tip with a sharp, fine point, 35 mm long, 3.5 mm wide in males, 40 mm long, 5 mm wide in females. Involucral leaves similar to upper leaves, crowded, pale green or yellow, not concealing flowerhead. Male flowerhead 11 mm long, 13 mm across, globose, usually clustered at the ends of branchlets, *flowers dark red*, with a pleasant scent. *Male floral bud club-shaped*. Male floral bract hairless. Female flowerhead grows in length while flowering, up to 35 mm long, 16 mm across, with dark red flowers. *Cones abutting towards base, up to 100 mm long*, 45 mm in diameter; bracts spreading, brown. Fruits 9.5 mm long, 8 mm wide, compressed, flat.
DISTRIBUTION: Langeberg, Outeniqua and Kouga Mountains; Swartberg; Touwsberg; Rooiberg.
HABITAT: Montane on sandstone soils, 600-1400 m. STATUS: Dense stands, which are vulnerable to fire, are most common. FLOWERS: October and November. FRUITS: Retained.

*Leucadendron comosum* subsp. *homaeophyllum* (Meisn.) I. Williams

Villiersdorp Ridge-cone Conebush    **Plate 111**

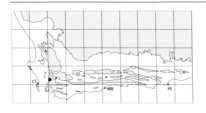

An erect shrub up to 1.7 m tall, with a single main stem. *Leaves needle-like, 24-33 mm long, 1 mm wide in both sexes*, hairless. *Involucral leaves similar to foliage leaves, not crowded*, pale green or yellow, not concealing flowerhead. *Male flowerhead 9 mm long, 10 mm across*, globose, usually clustered at ends of branchlets, flowers dark red, with a pleasant scent. Male floral bud club-shaped. *Male floral bracts densely covered with hairs.* Female flowers and cones undescribed.
DISTRIBUTION: Stettyns Mountains above High Noon and Du Toit's Kloof Pass above the tunnel.
HABITAT: Montane, on sandstone soils, 600-1000 m. STATUS: Known only from an unidentified locality, this subspecies was thought to be extinct until recently found again. FLOWERS: December. FRUITS: Retained.

*Leucadendron platyspermum* R. Br.                    Plate-seed Conebush    **Plate 111**

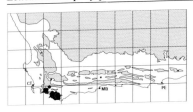

An erect shrub, male plants up to 1.3 m tall, female plants up to 1.7 m tall. Leaves up to 40 mm long, 5 mm wide in males, up to 70 mm long, 13 mm wide in females, oblanceolate, tip with a recurved, blunt, fine point which is flattened in female plants, narrowed to base. Male flowerhead 13 mm long, 12 mm across, terminal, almost cylindrical, with a *dense tuft of long, white hairs* at the tip which drop as flowers open. Involucral bracts oblanceolate, with soft hairs. Female flowerhead 28 mm long, 14 mm across, 7 mm long, with lanceolate involucral bracts covering lower half of flowerhead. Cones with a stout stalk, 50 mm long, 40 mm wide; *bracts double-ridged, abutting in a single spiral, hairless. Fruits 15 mm long, 32 mm wide, compressed, flat*, released after the adult plant has died by the root of the germinating seed pushing it out of the cone.
DISTRIBUTION: Donkerhoekberg near Villiersdorp; Groenland and Kleinmond Mountains from Houhoek to Elim Flats. HABITAT: Sandy and shale soils, 0-1350 m. STATUS: *Red Data Book* status: Vulnerable, due to flower-picking and agriculture. Occurs as very dense, isolated stands.
FLOWERS: September. FRUITS: Retained.

## *BRABEJUM* L.  The Wild Almond

> The genus *Brabejum* is the only naturally occurring African member of the Proteaceae which has *2 flowers per floral bract*. This feature is a characteristic of the Australian Proteaceae in the subfamily Grevilleoideae to which *Brabejum* is most closely related. The genus can also be identified by the *flowers being borne in dense, spike-like racemes, and having long stalks, the leaves occurring in whorls of 4-9, and by the large, densely velvety, almond-shaped fruits.*

*Brabejum stellatifolium* L.                                                  Wild Almond     **Plate 112**

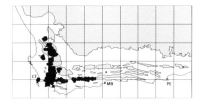

A tall tree reaching a height of 8 m, capable of resprouting at the base when burned. *Leaves in whorls of 6, occasionally 4-9* (hence 'stellate' meaning star-like), *simple*, 100-160 mm long, 15-25 mm wide, margin sharply toothed; stalk 10-15 mm long. Young leaves rusty golden. *Flowerhead a dense, spike-like raceme*, 60-90 mm long, 20 mm wide, with flowers arranged in many whorls of 10 flowers each. Flowers 5 mm long, with 4 totally free perianth segments, with a long stalk, subtended by deciduous, velvety, brown bract, anthers borne on stalks. *Fruits almond-shaped*, 20-45 mm long, 30 mm across, initially magenta, turning velvet-brown.

DISTRIBUTION: Gifberg to Hottentots-Holland Mountains to Klein River Mountains; Cape Peninsula; Riviersonderend Mountains and Langeberg to Gouritz River. HABITAT: Riverine, 0-1000 m. STATUS: Although often seen as scattered plants, it also frequently occurs as dense stands forming a riverine forest. FLOWERS: December and January. FRUITS: February to May. NOTE: Jan van Riebeeck planted the Wild Almond as a hedge around the early Cape settlement. These trees, now almost 350 years old, are a National Monument and can be seen at Kirstenbosch National Botanical Garden and on Wynberg Hill. The trees release cyanide when they are bruised. However, the poison can be released by bleaching, leaching or roasting the fruits, which can then be used as fodder, food or a substitute for coffee. The fruits cannot be stored; under natural conditions germination takes place soon after they drop so that seedlings can become established on the riverbank before the winter floods. The Wild Almond is related to Australia's Macadamia Nut (*Macadamia*) and to a very similar genus, *Panopsis*, in South America.

## *HAKEA* Schrad. **The Needlebushes**

The genus *Hakea* (subfamily Grevilleoideae) has been introduced into South Africa from Australia, primarily as a hedge plant. *Hakea salicifolia* (Vent.) Burtt *(=H. saligna* Knight) is popular serving this purpose in many areas of the country, and as yet does not pose a problem in fynbos. However, *H. drupacea, H. sericea* and *H. gibbosa* have become invasive, spreading rapidly and posing an enormous threat to vast areas of fynbos vegetation. An indigenous fungus has started to stunt these aliens' growth, and several weevil species which eat their seeds have been introduced to keep them under control.

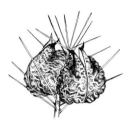

Needlebushes can be recognized by their *hard, needle-shaped leaves which have similar upper and lower surfaces.* The flowers, instead of being borne in a flowerhead, are generally borne in a small group in the leaf axils, sometimes forming catkins. They differ from those of most African Proteaceae in that *there are 2 flowers per floral bract and that 2 seeds develop from each flower.* The 2 seeds are protected from fire in *a hard, woody follicle,* and each has a flat, membranous wing on 1 side only.

*Hakea drupacea* (Gaertn.) Roem. & Schult.     Sweet Needlebush     **Plate 112**

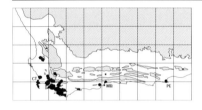

An erect shrub or tree resembling a small Stone Pine in shape and size when mature. *Leaves divided,* 70-100 mm long, consisting of many rigid needles 30-50 mm long, with silky hairs when young, hairless when mature. *Flowers produced in dense catkin-like clusters, cream. Pollen pink. Follicles with lacquered appearance,* with 2 prominent horns recurved to meet at the tip, borne in clusters.

DISTRIBUTION: Piketberg; Cape Peninsula to Agulhas, with outlying populations near Mossel Bay and Port Elizabeth. HABITAT: Sandstone and granite soils, 0-1000 m. STATUS: Dense stands occur on the Cape Peninsula, elsewhere usually encountered as scattered plants. FLOWERS: May and June. FRUITS: Retained.

NOTE: Native to southern Western Australia on granite soils. Probably introduced into South Africa in the 1830s, it was well established by the start of the 20th century. It has not spread as rapidly as the other species, requiring 6 years to flower and set seed. However, it has recently been appearing in much larger numbers in remote areas and is obviously spreading rapidly. It has not yet been considered enough of a problem to warrant biocontrol measures.

*Hakea sericea* Schrad.                                    Silky Needlebush    **Plate 112**

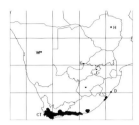

A shrub usually 2-3 m tall, reaching 5 m in dense stands. *Leaves needle-like, 30-40 mm long, 1 mm wide*, tip sharply pointed, with downy hairs, hairless when mature. Creamy flowers borne in profusion, giving bushes a white appearance, each flower on a 4 mm-long stalk with silky hairs. Follicles with 2 horns on the beaked tip, each growing in same direction as its stalk.
DISTRIBUTION: Cederberg to Grahamstown, with an outlier in Pondoland (Eastern Cape and adjacent KwaZulu-Natal).
HABITAT: Sandstone and shale soils, 0-1400 m. STATUS: Common as scattered plants everywhere, forming dense, impenetrable stands if not controlled. FLOWERS: June to September. FRUITS: Retained.
NOTE: A native of southeastern Australia in a wide variety of habitats. In South Africa it was introduced by 1830 as a hedge plant, and later to bind sand and as firewood. Several weevil and moth species have been released to control *H. sericea*. All have been carefully screened to ensure that they will feed only on this needlebush. The Silky Needlebush fruit weevil *Erytenna consputa* has proved most successful, reducing seed production by 90%. More recently, weevils that eat flower buds and leaves have also been released, and the Silky Needlebush seed moth *Carposina autologa* attacks the mature cones. An indigenous fungus, *Colletotrichum gloeosporoides*, has migrated from our proteas to the Silky Needlebush, where it manifests as patches of resinous gum on the stems and as a leaf rust. It causes widespread deaths, especially in the southern Cape. With these biocontrol agents in place, infestations of Silky Needlebush are declining in density. However, it will be necessary to maintain populations of the species in order to keep alive healthy populations of the biocontrol agents. Whether we like it or not, the Silky Needlebush is now a fynbos species.

*Hakea gibbosa* (Sm.) Cav.                                 Rock Needlebush    **Plate 112**

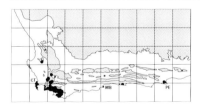

A bushy shrub or tree up to 4 m tall. *Leaves needle-like, 40-80 mm long, 1-2 mm wide*, tip sharply pointed, covered with dense, shaggy hairs when young, becoming hairless. Flowers dark cream. Follicles 20-35 mm long, 3 mm wide, with 2 sharp horns on the beaked tip, each growing at right angles to its stalk.
DISTRIBUTION: Cape Peninsula to Caledon, with outliers at Piketberg and Port Elizabeth. HABITAT: Sandstone soils, 0-1000 m. STATUS: Rapidly forms dense stands, but occasionally occurs as scattered plants. FLOWERS: June to September. FRUITS: Retained.
NOTE: Endemic to New South Wales near Sydney, it was cultivated in the Caledon area for firewood in the 19th century. Although it has become a major problem in the mountains of the Houhoek to Elim region, it has not yet been considered important enough to warrant biocontrol.

## *GREVILLEA* R.Br. ex Knight  **The Silky Oaks**

The genus *Grevillea* is characterized in South Africa by leaves which have *markedly different upper and lower surfaces. The flowers are borne in pairs per floral bract and the ovary forms a thin-walled or leathery follicle.*

*Grevillea robusta* Cunn. ex R. Br.  Silky Oak  **Plate 112**

*A tall tree up to 35 m.* Leaves to 300 mm long, *green above, with grey, silky hairs below, pinnately divided.* Flowerhead a toothbrush-like raceme up to 120 mm long, *orange, in clusters on short branchlets.* Flowers with a 10 mm-long stalk, producing copious nectar. Perianth 6 mm long. Style 20 mm long.
DISTRIBUTION: Planted throughout southern Africa, and becoming naturalized in the Eastern Cape, KwaZulu-Natal and the lowlands of Mpumalanga and Northern Province.
HABITAT: Wooded grassland and woodlands. STATUS: Scattered trees. FLOWERS: All year.
FRUITS: Released a few months after flowering.

*Grevillea banksii* R. Br.  Scarlet Silky Oak  **Plate 112**

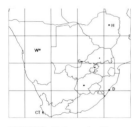

A tall, erect, open shrub up to 8 m tall, but with prostrate, creeping and bushy variants. Leaves up to 250 mm long, *green above, with grey, silky hairs below, deeply incised into 5-11 lobes.* Flowerhead terminal or axillary at the tips of branches, 100 mm long, a cylindrical raceme. *Perianth pinkish red, hairy on outer surfaces.* Style 40 mm long, red, with a yellow, disc-like pollen presenter.
DISTRIBUTION: Naturalized in southern KwaZulu-Natal.
HABITAT: Wooded grasslands and forest. STATUS: Capable of forming dense, isolated stands. FLOWERS: All year.
FRUITS: Released a few months after flowering.
NOTE: This species is reputed to be a serious potential invader in southern KwaZulu-Natal, where several extensive stands have become established. It needs to be carefully monitored and eliminated timeously. Its success as an invader is due in part to its ability to self-pollinate and thus set seed in isolation.

# EXTINCT SPECIES

It is not generally realized that we are on the verge of losing our proteas. More than one-third of them are listed in the *Red Data Book* for plants, which lists species threatened or potentially threatened by mankind. Amongst our proteas some 35 species are considered to be 'Endangered with extinction', and a further 46 species are 'Vulnerable to extinction'. The former category is used for species in imminent danger of extinction, whereas the latter is used for species which will become extinct if the threats to which they are exposed continue unabated. Another 76 species are listed as 'Rare' because their small populations or limited distribution range would make them vulnerable if their habitat were to be developed or transformed in any way.

It is vital that *Red Data Book* species are preserved, and they should not be picked, disturbed or damaged in any way. If you believe you may have found a new population or locality of a *Red Data Book* species, please inform your local branch of the Wildlife Society, Botanical Society or Mountain Club, and they will inform the relevant authorities. If you live near a population of a *Red Data Book* species, you may consider setting up a watchdog group in order to monitor it and foster its survival. Contact the Botanical Society for guidelines on how best to achieve this.

Please be aware that many of these species are very susceptible to trampling as well as to diseases such as dieback, rootrot or any other fungal and bacterial disease that you may carry on your shoes from your garden into the wild. Thus it is vital that you keep your distance lest you kill them.

The following species are extinct both in the wild and in cultivation. The *Red Data Book* definition of 'Extinct' is that the species has not been recorded during the last 50 years, or it has been eliminated (by, for example, agriculture, urbanization or flower-picking) from all known colonies.

Two species have not been seen for the past ten years. These are *Serruria furcellata* and *Serruria aemula congesta*. The former, known from the Kraaifontein and Brackenfell areas of the Cape Flats, could not be relocated at any of its historical localities during the period of the Protea Atlas Project. In 1987 fewer than 250 plants remained at Northpine on the Cape Flats, but by 1990 mowing had eliminated this last known locality for this species, and it is extremely unlikely that any suitable habitat remains for its long-term survival. Two plants still exist at the Cape Flats Nature Reserve nursery at the University of the Western Cape, and cuttings have been made from these for propagation at Kirstenbosch. However, with no suitable sites available to re-establish this species within its old redistribution range, it must be considered extinct in the wild.

*Serruria aemula congesta* occurred from Eersterivier to Macassar on the Cape Flats. The last known plants were seen at Penhill and Bleak House in 1985. The subspecies is apparently not in cultivation and must be considered totally extinct. As in the case of the other two forms of this species, urbanization and agriculture are the primary reasons for its decline. Whereas *S. a. aemula* is protected in the Plattekloof Natural Heritage Site at Edgemead, and *S. a. foeniculacea* occurs in the Rondevlei Bird Sanctuary, there are no nature reserves in the far eastern Cape Flats that conserve fynbos vegetation.

The situation in Cape Town regarding endangered plants is grave. The city has the highest number of *Red Data Book* species of any city in the world. Other protea species threatened with extinction within Cape Town include *Diastella proteoides*, *Leucadendron levisanus*, *Serruria cyanoides* and *S. trilopha*. A survey for the Cape Flats has been done and priority sites for conservation have been identified. However, veld maintenance is inadequate, with managers using bush-cutting and mowing, which kill most indigenous species, instead of fire to rejuvenate veld. Alien plants and dumping are major additional threats. Since many of our proteas occur nowhere else in the world, it is our duty – and ours alone – to conserve them.

## *Leucadendron grandiflorum* — Wynberg Conebush

*Leucadendron grandiflorum* was described in 1806 only from a male plant grown in George Hibbert's garden in England. No herbarium specimen has been found, so a description and a drawing are the only existing evidence that this species once occurred. Seed was collected on 'Wynberg Mountain' (presumably Wynberg Hill) by James Niven in about 1800, and no plant has been seen since. Nothing else is known about this species, although it is clearly related to the Crown Conebushes. However, some confusion has been caused by the name *L. grandiflorum* having also been given to what is now *L. tinctum* and allied species in the Sun Conebush grouping.

If *L. grandiflorum*'s habitat requirements were similar to those of the closely related *L. globosum,* it probably occurred on the southern side of Wynberg Hill near the crest, between Kirstenbosch and the Wynberg Military Hospital.

## *Leucadendron spirale* — Wolseley Conebush

This conebush is undoubtedly the 'ugly duckling' in the genus. Describing it in 1809, Richard Salisbury noted that 'cuttings grow freely, but possessing little beauty it should only be admitted in extensive collections'. Indeed, few people would recognize it as a conebush, as its leaves are small and ericoid, and the fully mature cones are only 20 mm in diameter.

*Leucadendron spirale* has been collected only four times in the past: James Niven found it in 1801 at the Breede River; Leopold Mund collected it at the same locality in 1819; James Bowie gives as his locality the swamps at Soetmelkrivier and Langkloof (but he has a reputation for giving incorrect localities); and Alfred Meebold collected it in 1933, describing the locality as 'Wolseley, heath, containing only few species, but river ground and swampy ground, few hours only'. If the Breede River and Wolseley localities are correct, most of its habitat has probably been ploughed up, but small pockets of plants may still exist.

# GLOSSARY

In this field guide, technical terms have been kept to a minimum. In the leaf and bract illustrations following, the equivalent botanical term is given in brackets after the simplified term that has been used.

## Leaf and bract shapes

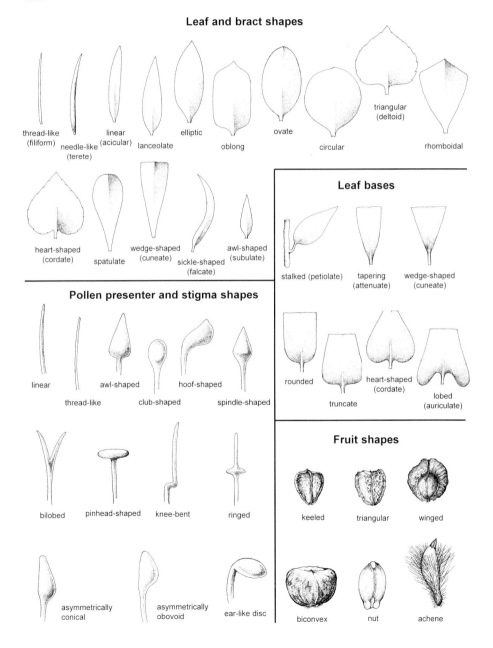

thread-like (filiform)

needle-like (terete)

linear (acicular)

lanceolate

elliptic

oblong

ovate

circular

triangular (deltoid)

rhomboidal

heart-shaped (cordate)

spatulate

wedge-shaped (cuneate)

sickle-shaped (falcate)

awl-shaped (subulate)

### Leaf bases

stalked (petiolate)

tapering (attenuate)

wedge-shaped (cuneate)

rounded

truncate

heart-shaped (cordate)

lobed (auriculate)

### Pollen presenter and stigma shapes

linear

thread-like

awl-shaped

club-shaped

hoof-shaped

spindle-shaped

bilobed

pinhead-shaped

knee-bent

ringed

asymmetrically conical

asymmetrically obovoid

ear-like disc

### Fruit shapes

keeled

triangular

winged

biconvex

nut

achene

*achene:* A small, dry fruit bearing a single seed which is not released; instead the entire fruit is dispersed. In proteas achenes with very hard, woody outer coatings are called nuts. Cf. *follicle.*

*adpressed:* Lying flat against (usually referring to hairs or bracts).

*anther:* The pollen-bearing sacs of the male part (stamen) of the flower. In most of the southern African proteas the anthers are stalkless.

*awn:* A stiff, bristle-like extension of the perianth limb, or other plant part.

*axil:* The upper angle formed between a stem and a leaf or bract.

*axillary:* Arising from the axil.

*beard:* A dense tuft of long hairs arising from the upper portion of an involucral bract or leaf. In this book the term is not used for either a fringe of hairs or a cone of awns.

*bract:* A leaf, modified so that it no longer resembles a leaf, which has a flower or flowerhead in its axil.

*callus:* A thickened portion of the leaf margin, usually at the leaf tip or, in the Pincushion allies, at each tooth of the leaf.

*capitulum:* A flowerhead type comprising a flattened head on which stalkless flowers are closely packed.

*channelled:* With a groove running along the upper length of the organ.

*claw:* The portion of the perianth segment that connects the tube and the limb.

*coma:* A rounded tuft of young, silky leaves at the top of a flowering branch, found mainly in some *Mimetes* species.

*compound flowerhead:* A flowerhead which comprises smaller groups of flowerheads, termed headlets in this book. In the southern African proteas these occur mainly in the Spiderhead allies, where the flowerhead may comprise a panicle of racemes or capitula (in *Serruria*), or a spike or raceme of capitula (in *Paranomus, Spatalla* and *Sorocephalus*).

*cone: 1)* In *Leucadendron*, a cone-shaped seedhead formed by the large floral bracts.
2) In some *Protea* flowerheads, a cone-shaped projection formed by the very long awns on the perianth segments. Often called a beard, but in this book the term 'beard' refers only to the hairs on the involucral bracts of *Protea* species.

*cone bracts:* In *Leucadendron*, the floral bracts which have become woody and form the cone.

*corymbiform:* Describing a flowerhead which is a raceme and in which the outer flower stalks are longer than the inner ones, resulting in the flowerhead being flat-topped.

*dambo:* A seasonal swamp or vlei found in miombo savanna, in which grass but no trees grow.

*decumbent:* With branches lying on the ground, tips erect.

*denticle:* A minute, tooth-like projection.

*dimorphic:* 1) Having two shapes, e.g. the two leaf shapes of *Paranomus* species.
2) In *Leucadendron*, where the male and female plants have bushes, leaves, flowers or cones of different sizes.

*dioecious:* Having plants of separate sexes, with some bearing only male flowers and others bearing only female flowers. In the protea family, the *Leucadendron* and *Aulax* genera have dioecious plants. Most plant species are hermaphrodite, bearing flowers with both male and female parts.

*ecotone:* An overlapping boundary between two vegetation types or soils.

*elaiosome:* The fleshy structure on ant-dispersed protea fruits which is consumed by the ants. It may be a fleshy lump at the base of the fruit or it may cover the entire fruit.

*entire:* Having an undivided margin.

*floral bract:* A bract at the base of a flower, i.e. subtending it. In *Leucadendron* the floral bracts form the fruit-bearing cone. Cf. *involucral bract.*

*flower:* The reproductive unit of flowering plants. In proteas they consist of (from tip to base): one female organ (comprising the stigma, style and ovary); four male organs (the stamens, comprising anthers and filaments); four nectaries; four perianth segments (or tepals); and a floral bract. In the protea family the flowers are relatively inconspicuous and are massed into showy flowerheads.

*flowerhead:* Any arrangement of more than one flower. Also called an inflorescence.

*follicle:* A fruit occuring in *Hakea* and *Grevillea.* It bears two or more seeds and, on ripening, splits down one side to release the seeds.

*glandular tooth:* A nectar-secreting gland at the tip of a leaf. *Leucospermum* and *Mimetes* species are characterized by their many teeth. Cf. *callus, nectary.*

*glaucous:* Describing leaves with a blue-green or grey colour given them by a waxy layer (or bloom).

*habit:* The form and shape of a plant; its characteristic growth form and appearance.

*headlet:* A cluster of flowers which forms part of a larger flowerhead. Typically in the proteas the headlet is a raceme or a capitulum.

*imbricate:* Overlapping as do the tiles on a roof. The term may refer to leaves, bracts or perianth segments.

*involucral bracts:* A rim of bracts surrounding a flowerhead or on the stalk of the flowerhead. Involucral bracts do not subtend a flower and are thus barren.

*involucral receptacle:* The base or stalk of an involucre bearing the flowers.

*involucre:* 1) A rim of bracts or leaves surrounding a flowerhead.
2) A headlet comprising a capitulum or dense raceme.

*lax:* Loose, not compact or dense. Usually describing flowerheads in which the headlets or flowers are well spaced along the stalk.

*limb:* The portion of the perianth segment bearing the anthers, and furthest from its base. It is usually expanded and rounded to contain the anthers.

*morphology:* The study of shape, form and external structure.

*mucro:* A sharp point, often initially soft and fleshy, but hard and cartilaginous when mature; *mucronate* (adj.).

*myrmecochory:* Seed dispersal by ants, in which ants carry fruits underground into their nest to eat the elaiosome surrounding the fruit.

*nectary:* A nectar-secreting gland found either on the leaves, where they are called glandular teeth or extrafloral nectaries, or in the flower, where they are often called hypogynous glands or floral nectaries, and are thought to be the 'petals' in proteas.

*nut:* A dry fruit that is surrounded by a woody and extremely hard coat. It bears a single seed which is not released. In the southern African proteas all nuts are also achenes.

*ob-:* Referring to leaf or flowerhead shapes in which the broadest portion is more than halfway from the point of attachment.

*ovary:* The base of the female organ of the flower which, in southern African proteas, contains a single ovule. After pollination it develops into the fruit containing the seed.

*panicle:* A racemose flowerhead in which the flowers or headlets are borne on branched stalks.

*pendulous:* Hanging upside down from a branch.

*perianth:* The floral parts of a flower outside the sexual parts. In some flowers – but not those of proteas – these are the petals and sepals. In proteas each flower has four perianth segments in a ring around the ovary.

*perianth segments:* Individual parts forming the perianth. Each segment comprises a claw, which is thin, and a limb bearing an anther. The base of the claw is usually fused with the other three segments into a tube.

*persistent:* Long-lived; remaining for a long time, as opposed to being shed or becoming rubbed off.

*Pincushion allies:* The genera *Diastella, Leucospermum, Mimetes, Orothamnus* and *Vexatorella.* They are characterized by having glandular teeth or calluses at the tips of the leaves and by the distinctive elaiosome which covers their fruits.

*plant community:* A group of plants sharing the same environment and interacting with one another.

*pollen presenter:* A modified portion of the style on which pollen adheres and from which pollen is transferred onto a pollinator as the flower opens.

*promiscuous:* Readily interbreeding with other species to form hybrids.

*prostrate:* Lying on the ground; usually referring to bushes with creeping stems.

*protea:* Any member of the protea family (Proteaceae), as defined by the International Protea Association. In this book members of the genus *Protea* are referred to as sugarbushes.

*raceme:* A flowerhead type in which the youngest flowers occur at the tip and which is thus capable of indefinite elongation; *racemose* (adj.).

*Recent:* An epoch of the Quaternary period which spans the time from 10 000 years ago to the present.

*receptacle:* A flat, concave or domed base on which the flowers of a capitulum-type flowerhead are borne.

*recurved:* Curved backwards or downwards.

**Red Data Book for plants:** A listing of plant species which are threatened or potentially threatened by the activities of mankind. The major categories are: Extinct (no longer known from the wild); Endangered (in danger of extinction as a result of human activities); Rare (at risk, but not yet Vulnerable or Endangered); and Vulnerable (likely to become Endangered soon).

*rhizome:* A horizontally creeping underground stem with branches. As the older portions of the stem may die without harming the plant, *Protea* species with rhizomatous stems may live to a great age and fragment into many plants covering large areas.

*rootstock:* A woody, rounded, fire-resistant stem base, usually partially underground, from which many (usually erect) stems arise after the aerial parts of the plant have been destroyed by fire. Also known as bole or lignotuber.

*scabrous:* With a rough surface, often feeling like sandpaper. The leaves of the Dwarf-tufted Sugarbushes and Clay Conebushes are covered with modified hairs, or denticles, which give them a rough texture.

*scale leaves:* Reduced brown leaves on underground stems. When they are considerably reduced they are called scales.

*seedhead:* A mass of fruit and floral parts, developed from a flowerhead, in which the fruits are stored and protected. In *Protea* the seedhead is formed by the involucral bracts around the fruit; in female plants of *Leucadendron* it is formed by the floral bracts. *Cf. cone.*

*serotiny:* The retention of fruits on the plant in protective cones or seedheads for long periods. In proteas this is for protection from fire and predation.

**Spiderhead allies:** The genera *Paranomus, Serruria, Spatalla* and *Sorocephalus*. These are characterized by their divided or needle-like leaves and compound flowerheads.

*spike:* A flowerhead type in which stalkless flowers are borne in a racemose arrangement.

*spreading:* Held at right angles to the stem and usually horizontal to the ground.

*stamen:* The male organs of a flower comprising the anther and a stalk or filament. In proteas the filament is usually absent and the stamen is attached to the perianth segment at the base of the limb.

*stigma:* The tip of the female organ of the flower which traps pollen transported by pollinators or wind. In proteas it is situated at the tip of the pollen presenter.

*style:* The stalk of the female organ of the flower which connects the stigma with the ovary. In proteas the portion below the tip is swollen to form a pollen presenter.

*sub-:* Nearly.

*subtend:* Occurring immediately below and close to, as a bract subtending a flower.

*talus:* A steep mass of rubble at the base of a cliff or steep slope.

*terminal:* Situated at the apex or tip of the branch.

**Tertiary:** The period from 65 million years ago to 2 million years ago, during which many limestone and sandy rocks were formed.

*tooth:* see **glandular tooth**.

*tube:* A basal ring which is formed by the claws of the perianth segments, may surround the ovary, and stores nectar.

*umbel:* A flowerhead type in which all the flower stalks arise from the same point. These flowerheads tend to be flat- or dome-topped, with the headlets at a similar level.

*whorl:* A ring of plant parts (e.g. leaves, bracts) around a stem, usually well separated from the next whorl.

# REFERENCES AND FURTHER READING

BEARD, J.S. 1963. The Genus *Protea* in Tropical Africa. *Kirkia* 3: 138-206.

BEARD, J.S. 1993. *The Proteas of Tropical Africa.* Kangaroo Press, Kenthurst, NSW, Australia.

BROEMBSEN, S.L. & BRITS, G.J. 1986. Control of *Phytophthora* Root Rot of Proteas in South Africa. *Acta Horticulturae* 185: 201-207.

BRUMMITT, R.K. & MARNER, S.K. 1993. Proteaceae. In: *Flora of Tropical East Africa.* Royal Botanic Gardens, Kew.

BRUMMITT, R.K. & POWELL, C.E. 1992. *Authors of Plant Names.* Royal Botanic Gardens, Kew.

CHISUMPA, S.M. & BRUMMITT, R.K. 1987. Taxonomic Notes on Tropical African Species of *Protea. Kew Bulletin* 42: 815-853.

CLAASSENS, A.S. 1986. Some Aspects of the Nutrition of Proteas. *Acta Horticulturae* 185: 171-179.

COLLINS, B.G. & REBELO, A.G. 1987. Pollination Biology of the Proteaceae in Australia and Southern Africa. *Australian Journal of Ecology* 12: 387-421.

GEORGE, A.S. 1984. *An Introduction to the Proteaceae of Western Australia.* Kangaroo Press, Kenthurst, NSW, Australia.

GOLDBLATT, P. & MANNING J. 2000. Cape Plants: A Conspectus of the Cape Flora of South Africa. *Strelitzia* 9.

GUNN, M. & CODD, L.E. 1981. *Botanical Exploration of Southern Africa.* Balkema, Cape Town.

HALL, A.V. & VELDHUIS, H.A. 1985. South African Red Data Book. Plants: Fynbos and Karoo Biomes. *South African National Scientific Programmes Report* No. 117.

HILTON-TAYLOR, C. (unpublished). *Red Data Book for Plants in South Africa.* National Botanical Institute, Cape Town.

HUTCHINSON, J., PHILLIPS, E.P. & STAPF, O. 1912. Proteaceae. In: *Flora Capensis.* Lovell Reeve & Co., London.

KNOX-DAVIES, P.S., VAN WYK, P.S. & MARASAS, W.F.O. 1986. Diseases of Proteas and their Control in the South-western Cape. *Acta Horticulturae* 185: 189-200.

LAMONT, B.B. 1986. The Significance of Proteoid Roots in Proteas. *Acta Horticulturae* 185: 163-170.

LEVYNS, M.R. 1970. A Revision of the Genus *Paranomus* (Proteaceae). *Contributions from the Bolus Herbarium* 2.

MATTHEWS, L.J. 1993. *The Protea Grower's Handbook.* Bok Books, Durban.

MATTHEWS, L.J. & CARTER, Z. 1983. *South African Proteaceae in New Zealand.* Matthews, Manakau.

MATTHEWS, L.J. & CARTER, Z. 1993. *Proteas of the World.* Bok Books, Durban.

PRECIS. 1995. Proteaceae. Electronic update of M. Jordaan. In: Arnold, T.H. & De Wet, B.C. (eds). Plants of Southern Africa: Names and Distribution. *Memoirs of the Botanical Survey of South Africa* No. 62. National Botanical Institute, Pretoria.

REBELO, A.G. (ed.) 1989-1995. *Protea Atlas Newsletter* 1-27. Protea Atlas Project, Cape Town.

REBELO, A.G. 1991. *Protea Atlas Manual.* Protea Atlas Project, Cape Town.

REBELO, A.G. 1994. Using the Proteaceae to Design a Nature Reserve Network and Determine Conservation Priorities for the Cape Floristic Region. In: Forey, P.L., Humphries, C.J. & Vane-Wright, R.I. (eds) *Systematics and Conservation Evaluation.* 375-396. Clarendon Press, Oxford.

REBELO, A.G. 1995. *A Checklist of Southern African Proteas.* Protea Atlas Project, Cape Town.

REBELO, A.G. & ROURKE, J.P. 1986. Seed Germination and Seed Set in Southern African Proteaceae: Ecological Determinants and Horticultural Problems. *Acta Horticulturae* 185: 75-88.

ROURKE, J.P. 1969. Taxonomic Studies on *Sorocephalus* R.Br. and *Spatalla* Salisb. *Journal of South African Botany,* Supplementary Vol. 7.

ROURKE, J.P. 1972. Taxonomic Studies on *Leucospermum* R.Br. *Journal of South African Botany,* Supplementary Vol. 8.

ROURKE, J.P. 1976. A Revision of *Diastella* (Proteaceae). *Journal of South African Botany* 42: 185-210.

ROURKE, J.P. 1982. *The Proteas of Southern Africa.* Centaur, Johannesburg.

ROURKE, J.P. 1984. A Revision of the Genus *Mimetes* Salisb. (Proteaceae). *Journal of South African Botany* 50: 171-236.

ROURKE, J.P. 1984. *Vexatorella* Rourke, a New Genus of the Proteaceae from Southern Africa. *Journal of South African Botany* 50: 373-391.

ROURKE, J.P. 1987. The Inflorescence Morphology and Systematics of *Aulax* (Proteaceae). *South African Journal of Botany* 53: 464-480.

SMITH, C.A. 1966. Common Names of South African Plants. *Botanical Survey Memoir* 35.

TANSLEY, S.A. 1988. The Status of Threatened Proteaceae in the Cape Flora, South Africa, and the Implications for their Conservation. *Biological Conservation* 43: 227-239.

VOGTS, M. 1982. *South Africa's Proteaceae: Know Them and Grow Them.* C. Struik, Cape Town.

VON BREITENBACH, F. 1986. Notes on the Arborescent Proteaceae of Southern Africa. *Journal of Dendrology* 6: 1-45.

WILLIAMS, I.J.M. 1972. A Revision of the Genus *Leucadendron* (Proteaceae). *Contributions from the Bolus Herbarium* 3.

WRIGLEY, J.W. & FAGG, M. 1989. *Banksias, Waratahs and Grevilleas and All Other Plants in the Australian Proteaceae Family.* Collins, Sydney.

# INDEX TO COMMON NAMES

Spiderhead, Wynberg 99
Spinning Top 186
Spoon, Erica-leaf 125
Spoon, Fine-leaf 124
Spoon, Kink-style 122
Spoon, Lax 129
Spoon, Lax-stalked 126
Spoon, Long-tube 128
Spoon, Medusa 123
Spoon, Needle-leaf 123
Spoon, Palmiet 122
Spoon, Pink-stalked 125
Spoon, Shaggy-hair 127
Spoon, Shiny 124
Spoon, Silky 124
Spoon, Silver-leaf 129
Spoon, Spike 123
Spoon, Swan-head 128
Spoon, Swan-neck 128
Spoon, White-stalked 125
Spoon, Woolly 126
Spoon, Woolly-hair 127
Stinkblaarsuikerbos *see* Sugarbush, Stink-leaf
Strooimeisie *see* Spiderhead, Rose
Sugarbush, African 43
Sugarbush, Awl-leaf 31
Sugarbush, Barberton 41
Sugarbush, Bashful 51
Sugarbush, Bishop 66
Sugarbush, Black-beard 55
Sugarbush, Black-rim 73
Sugarbush, Blyde 41
Sugarbush, Bot River 49
Sugarbush, Broad-leaf 48
Sugarbush, Brown-beard 57
Sugarbush, Burchell's 50
Sugarbush, Cascade 66
Sugarbush, Ceres 75
Sugarbush, Channel-leaf 60
Sugarbush, Chimanimani 38
Sugarbush, Clanwilliam 36
Sugarbush, Clasping-leaf 29
Sugarbush, Cloud 35
Sugarbush, Common 32, 52
Sugarbush, Common Ground 69
Sugarbush, Common Shuttlecock 65
Sugarbush, Dagger-leaf 72
Sugarbush, Dainty 34
Sugarbush, Drakensberg 35
Sugarbush, Dwarf Grassland 34
Sugarbush, Dwarf Northern-woodland 39
Sugarbush, Dwarf Savanna 42

Sugarbush, Dwarf Silver 48
Sugarbush, Forest 65
Sugarbush, Frosted 47
Sugarbush, Green 56
Sugarbush, Grey-leaf 54
Sugarbush, Groove-leaf 74
Sugarbush, Harts-tongue-fern 46
Sugarbush, Heart-leaf 30
Sugarbush, Hidden 75
Sugarbush, Hoary 46
Sugarbush, Hottentot 64
Sugarbush, Inyanga 44
Sugarbush, Kamiesberg 77
Sugarbush, King 45
Sugarbush, Kleinmond 70
Sugarbush, Kouga 68
Sugarbush, Krantz 37
Sugarbush, Ladismith 53
Sugarbush, Lance-leaf 53
Sugarbush, Large-leaf 71
Sugarbush, Large-nut 36
Sugarbush, Leafy 68
Sugarbush, Limestone 49
Sugarbush, Linear-leaf 31
Sugarbush, Long-leaf 51
Sugarbush, Malawi 33
Sugarbush, Manica 33
Sugarbush, Mountain-rose 74
Sugarbush, Narrow-leaf 55
Sugarbush, Nodding 77
Sugarbush, Northern 39
Sugarbush, Northern Woodland 39
Sugarbush, Patent-leaf 30
Sugarbush, Pink 57
Sugarbush, Potberg 65
Sugarbush, Queen 58
Sugarbush, Red 58
Sugarbush, Reed-leaf 62
Sugarbush, Regal 39
Sugarbush, Rolled-leaf 71
Sugarbush, Rough-leaf 61
Sugarbush, Saddleback 40
Sugarbush, Sandpaper-leaf 61
Sugarbush, Sawedge 59
Sugarbush, Scarlet 76
Sugarbush, Sickle-leaf 33
Sugarbush, Silver 48
Sugarbush, Smooth-leaf 70
Sugarbush, Stink-leaf 50
Sugarbush, Strap-leaf 56
Sugarbush, Sulphur 76
Sugarbush, Swan 74

# INDEX TO SCIENTIFIC NAMES

Figures printed in italic refer to plate numbers or, in the case of extinct species, the number of the page on which an illustration may be found.

Included in this index are the more common synonyms for species and genera. Current names, and therefore those used in the book, are printed in bold, and the authors of these species can be found under the relevant entry in the text. Authors of synonyms are given only in cases where identical names may cause confusion.